C0-AJR-311

THE GRASSES OF MISSOURI

THE GRASSES
OF
MISSOURI

Clair L. Kucera

University of Missouri Studies Volume XXXV

UNIVERSITY OF MISSOURI PRESS
COLUMBIA

Library of Congress Catalog
Card Number 61-5880

Printed and Bound in the United States of America

PREFACE

This manual is a systematic presentation of the grass flora of Missouri. Upon initiation of this project eight years ago, no treatment of similar scope was available. On this basis alone, a need was indicated for a current assessment of the flora on a state-wide basis. Preparing a work of this kind requires intensive field and herbarium survey, analysis, and interpretation. This course of endeavor provides valuable information about the distribution of each species, as well as certain aspects of its ecology. In turn, these data are important adjuncts to a more accurate understanding of the relationships existing between closely related species and groups of species.

Concerning the species concept and related problems, the writer adopts a generally conservative view. A few revisions have been effected. In each case, the change involved a reduction from the rank of species to varietal status. Nomenclatural changes were made where deemed necessary, but these have been kept to a minimum. In this way, a certain measure of stability is maintained and additions to an already extensive synonomy are avoided. There are some areas where established combinations are difficult to evaluate and these may be questionable. It is felt that acceptance of these earlier interpretations is advisable until more specific information is available. In some instances it would seem that such combinations have been made without sufficient basis, although they may have appeared valid at the time. The question arises as to the selection of a standard treatment, on which to base the present work. In this study, no single standard reference was followed exclusively regarding nomenclature and classification. Rather, that part of a work was adopted which was considered most satisfactory from a particular viewpoint. In general, however, decisions involving a choice in arrangement or usage were resolved by reference to Hitchcock (*Manual of Grasses,* 1951) or Gleason (*Illustrated Flora of the United States,* 1952).

Basically, this manual serves two purposes. It is an up-to-date compilation of all native and naturalized species known to occur within the borders of the state. Thus it affords a record of our flora. It also provides information concerning the distributional status of each species. Secondly, it enables the observer to identify specimens with which he is not familiar. It is hoped this function will enhance the possibilities of stimulating greater interest and study in the uncultivated grasses.

This book was completed through the invaluable assistance of many individuals. For this help and cooperation, the author wishes to express his sincere appreciation. Special thanks are due David B. Dunn, Department of Botany, University of Missouri, for his critical examination of the manuscript, and for his numerous helpful suggestions. Julian Steyermark, formerly of the Chicago Natural History Museum, gave freely of data and herbarium material drawn from his many years of association with the Missouri flora. To him the author is deeply indebted for this expression of generosity. The herbarium and library assistance given from time to time by Jason Swallen, Smithsonian Institution, and George Van Schaack, Missouri Botanical Garden, is recognized with gratitude. Deeply appreciated also is the opportunity to examine the numerous collections made in southwestern Missouri by E. J. Palmer. Acknowledgment is made concerning the reproduction and use of drawings from the *Manual of the Grasses of the United States*. Most of the illustrations employed here came from this source. Finally, the author wishes to thank the University Research Council for financial aid in carrying on this project and bringing the work to completion.

C. L. K.

Department of Botany
University of Missouri
January, 1961

CONTENTS

INTRODUCTION

The grasses comprise a large, distinctive family, the Gramineae.[1] They are the most widely distributed of flowering plants. Representatives occur in all latitudes under a wide range of physical conditions. In various parts of the world large regions are characterized by a grass life form. There are approximately 600 genera and possibly as many as 6 to 8,000 species according to some estimates. From the viewpoint of utilization, the grasses are the most important of all plants, among which are included corn, wheat, rice, sugar cane, various bamboos, and numerous forage species. By its diversification, adaptiveness, and universal distribution, the grass family is also the subject of particular academic interest. Numerous and varied studies are conducted dealing with a wide range of basic problems, all of which contribute to our knowledge of the grass family.

The grass plant has characteristic features easily distinguished from most other plants. The sedges, Cyperaceae, and the rushes, Juncaceae, appear "grass-like," but these too are easily separated. Classification of the grasses is based primarily on the *spikelet*. This is the basic unit of the inflorescence which characterizes the family as a whole, setting it apart from all others with the exception of the sedges. The spikelet is a reduced series of bracts, consisting of one or more flowers. No perianth as observed in most other flowering plants is present. A generalized spikelet is shown in Figure 1-A. The two lowermost bracts are *glumes*.

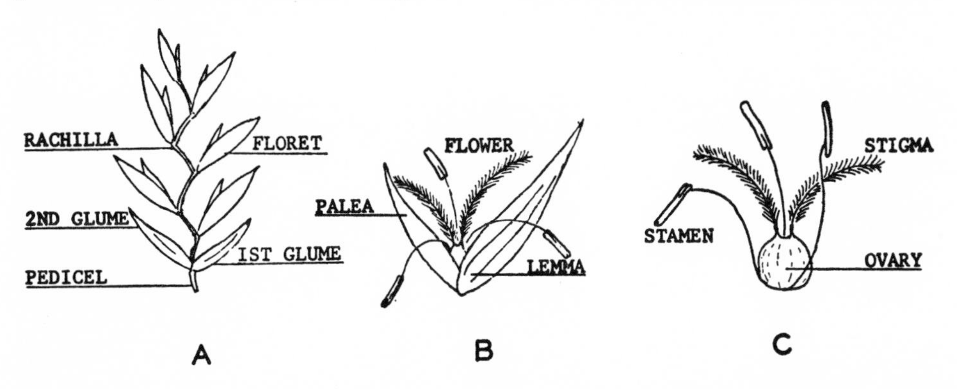

FIG. 1.—A. Spikelet consisting of six florets; B. Floret; C. Flower.

Above these, the *florets* are attached at the joints of the *rachilla* in an alternating, 2-ranked arrangement. An extracted floret is shown in Figure 1-B, consisting of (1) two bracts called the *lemma* and *palea,* and (2) the true flower. The lemma is usually the larger and is on the side away from the rachilla. Sterile florets occur in some genera. The perfect or bisexual *flower* consists of stamens and pistil (1-C). In several genera the flowers are unisexual. The usual number of stamens is three, although there are several exceptions, sometimes with only one, or as many as six. The filament of the grass stamen is typically elongate and slender. The pistil

[1] The alternate designation is Poaceae.

consists of a distinctly feathery stigma and a 1-seeded ovary, the latter developing as the *grain* or *caryopsis*. At the base of the flower two minutes scales, or *lodicules,* are noticeable in some grasses.

There are two types of spikelet *articulation* or separation which provide a basic division in classifying grasses. In the first group the rachilla becomes discontinuous above the glumes at maturity, the latter remaining on the *pedicel* as more or less persistent bracts. In the second group, the spikelet separates below the glumes and falls intact. The spikelets of some grasses are more or less rounded or circular in cross-section. For others some degree of *compression* is exhibited. In one type, the spikelet is laterally compressed, as if flattened from the sides (Figure 2-A). The midvein of the various bracts forms the keel. Bluegrass and redtop are examples of this type. The other type is dorsally compressed in which the back (midvein) is rounded or flattened (Figure 2-B). This characteristic is exemplified by crabgrass and panicum. Spikelets with lateral compression

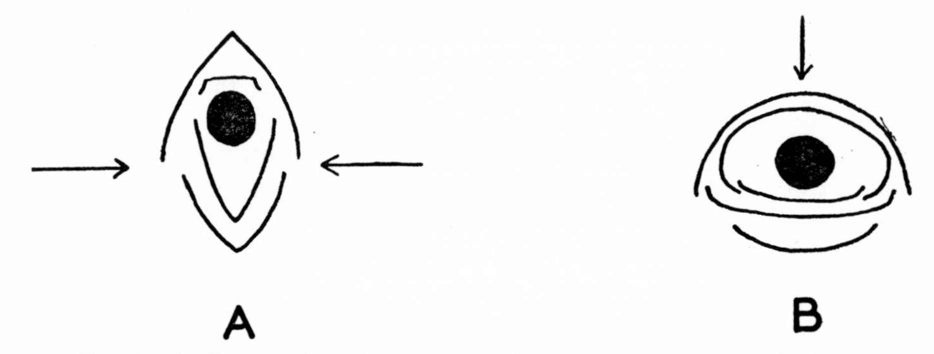

FIG. 2.—A. Cross-section of spikelet showing lateral compression; B. Cross-section showing dorsal compression.

separate above the glumes; however, exceptions do occur as in the woodreed, *Cinna.* The number of florets in the group with lateral compression varies from one to many. In the group with dorsal compression, the articulation is always below the glumes and the spikelets have only one perfect floret. Sterile florets are also present in some species. Articulation and compression are generally correlated and together provide a basis on which the family may be divided into two large subgroups.

Inflorescence types in grasses include the spike, raceme, and panicle (Figures 3-A, B and C). There are modifications of these in which panicles or racemes may appear spike-like. For example, the inflorescence of timothy, *Pheum,* is actually a panicle; however, because of the reduced lateral branches it is similar in appearance to a true spike. The most common inflorescence is the panicle. The inflorescence may be terminal or axillary (from the sheaths), or both. One section of *Panicum* commonly has terminal as well as reduced, sheathed panicles, the first appearing as a vernal phase, the second later in the season. In addition to the regular inflorescence, *cleistogamy* occurs in some grasses. In the latter, the spikelets remain closed and the florets generally concealed, so that the flowers are self-pollinated. The wild oatgrass, *Danthonia,* is an example of this type of flowering.

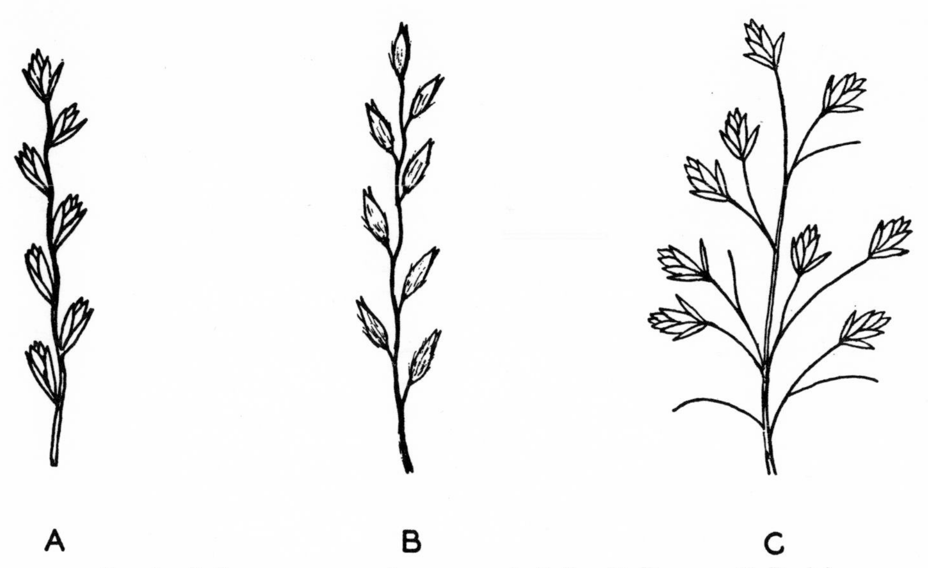

FIG. 3.—Inflorescence types in grasses: A. Spike; B. Raceme; C. Panicle.

Several vegetative characters of the grass are useful supplementary aids in classification and recognition. Leaf arrangement is *two-ranked,* from opposite sides of the stem, in contrast to the three-ranked condition of sedges and rushes. The *culm,* or stem, is jointed, generally hollow or pithy, and round in cross-section. The stem of sedges is usually solid and three-angled. In the rushes, the stem is round in cross-section and also hollow, but lacks the conspicuous joints or nodes of the grass plant. The leaf of grasses consists of a blade and a sheath, the latter encircling the culm (Figure 4-A). The sheath of most grasses is "open" in which case the margins are not fused but merely overlap. This is in contrast to the

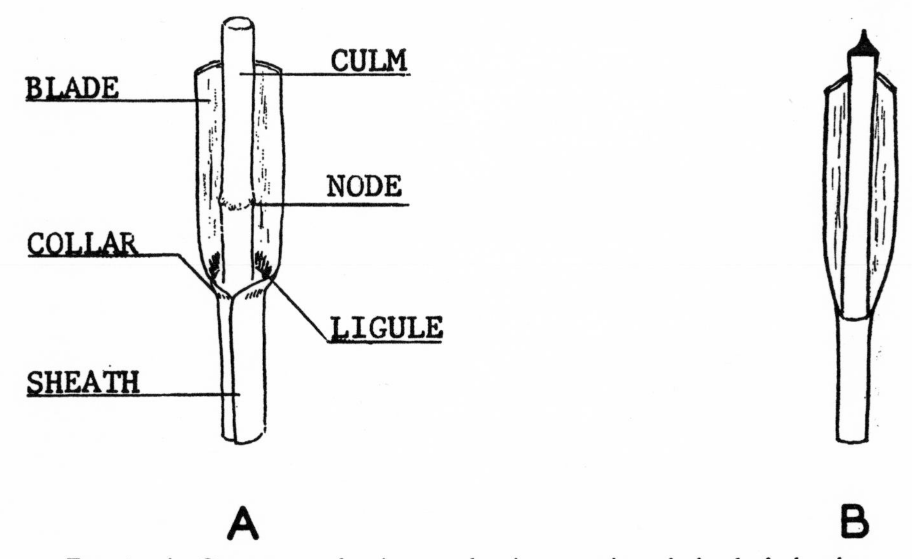

FIG. 4.—A. Grass stem showing overlapping margins of the leaf sheath; B. Sedge stem showing 'closed' sheath.

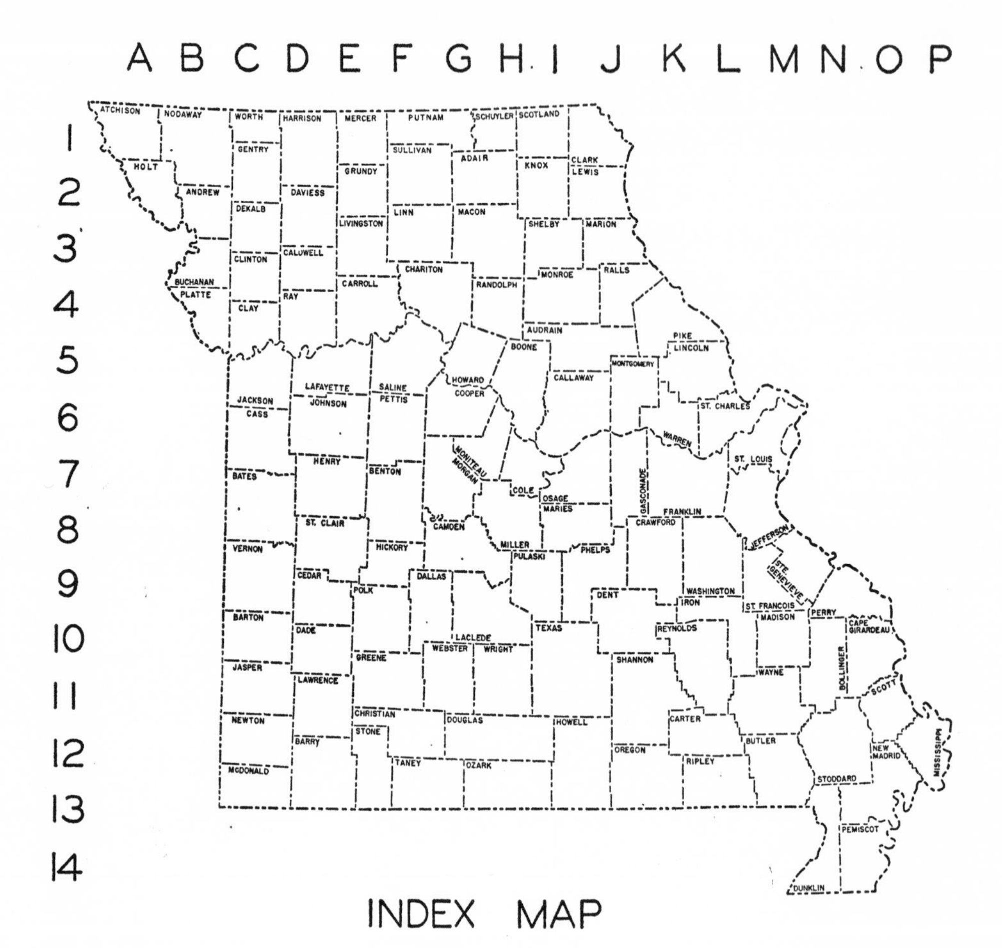
A B C D E F G H I J K L M N O P
1
2
3
4
5
6
7
8
9
10
11
12
13
14
ATCHISON
NODAWAY
WORTH
HARRISON
MERCER
PUTNAM
SCHUYLER
SCOTLAND
GENTRY
SULLIVAN
ADAIR
CLARK
HOLT
GRUNDY
KNOX
LEWIS
ANDREW
DAVIESS
DEKALB
LINN
MACON
LIVINGSTON
SHELBY
MARION
CLINTON
CALDWELL
CHARITON
MONROE
RALLS
BUCHANAN
PLATTE
CARROLL
RANDOLPH
RAY
CLAY
AUDRAIN
PIKE
BOONE
LINCOLN
MONTGOMERY
HOWARD
CALLAWAY
LAFAYETTE
SALINE
COOPER
JACKSON
JOHNSON
PETTIS
ST. CHARLES
CASS
WARREN
MONITEAU
MORGAN
HENRY
BENTON
ST. LOUIS
BATES
COLE
OSAGE
GASCONADE
MARIES
FRANKLIN
ST. CLAIR
CAMDEN
CRAWFORD
JEFFERSON
MILLER
VERNON
HICKORY
PULASKI
PHELPS
STE. GENEVIEVE
CEDAR
DALLAS
POLK
DENT
WASHINGTON
IRON
ST. FRANCOIS
PERRY
BARTON
MADISON
CAPE GIRARDEAU
DADE
TEXAS
REYNOLDS
LACLEDE
WEBSTER
WRIGHT
GREENE
SHANNON
JASPER
WAYNE
BOLLINGER
LAWRENCE
SCOTT
CHRISTIAN
NEWTON
DOUGLAS
HOWELL
CARTER
STONE
BUTLER
BARRY
OREGON
NEW MADRID
MISSISSIPPI
TANEY
OZARK
RIPLEY
McDONALD
STODDARD
PEMISCOT
DUNKLIN

INDEX MAP

COUNTIES

County	Location
Adair	2-G
Andrew	2-B
Atchison	1-A
Audrain	5-I
Barry	12-D
Barton	10-C
Bates	7-C
Benton	7-F
Bollinger	10-N
Boone	5-H
Buchanan	3-B
Butler	12-M
Caldwell	3-D
Callaway	6-I
Camden	8-G
Cape Girardeau	10-N
Carroll	4-E
Carter	11-K
Cass	6-C
Cedar	9-D
Chariton	4-G
Christian	11-F
Clark	1-J
Clay	4-C
Clinton	3-C
Cole	7-H
Cooper	6-G
Crawford	8-K
Dade	10-D
Dallas	9-G
Daviess	2-D
DeKalb	2-C
Dent	9-J
Douglas	12-G
Dunklin	14-M
Franklin	7-K
Gasconade	7-J
Gentry	2-C
Greene	11-F
Grundy	2-E
Harrison	1-D
Henry	7-E
Hickory	8-F
Holt	2-A
Howard	5-G
Howell	12-I
Iron	10-L
Jackson	5-C
Jasper	11-C
Jefferson	8-L
Johnson	6-D
Knox	2-I
Laclede	9-G
Lafayette	5-D
Lawrence	11-D
Lewis	2-J
Lincoln	5-K
Linn	3-F
Livingston	3-E
McDonald	12-C
Macon	3-G
Madison	10-L
Maries	8-I
Marion	3-J
Mercer	1-E
Miller	8-H
Mississippi	12-O
Moniteau	7-H
Monroe	4-I
Montgomery	6-J
Morgan	7-G
New Madrid	13-O
Newton	12-C
Nodaway	1-B
Oregon	12-J
Osage	7-I
Ozark	13-H
Pemiscot	14-N
Perry	9-N
Pettis	6-F
Phelps	9-J
Pike	4-K
Platte	4-B
Polk	9-F
Pulaski	9-I
Putnam	1-F
Ralls	4-J
Randolph	4-H
Ray	4-D
Reynolds	10-K
Ripley	12-K
St. Charles	6-L
St. Clair	8-D
St. Francois	9-M
Ste. Genevieve	9-M
St. Louis	7-M
Saline	5-F
Schuyler	1-H
Scotland	1-I
Scott	11-N
Shannon	11-J
Shelby	3-I
Stoddard	12-N
Stone	12-E
Sullivan	2-F
Taney	13-F
Texas	10-I
Vernon	9-C
Warren	6-K
Washington	9-K
Wayne	11-L
Webster	11-G
Worth	1-C
Wright	11-H

"closed" sheaths of sedges and most rushes. In these plants the sheath is a closed cylinder (Figure 4-B). Several grasses, however, have closed sheaths, including the bromes, *Bromus,* and *Melica.* The external junction of the blade and the sheath is called the *collar.* On the inner side is the *ligule.* It varies in size, shape, and texture and is an important and consistent character in classification. In the Indian grass, *Sorghastrum,* the ligule is conspicuous and rigid whereas in orchard grass, *Dactylis,* it is also conspicuous but hyaline. The ligule consists of a tuft of hairs in one section of *Panicum;* in the wild millet, *Echinochloa,* no ligule is present. Some genera, particularly in the tribe *Hordeae,* are characterized by the presence of *auricles,* two small, curved appendages, one on each side of the collar.

Most grasses are perennials. These usually form bunches or tufts of varying size, or a continuous sod. The prairie bluestem, *Andropogon,* is a bunch grass. Characteristic sod-formers are bluegrass, *Poa,* developing from rhizomes, or Bermuda grass, *Cynodon,* spreading by stolons or surface runners. These propagative organs, which are actually stems, are poorly developed or absent in bunch grasses.

Many species of native grasses are generally distributed throughout Missouri. Others have a more limited range and occur predominantly in a particular region, such as the northern prairie counties or the Ozarks region. A few are distinctly local and are found, according to our present knowledge, in a given locality. Various species, some of foreign origin, are adventives. In some cases these have spread widely from the point of ingress. Introductions intended for domestic purpose occasionally escape cultivation and have become naturalized.

In this manual of the Missouri grasses, all native and naturalized species persisting without cultivation are treated. Twelve of the 14 tribes of the grass family listed for the United States (Hitchcock, 1951) are represented by native Missouri species. There are 79 genera and 245 species. In addition there are a number of recognized varieties and forms. Approximately 50 per cent of the species in the state occur also in the eight states which border Missouri. Perennial species are approximately five times as numerous as annual species.

Keys to all known Missouri species are included. Identification of an unknown specimen begins with the determination of the tribe. This is followed by successive delineation through keys to genus, and lastly to the species. If there are fewer than three species in a genus, no key is given. Every genus and species is described. All analytical measurements are based on actual specimens unless otherwise stated. These are expressed in the metric system for which abbreviations and English conversions are as follows: one meter (m.) = 39.37 inches; one centimeter (cm.) = 2/5 inches; one millimeter (mm.) = 1/25 inches. Spikelet characters of each species are illustrated, and in many cases inflorescence and habit drawings are also provided. Missouri distributions, habitat data, and general period of flowering are based on field observations and herbarium studies. County locations may be determined from the accompanying index map of the state. Notes concerning economic values of pertinent species are included. A remarks section is included under various species where additional evaluation or discussion is necessary. General distribution data are based primarily on Hitchcock (1951), and to a limited extent on USDA Handbook No. 58, Weintraub (1953).

Attention is called to current regulations governing nomenclature, as required by the 1952 International Code of Botanical Nomenclature. For example, *Poa pratensis* L. is the technical designation which Linnaeus gave to Kentucky bluegrass. Since there are no subspecific differences, no additional division is required. However, in those species where recognized varieties or forms do exist, additional designations are involved. As an illustration, *Elymus virginicus* L., a wild rye, includes several varieties. The typical variety, from which the other elements are separated, is designated by repetition of the specific epithet. This procedure allows for standardization and eliminates the use of such terms as *typicus* and *genuinus* employed in the past. Thus, *E. virginicus* var. *virginicus* refers to the typical variety, and *E. virginicus* var. *glabriflorus* to one of the several varieties. In this text, when concerned with such infraspecific differences, the initial description encompasses the whole range of variation for the species. Differentiating measurements or characters are used in separating the typical variety or form from the other entities. For purposes of clarification, synonyms used in well-known manuals are given in parentheses.

When making collections for study, specimens should be as complete as possible and include flowering material. Date, location, and pertinent habitat data are recorded at the time of collection. Plants should be pressed and dried, and stored in folders for later reference. Examination of the grass spikelet may require the use of a dissecting microscope, or, if this is not available, a good hand lens. In addition, a dissecting needle, tweezers, and metric rule are useful. Specimens for which verification of identification is requested should be sent to the Department of Botany, University of Missouri, together with appropriate collection information.

KEY TO THE TRIBES

1. Spikelets laterally compressed, as if from the sides, articulated or separating above the persistent glumes; florets 1-several, rarely unisexual, species herbaceous, or woody, bamboo-like in *Arundinaria*....2

1. Spikelets with dorsal compression, articulated below the glumes; florets 1; sometimes spikelets paired, one usually sessile, the other pedicellate and mostly sterile; or all spikelets unisexual; plants herbaceous....10

   2. Plants tall, woody, leafy, with overlapping sheaths....Tribe I. BAMBUSEAE, p. 14

   2. Plants herbaceous....3

3. Spikelets sessile, arranged either on 1 side or opposite sides of the rachis or central axis; spikes solitary, terminal, or if several, racemose or digitate....4

3. Spikelets pedicellate, in racemes or panicles, or clustered on short branches in dense, spikelike racemes or panicles....5

   4. Spikelets in rows on opposite sides of the central, jointed axis....Tribe III. HORDEAE, p. 66

   4. Spikelets on 1 side of the continuous rachis; spikes 1-several....Tribe VI. CHLORIDEAE, p. 137

5. Spikelets with 2 or 3 to many perfect flowers....6

5. Spikelets with 1 perfect flower, sterile bracts sometimes present, or unisexual....7

   6. Glumes long, usually reaching the uppermost floret (1st glume sometimes shorter); awns of lemmas attached dorsally when present....Tribe IV. AVENEAE, p. 87

   6. Glumes shorter, not exceeding the lowermost floret; awns attached apically or near tip when present....Tribe II. FESTUCEAE, p. 16

7. Glumes minute or lacking....8

7. Glumes present and conspicuous....9

   8. Spikelets strongly compressed, distinctly keeled; florets perfect....Tribe III. ORYZEAE, p. 155

   8. Spikelets not compressed; florets unisexual....Tribe IX. ZIZANIEAE, p. 158

9. Sterile lemmas or bracts 2, beneath and attached to the fertile floret....Tribe VII. PHALARIDEAE, p. 152

9. Sterile lemmas not present....Tribe V. AGROSTIDEAE, p. 98

   10. Glumes of thinner texture than the fertile floret; sterile lemmas also thin, about equal to and opposite the 2nd glume; 1st glume smaller or lacking....Tribe X. PANICEAE, p 160

   10. Glumes thick, hardened; sterile lemma and fertile floret thin....11

11. Inflorescence appearing similar throughout; spikelets in pairs, one mostly sessile and perfect, the other pedicellate, mostly sterile and reduced....Tribe XI. ANDROPOGONEAE, p. 208

11. Inflorescence consisting of staminate and pistillate spikelets, in our native species the latter beneath, appearing as a hardened, cylindrical axis....Tribe XII. TRIPSACEAE, p. 223

KEYS TO THE GENERA

TRIBE I. BAMBUSEAE

A single native genus in Missouri..1. *Arundinaria,* p. 14

TRIBE II. FESTUCEAE

Key to Genera

1. Spikelets with conspicuous, straight hairs as long or longer than florets; panicles large, plumose; coarse, leafy-stemmed perennials sometimes to 5 m. or more in height 2
1. Spikelets lacking long, straight hairs which equal florets; plants varying from weak to relatively stout habit, but seldom more than 1.5 m. in height..3
   2. Rachilla glabrous; lemmas long-hairy; tall exotic species, rarely self-established.... ....12. *Arundo,* p. 59
   2. Rachilla with long hairs exceeding lemmas, the latter glabrous; native species, primarily in the northern counties..13. *Phragmites,* p. 59
3. Spikelets unisexual; plants dioecious, perennial, spreading by rhizomes.. ....9. *Distichlis,* p. 53
3. Spikelets with perfect flowers (except for the annual and rare *Eragrostis reptans* which is dioecious, rooting at the nodes)..4
   4. Spikelets in dense, 1-sided, glomerule-like clusters..11. *Dactylis,* p. 56
   4. Spikelets not arranged in dense, 1-sided clusters..5
5. Spikelets with the lowermost floret empty; open, drooping panicles with wide, conspicuously flattened spikelets..10. *Uniola,* p. 54
5. Spikelets without empty floret below the fertile lemmas..6
   6. Lemmas with 3 conspicuous nerves..7
   6. Lemmas with 5 or more nerves, sometimes intermediate nerves faint or indistinct 10
7. Nerves of the lemmas hairy; lemmas with a minute awn or awns from notched or lobed apex..8
7. Nerves of the lemmas smooth; lemmas awnless or with merely acuminate tip 9
   8. Palea with a conspicuous, pubescent fringe on upper part; annuals.. ....16. *Triplasis,* p. 64
   8. Palea lacking a fringe on the upper part, pubescent only on the lower part; perennials..15. *Tridens,* p. 61
9. Spikelets closely overlapping, laterally flattened; grain not protruding.. ....7. *Eragrostis,* p. 41
9. Spikelets distant, in narrow panicles; florets distended, with protruding grains............ ....8. *Diarrhena,* p. 50
   10. Lemmas usually with a bidentate apex; sheaths closed..11
   10. Lemmas with an entire apex; sheaths open..12
11. Spikelets with 2 or 3 florets, awnless, with several empty lemmas above fertile florets..14. *Melica,* p. 59
11. Spikelets with more florets, mostly awned, no empty lemmas above.. ....2. *Bromus,* p. 16
    12. Nerves of lemma all conspicuous, parallel near tip; palea sometimes exceeding the lemma; perennial species of damp or aquatic habitats........5. *Glyceria,* p. 32
    12. Nerves obscure, or not all conspicuous, converging at tip of lemma; palea nearly equal to or shorter than the lemma; species of general habitat conditions, or, occasionally from spring branches as for *Poa annua* var. *reptans*....................13
13. Lemmas awnless, keeled along the back, with mostly cobwebby hairs at the base, or with pubescent nerves..6. *Poa,* p. 34
13. Lemmas awned or awnless, rounded on back, lacking cobwebby hairs at the base 14
    14. Lemmas acuminate, aristate, or awned..3. *Festuca,* p. 24
    14. Lemmas blunt, thin, membraneous at the apex, sometimes lacerated................ ....4. *Puccinellia,* p. 31

TRIBE III. HORDEAE

Key to Genera

1. Spikelets 1 at each joint of the rachis..........2
1. Spikelets 2 to several at each joint, but in some species only 1 perfect one, the rest smaller, sterile, though similarly awned..........6
   2. Spikelets several-flowered, with an edge to the rachis, the inner (1st) glume absent except in terminal spikelets..........25. *Lolium*, p. 85
   2. Spikelets with a flat side to the rachis..........3
3. Spikelets cylindrical; glumes conspicuously-veined with an off-center awn..........19. *Aegilops*, p. 69
3. Spikelets compressed, not cylindric; glumes awned from the center of the apex, or with acute tip..........4
   4. Lemmas symmetrical, the keel in the middle..........17. *Agropyron*, p. 66
   4. Lemmas asymmetrical, the keel displaced to 1 side..........5
5. Glumes broad, ovate, 3-nerved..........18. *Triticum*, p. 69
5. Glumes narrow, tapering, 1-nerved..........20. *Secale*, p. 71
   6. Perfect spikelets 1-flowered, 1 at each node with 2 lateral spikelets which are reduced and awned..........24. *Hordeum*, p. 81
   6. Perfect spikelets 2 or more flowered, more than 1 at each node..........7
7. Spikelets 2 at a node, with long flexuous, wide-spreading awns; glumes extremely narrow, bases not much wider than the awns; rare, a western species..........22. *Sitanion*, p. 78
7. Spikelets 2 or more, awned; glumes thickened, bases wider than the awns; common species of prairie and woodland..........21. *Elymus*, p. 73

TRIBE IV. AVENEAE

Key to Genera

1. Spikelets, excluding awns, 1 cm. or more in length..........2
1. Spikelets less than 1 cm. long..........3
   2. Glumes conspicuously veined, up to 2.5 cm. long; introduced annuals with flat, wide leaves..........30. *Avena*, p. 91
   2. Glumes not conspicuously veined, 9-13 mm. long; native perennials with curling, narrow leaves from tufted bases..........33. *Danthonia*, p. 97
3. Lemmas with bent awns, more than 5 mm. in length..........4
3. Lemmas awnless, or if awns present, 1-4 mm. long..........5
   4. Spikelets 2-flowered; only the lower floret conspicuously awned; glumes of similar width; leaf blades more than 5 mm. wide..........31. *Arrhenatherum*, p. 93
   4. Spikelets 3-4 flowered; lemmas awned; 1st glume smaller, narrower than the 2nd; if 2-flowered, leaf blades less than 5 mm. wide..........28. *Trisetum*, p. 90
5. Articulation above the glumes, the latter persistent..........6
5. Articulation below the glumes, the spikelets falling entire (see also *Trisetum pensylvanicum*)..........7
   6. Lemmas all awnless..........26. *Koeleria*, p. 87
   6. Only the upper lemma with a delicate awn attached from below the middle, the lower one usually awnless..........29. *Aira*, p. 91
7. Glumes similar; sterile floret with a short, curving awn; sheaths velvety-hairy; introduced species..........32. *Holcus*, p. 97
7. Glumes dissimilar, the 1st narrow, linear, the 2nd broader, obovate; short awns if present not curving; sheaths not velvety; native species......27. *Sphenopholis*, p. 87

TRIBE V. AGROSTIDEAE

Key to Genera

1. Inflorescence cylindrical, compact, a spike-like panicle; plants lacking rhizomes........2
1. Inflorescence not cylindrical, with more diffuse or open branching of the panicles, sometimes compact or congested..........4
   2. Glumes awned, equal, much overtopping the floret..........39. *Phleum*, p. 110
   2. Glumes awnless, equal to or shorter than floret..........3
3. Lemmas awned from back; glumes with dorsal cilia..........38. *Alopecurus*, p. 107
3. Lemmas awnless; glumes not ciliate..........42. *Heleochloa*, p. 126
   4. Articulation below the glumes, spikelets falling entire; floret with a short stipe..........37. *Cinna*, p. 107
   4. Articulation above the glumes; the glumes persistent, only the floret falling........5

5. Lemmas rather thick, rigid, with hardened, obtuse to mostly sharp-pointed bases 6
5. Lemmas mostly thin, not extending into hard, pointed bases....8
   6. Lemmas with 3 awns....46. *Aristida,* p. 131
   6. Lemmas single-awned....7
7. Base of the lemma extending into a sharp point; lemma with a long, bent, twisted awn....45. *Stipa,* p. 129
7. Base of the lemma blunt; awn not twisted, somewhat flexuous....44. *Oryzopsis,* p. 127
   8. Lemmas awned from the tip....9
   8. Lemmas awnless, or awned dorsally, or below the tip....10
9. Rachilla extended as a short joint behind the palea....43. *Brachyelytrum,* p. 127
9. Rachilla not extended....40. *Muhlenbergia,* p. 110
   10. Lemmas with tufted hairs at the base, equal to or exceeding half the length of the body....11
   10. Lemmas without basal hairs, if present then sparse and much shorter....12
11. Lemmas awned; both glumes equal to or exceeding the floret....34. *Calamagrostis,* p. 98
11. Lemmas awnless; 1st glume much shorter than the floret....35. *Calamovilfia,* p. 100
   12. Lemmas 1-nerved, awnless; 1st glume usually shorter than floret....41. *Sporobolus,* p. 118
   12. Lemmas 2-3-nerved, awned or awnless; 1st glume about equal to or exceeding the floret....36. *Agrostis,* p. 100

TRIBE VI. CHLORIDEAE

Key to Genera

1. Spikelets unisexual, the staminate ones in exserted, solitary, 1-sided spikes, 1.5 cm. or less in length; plants stoloniferous....56. *Buchloe,* p. 150
1. Spikelets having perfect flowers; plants lacking stolons (except in *Cynodon,* which has digitate spikes)....2
   2. Inflorescence consisting of spikes, digitate or digitate-like, or spikes in whorls....3
   2. Inflorescence consisting of spikes, these racemose or paniculate, not digitate....5
3. Spikelets awned, 2-flowered, the upper floret sterile....54. *Chloris,* p. 147
3. Spikelets awnless, 1-several-flowered....4
   4. Spikelets 1-flowered; stoloniferous, sod-forming plants....49. *Cynodon,* p. 139
   4. Spikelets several-flowered; annual plants with wide, flattened culms near base, forming isolated tufts....48. *Eleusine,* p. 139
5. Spikes dense, thick, with crowded spikelets; perfect flowers, mostly 1....6
5. Spikes slender, diffuse; spikelets distant; perfect flowers, 1-several....8
   6. Spikelets laterally flattened, broad as long, or nearly so, awnless....51. *Beckmannia,* p. 142
   6. Spikelets elongate, awned....7
7. Spikelets with 1-several sterile, awned florets above the perfect floret; plants less than 1 m. tall....55. *Bouteloua,* p. 149
7. Sterile florets lacking; tall, coarse plants exceeding 1 m....52. *Spartina,* p. 144
   8. Spikelets with several perfect flowers....47. *Leptochloa,* p. 137
   8. Spikelets with only 1 perfect flower....9
9. Spikelets awned; flower stalks with numerous branches or spikes....53. *Gymnopogon,* p. 144
9. Spikelets awnless; flower stalks diffuse, spikes distant along the central axis....50. *Schedonnardus,* p. 142

TRIBE VII. PHALARIDEAE

Key to Genera

1. Spikelets with awned florets; glumes strongly unequal in length....57. *Anthoxanthum,* p. 152
1. Spikelets awnless; glumes of similar length....58. *Phalaris,* p. 152

TRIBE VIII. ORYZEAE

Key to Genera

1. Glume-like bracts (sterile lemmas) present; introduced cereal plant; annual....59. *Oryza,* p. 155
1. Glume-like bracts absent; native perennials with short rhizomes....60. *Leersia,* p. 155

TRIBE IX. ZIZANIEAE

Key to Genera

1. Staminate and pistillate spikelets on separate branches, the latter in the upper part of the panicle; awn exceeding the lemma of pistillate floret..............61. *Zizania,* p. 158
1. Staminate and pistillate spikelets appearing on the same branches of panicle; pistillate floret with an awn shorter than lemma.........................62. *Zizaniopsis,* p. 158

TRIBE X. PANICEAE

Key to Genera

1. Spikelets several, enveloped in a spiny, globose involucre or bur..71. *Cenchrus,* p. 207
1. Spikelets not forming a spiny bur..........2
   2. Spikelets subtended by several bristles, the inflorescence compact, somewhat cylindric and spike-like..........70. *Setaria,* p. 201
   2. Spikelets not subtended by bristles; the inflorescence an open panicle, or consisting of several ascending or spreading spike-like racemes..........3
3. Spikelets nearly sessile or short-stalked, in spike-like racemes..........4
3. Spikelets stalked, in panicles (spike-like racemes in 3 species of *Panicum,* see spp. 27, 28, and 29, in this genus)..........8
   4. Glumes and sterile lemma usually awned, sometimes merely apiculate, usually crowded in numerous, dense racemes; 1st glume conspicuous..........69. *Echinochloa,* p. 199
   4. Glumes and sterile lemma awnless, arranged in 2 rows on 1 side of the raceme; 1st glume reduced or absent (conspicuous in *Brachiaria*)..........5
5. 1st glume conspicuous..........66. *Brachiaria,* p. 166
5. 1st glume absent or minute..........6
   6. Fertile lemma short-awned or merely apiculate; spikelet with a short stipe below..........65. *Eriochloa,* p. 163
   6. Fertile lemma awnless..........7
7. Spikelets ovate to orbicular, convex on 1 side, with other side flat and away from rachis..........67. *Paspalum,* p. 166
7. Spikelets elliptic to lanceolate, not flattened on 1 side..........63. *Digitaria,* p. 160
   8. 1st glume minute or absent; fertile lemma thin, the edges not inrolled..........64. *Leptoloma,* p. 163
   8. 1st glume present, at least one-fourth as long as the 2nd glume; fertile lemma thick, the edges inrolled..........68. *Panicum,* p. 173

TRIBE XI. ANDROPOGONEAE

Key to Genera

1. Lower and upper spikelet of each pair pedicellate; tall, clump grasses with whitish, plume-like panicles..........72. *Miscanthus,* p. 208
1. Lower spikelet of each pair sessile, only the upper spikelet pedicellate..........2
   2. Spikelets of each pair similar, and perfect; spikelets long tufted at the base, if not, then with a slender, straight awn 1 cm. or more in length..........73. *Erianthus,* p. 208
   2. Spikelets dissimilar, the sessile one perfect, the other (pedicellate) reduced, or sterile, sometimes staminate..........3
3. Spikelets recessed in a cylindrical pencil-like rachis..........78. *Manisurus,* p. 222
3. Spikelets in spreading racemes, or panicles..........4
   4. Pedicellate spikelet absent; rachis and pedicels bearded; inflorescence a light-brown panicle..........77. *Sorghastrum,* p. 219
   4. Pedicellate spikelet present..........5
5. Inflorescence a smooth-branching, terminal, open panicle..........76. *Sorghum,* p. 216
5. Inflorescence consisting of pubescent or feathery spike-like racemes, solitary, digitate or paniculate..........6
   6. Racemes jointed, separating into paired spikelets; leaves elongate..........75. *Andropogon,* p. 211
   6. Racemes not jointed; leaves short, ovate with cordate bases..74. *Arthraxon,* p. 210

TRIBE XII. TRIPSACEAE

A single native genus in Missouri ....79. *Tripsacum,* p. 223

KEYS TO SPECIES
With Descriptions and Illustrations

TRIBE I. BAMBUSEAE

1. ARUNDINARIA Michx.

Woody perennials, producing rhizomes; canes leafy, branching, or sometimes leafless, simple; panicles terminal or axillary; spikelets several-flowered, compressed-keeled, separating above the persistent glumes; glumes unequal, sharp-pointed; lemmas tapering, acuminate, awnless. This is the only genus of North American grasses with woody culms.

1. **Arundinaria gigantea** (Walt.) Muhl. GIANT CANE. Fig. 5.

Plants forming large clumps or colonies; culms coarse, bamboo-like, 1.5-7.5 m. tall, sometimes taller; sheaths telescoped, hispid, with auriculate bristles at the summit; leaf blades bluish-green, lanceolate, 1-3 cm. wide, with a petiolate base; spikelets pubescent, listed dimensions 2-7 cm. long, but specimens generally not flowering in Missouri.

Distribution: Southeastern United States, Florida to Texas, north to Missouri and Ohio Valley.

Missouri. Alluvial bottoms, stream banks, springs, southern Ozarks and Mississippi River region, south of a line from Perry west to McDonald counties, frequently abundant, forming dense stands, and providing usable forage from the new growth.

Remarks: According to some workers *A. tecta* (Walt.) Muhl., originally distinguished by the flowering canes being mostly leafless, is possibly a growth form of *A. gigantea.* Previous observations have indicated the presence of leafy as well as leafless canes developing from the same rootstocks. However, Gilly (1943) stated that there are two specific identities in the North American canes separated on spikelet characters, rather than on growth form. It was shown also that both types of spikelets may be associated with the so-called "tectoid" phase.

FIG. 5.—*Arundinaria gigantea.* Flowering shoot, × ½; two views of floret, × 2.

TRIBE II. FESTUCEAE

2. BROMUS L. BROME

Annuals or perennials; panicles terminal, generally open, with more or less spreading branches; spikelets several-flowered, usually large and exceeding 1 cm. in length, separating above the persistent glumes; glumes unequal; lemmas bidentate or sometimes entire, awned from below the apex, or awnless; grain pubescent at the summit, adhering to the palea. A characteristic feature of the genus is the closed sheath, thus differing from the open sheath of most other grasses.

Eleven species are reported in Missouri; eight of these are weedy annuals, adventive from the Old World and South America.

KEY TO MISSOURI SPECIES

1. Spikelets awnless, or with a short awn 1-2 mm. long; important forage perennial ....9. *B. inermis*
1. Spikelets distinctly awned (awnless or nearly so in the annual *B. Willdenowii,* with conspicuously flattened florets); introduced annuals or native perennials........2
   2. Perennials, usually in damp, shaded habitats........3
   2. Annuals, occurring in dry, open ground or waste areas........4
3. Sheaths mostly pubescent, not reaching the nodes; common species throughout the state........10. *B. purgans*
3. Sheaths mostly glabrous, exceeding and covering the nodes; scattered and infrequent species........11. *B. latiglumis*
   4. Florets and glumes flattened and keeled, awnless, or nearly so; rare species........1. *B. Willdenowii*
   4. Florets and glumes rounded on back, not flattened, distinctly awned in most specimens 5
5. 1st glume about 1 mm. wide, elongate, 1-nerved; awns of lemmas straight, usually 12-15 mm. long or more........6
5. 1st glume 2 mm. wide or more, not tapering to long tip, 3- (sometimes 5-) nerved; awns straight or divergent, mostly less than 10 mm. long........8
   6. Awns about 15 mm. long; panicles silvery-green with drooping spikelets; foliage pubescent; common roadside and waste ground species........8. *B. tectorum*
   6. Awns 20 mm. or more in length; rare or scattered species........7
7. 1st glume 8-10 mm. long; awns of lemmas about 20-25 mm. long........7. *B. sterilis*
7. 1st glume longer than 10 mm.; awns of lemmas exceeding 30 mm. in length........6. *B. rigidus*
   8. Sheaths mostly glabrous; blades about 5 mm. wide or wider (up to 10 mm. in some specimens); spikelets sometimes awnless or nearly so........4. *B. secalinus*
   8. Sheaths pubescent; blades narrower, usually less than 5 mm.; spikelets conspicuously awned........9
9. Panicles diffuse, branches delicate, drooping; awns divergent, up to 10 mm. long; sheaths conspicuously pubescent........2. *B. japonicus*
9. Panicles relatively compact, or if open then branches more rigid; awns straight; sheaths pubescent or sparsely so........10
   10. Panicles contracted with short branches; spikelets and foliage soft-pubescent; infrequent species........5. *B. mollis*
   10. Panicles open, the branches spreading; spikelets smooth; foliage in particular specimens only sparsely hairy; common species........3. *B. racemosus*

1. **Bromus Willdenowii** Kunth. RESCUE-GRASS. Fig. 6.

Annual; culms erect, to 1 m. tall; foliage mostly glabrous except for lower sheaths; leaf blades 3-5 mm. wide; panicles sparsely flowered, with stiffly ascending branches; spikelets sharply keeled, pale green, 2-3 cm. long; glumes nearly

FIG. 6.—*Bromus Willdenowii*, × 1.

equal, elongate; lemmas essentially glabrous, the nerves ciliate, 10-15 mm. long, awnless or nearly so. (*B. catharticus* Vohl.)

Distribution: Widely scattered in the United States, most common in the South; adventive from South America.

Missouri. Rare, reported from Jackson, Newton, and Jasper counties. Flowering in May-June.

Remarks: In a recent paper, Raven (1960), it was shown that the correct name for the widely distributed rescue grass is *B. Willdenowii* Kunth and should be used instead of *B. catharticus*.

2. **Bromus japonicus** Thumb. JAPANESE CHESS. Fig. 7.

Annual; culms 50 cm. or taller; foliage pubescent; leaf blades 3-6 mm. wide; panicles open, with spreading branches arranged in whorls; spikelets 2-3 cm. long; glumes unequal, the 1st 3-nerved, the 2nd 5-nerved; lemmas smooth, 8-9 mm. long, with a slender divergent awn. This species resembles the following, but differs by the more drooping habit of the panicle branches, and by the spreading awns. (Including *B. arvensis* L.)

FIG. 7.—*Bromus japonicus*, × 1.

Distribution: Widespread as a weed in the United States; introduced from the Old World.

Missouri. Waste areas, open ground, fields, generally distributed. Flowering in May-June.

3. **Bromus racemosus** L. CHESS. Fig. 8.

Annual; culms 40-100 cm. tall, resembling the preceding in general habit and also species 4 and 5; panicles open, the branches somewhat stiff; spikelets glabrous, becoming plump, 2-3 cm. long; glumes unequal, the 1st 3-nerved, the 2nd 5-nerved; lemmas 8-10 mm. long, with scarious margins, straight-awned. This species is distinguished from *B. japonicus* by the stiffer panicle branches and less divergent awns. Both are equally common in Missouri. (Including *B. commutatus* Schrad.)

Distribution: Widespread as a weed in the United States; introduced from Europe.

Missouri. Waste areas, open ground, fields, generally distributed. Flowering in May-June.

4. **Bromus mollis** L. SOFT CHESS. Fig. 9.

Annual; culms 50-100 cm. tall; foliage soft, downy-pubescent; leaf blades 3-5 mm. wide; panicles somewhat contracted with short, ascending branches; spikelets downy, 1.5-2.5 cm. long; glumes unequal, the 1st 3-nerved, the 2nd 5-nerved; lemmas about 8 mm. long, with broad scarious margins, and awned from a deeply 2-cleft apex.

Distribution: Widely scattered in the United States, particularly common in the California range; adventive from Europe.

Missouri. Rare and little known, reported on waste ground from Jackson and St. Louis counties. Flowering in May-June.

FIG. 8.—*Bromus racemosus,* × 1.

FIG. 9.—*Bromus mollis,* × 1.

5. **Bromus secalinus** L. CHESS. Fig. 10.

Annual; culms about 50 cm. or taller; foliage glabrous or nearly so; leaf blades 3-9 mm. wide; panicles open with spreading branches; spikelets glabrous, 1-2 cm. long; glumes oblong, short pointed; lemmas plump, 7-9 mm. long, with a short awn less than 5 mm. in length; margins of the mature lemmas becoming

FIG. 10.—*Bromus secalinus*. Plant, × ½; spikelet and floret, × 5.

inrolled, exposing the rachilla. This and the three preceding species are closely allied, characterized by annual weedy habit, the 1st glume 3-nerved, and the lemmas generally blunt-tipped.

Distribution: Widespread in the United States; adventive from Europe.

Missouri. Waste ground and grain fields, generally distributed. Flowering in May-June.

6. **Bromus rigidus.** RIP-GUT GRASS. Fig. 11.

Annual; culms erect, about 50 cm. or taller; foliage pubescent, the leaf blades 3-6 mm. wide; panicles few-flowered, with somewhat stiff branches; spikelets coarse, with sharp, tapering bases; glumes dissimilar, the 1st one narrow, 1-nerved, about 1.5 cm. long, the 2nd broader, 3-nerved and longer; lemmas 2.5-3 cm. long with straight awns 3-4 cm. or longer.

Distribution: Widely scattered in the United States; introduced from Europe. The sharp, awned spikelets may be injurious to livestock when present in hay.

Missouri. Rare and little known, reported on waste ground from Jackson and St. Louis counties. Flowering in May-June.

7. **Bromus sterilis** L. Fig. 12.

Annual, similar in general habit to species 6 but with smaller spikelets and shorter awns; lower sheaths pubescent but the leaf blades smooth or nearly so; panicles diffuse, few-flowered; glumes dissimilar; lemmas smooth or scabrous, about 1.5 cm. long, with straight awns 2-3 cm. in length.

FIG. 11.—*Bromus rigidus.* Spikelet, × 1.

FIG. 12.—*Bromus sterilis.* Spikelet, × 1.

Distribution: Widely scattered in the United States; introduced from Europe.

Missouri. Rare, waste areas and open ground, reported from Newton and Wright counties. Flowering in May-June.

FIG. 13.—*Bromus tectorum.* Plant, × ½; spikelet and floret, × 5.

8. **Bromus tectorum** L. DOWNY CHESS. Fig. 13.

Annual, forming small tufts; culms erect about 50 cm. or taller; foliage pubescent, the leaf blades 3-5 mm. wide; panicles soft, dense, silvery green, with slender, drooping branches; spikelets narrow, tapering to the base; 1st glume subulate, about 1 mm. wide, 1-nerved, the 2nd glume wider with scarious margins and 3-nerved; lemmas soft-pubescent, about 10 mm. long with a straight awn, 10-15 mm. in length. This and the two preceding species are closely related, characterized by the narrow, straight-awned spikelets with tapering bases, differing primarily in the size of the spikelet and awn length.

Distribution: Widely scattered in the United States, less common or absent in the Southeast; introduced from Europe.

Missouri. Dry soils on open ground, fields, and along roadsides, generally distributed, one of our most common annual bromes. Flowering in early May.

9. **Bromus inermis** Leyss. SMOOTH BROME. Fig. 14.

Perennial, forming a sod, spreading by rhizomes; culms erect, to 1 m. tall or more; nodes and foliage mostly glabrous, the leaf blades 5-15 mm. wide; panicles somewhat dense, 10-25 cm. long, the branches whorled, stiffly erect at maturity; spikelets narrow, somewhat cylindrical, 2-3 cm. long, becoming brownish; glumes awl-shaped, the 1st 1-nerved, the 2nd 3-nerved, both with thin, hyaline margins; lemmas glabrous, or rarely pubescent, also thin-margined, about 10 mm. long, awnless, or sometimes with short awn to 3 mm. in length; anthers conspicuous, 4-6 mm. long. Specimens with pubescent lemmas are sometimes designated as forma *villosa* (Mert. & Koch.) Fern.

Distribution: Primarily northern and western United States, less common in the South; introduced from the Old World as a forage species.

Missouri. Open ground, fields, most common in the northern counties. Specimens with pubescent lemmas occur only rarely. Flowering in June-July.

Remarks: Wagnon (1952) reduces the closely related *B. pumpellianus* to subspecific rank, *i.e.* subsp. *pumpellianus* (Scribn.) Wagnon, and includes it under *B. inermis*. It is distinguished by the usually pubescent nodes and leaf blades, and the more prominent auricles. This taxon is of American origin, ranging from Canada south to Colorado, but does not reach Missouri.

10. **Bromus purgans** L. CANADA BROME. Fig. 15.

Perennial, solitary or in small clumps; culms erect, to 1 m. or more tall; sheaths pubescent, or sometimes glabrous, usually shorter than the internode; leaf blades pilose to smooth, thin, lax, 5-15 mm. wide; panicles diffuse, with whorled, drooping branches; spikelets 1.5-3 cm. long; 1st glume 1-nerved, the 2nd 3-nerved, both with narrow, hyaline margins; lemmas pubescent or rarely smooth, 8-10 mm. long, distinctly awned. Specimens with glabrous sheaths are sometimes distinguished as forma *laevivaginatus* Wieg.

Distribution: Eastern and central United States, west to North Dakota and Texas.

Missouri. Damp, shaded ground and rocky slopes, usually on calcareous soils, generally distributed, but less common in the extreme southeast. Flowering in May-June, somewhat earlier than the following closely related species.

FIG. 14.—*Bromus inermis*. Plant, × ½; spikelet, × 2½.

FIG. 15.—*Bromus purgans*. Plant, × ½; spikelet, × 5.

Remarks: Wagnon (1952) employs *B. pubescens* Muhl. ex Willd. here instead of *B. purgans*. In turn the latter usage is construed to include *B. latiglumis*, the following species. Wagnon attributes to the Missouri flora *B. nottowayanus* Fern., which he suspects may be a hybrid and which possibly should be reduced to varietal status under his *B. pubescens*. Since there is some doubt about its specific rank, it is not included here.

11. **Bromus latiglumis** (Shear) Hitchc. Fig. 16.

Perennial, solitary or in small clumps; culms about 1 m. tall, generally resembling the preceding species; sheaths mostly glabrous, rarely pilose, with conspicuous auriculate flange at summit usually exceeding the internode; panicles diffuse with drooping branches; lemmas pubescent, about 10 mm. long, distinctly awned. Plants differing from the typically glabrous condition in having pilose sheaths are sometimes separated as forma *incana* (Shear.) Fern. (*B. purgans* of Wagnon, 1952.)

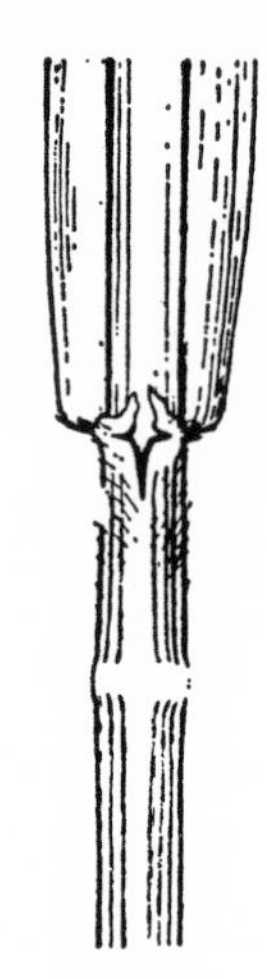

FIG. 16.—*Bromus latiglumis*, × 2.

Distribution: Northeastern United States and Canada, west to North Dakota, south to Missouri and mid-Atlantic region.

Missouri. Damp, shaded ground and alluvial banks, infrequent and scattered, mostly in the eastern counties. Flowering in July-August, generally later than the preceding species.

3. FESTUCA L. FESCUE

Annuals or perennials; panicles mostly terminal, narrow, compact, or diffusely spreading; spikelets several-flowered, separating above the persistent glumes; glumes mostly unequal; lemmas acuminate or pointed, or sometimes awned from the apex (apex not 2-cleft with an awn arising below the tip of lemma as in *Bromus*). The annual species are placed by some authors in the genus *Vulpia* K. C. Gmel.

KEY TO MISSOURI SPECIES

1. Plants annual, of slight habit, leaf blades at most 1 mm. wide, with involute or inrolled margins....2
1. Plants perennial, leaf blades much wider, flat, or mostly involute from basal clumps as in *F. rubra* and *F. ovina*....4
   2. Glumes very unequal, the 1st about one-fifth or less as long as the 2nd; florets large, the lemmas 5-6 mm. in length with an awn about 10 mm. long....1. *F. myuros*
   2. Glumes more equal, the 1st one-half or more as long as the 2nd; florets smaller, the lemmas 3-5 mm. in length, awned or awnless....3
3. Lemmas about 3 mm. long with long, delicate awn up to 10 mm. in length; infrequent species....3. *F. sciurea*
3. Lemmas usually larger, awn 1-5 mm. long, or awnless; common species on dry, thin soils....2. *F. octoflora*
   4. Plants with narrow or involute basal leaves less than 2 mm. wide, forming dense clumps; panicles contracted and spike-like....5
   4. Plants with flat leaves more than 2 mm. wide, solitary, few, or in clumps; panicles contracted or diffusely branched....6
5. Basal sheaths reddish, becoming fibrous at maturity; leaves about 1 mm. wide........6. *F. rubra*

5. Basal sheaths lighter colored, not becoming fibrous; leaves narrow, mostly involute ....5. *F. ovina*
   6. Leaf blades auriculate; spikelets linear, about 10 mm. long; introduced forage species..4. *F. elatior*
   6. Leaf blades not auriculate; spikelets shorter; native prairie and woods species........7
7. Panicles diffusely branched; spikelets scattered, not crowded; species of damp woods ....7. *F. obtusa*
7. Panicles somewhat contracted; spikelets plump, clustered toward ends of drooping branches; species of prairies and open woods..8. *F. paradoxa*

1. **Festuca myuros** L. RAT'S-TAIL FESCUE. Fig. 17.

Annual; culms 20-50 cm. tall, somewhat geniculate near base; foliage mostly glabrous; leaf blades narrow, with inrolled margins; panicles narrow, spike-like, 6-15 cm. long; spikelets 4-5 flowered; glumes very unequal, the 1st about 1 mm. long, the 2nd 4-5 mm. long; lemmas scabrous, about 5 mm. long, with awn twice as long or nearly so.

Distribution: Widely scattered in the United States; adventive from Europe.

Missouri. Rare, reported on open ground from Boone and St. Louis counties. Flowering in May-June.

2. **Festuca octoflora** Walt. SIXWEEKS FESCUE. Fig. 18.

Annual, with habit similar to the preceding species; foliage generally glabrous; sheaths shorter than the internodes; panicles contracted, spike-like to somewhat open, with short, ascending branches; spikelets 6-12 flowered; glumes dissimilar, the 1st about 1.5-3 mm. long, the 2nd 4-5 mm. long; lemmas smooth

FIG. 17.—*Festuca myuros.* Spikelet, × 5.

FIG. 18.—*Festuca octoflora.* Plant, × ½; spikelet, × 5.

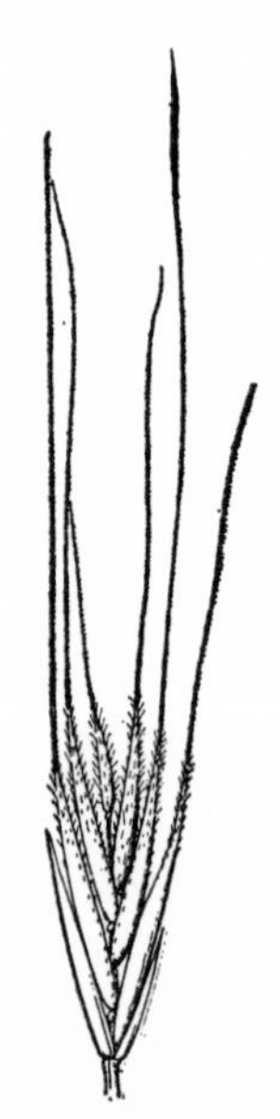

FIG. 19.—*Festuca sciurea.* Spikelet, × 5.

to scabrous, about 3 mm. or longer, with an awn 1-5 mm. long. This species differs from the preceding by the smaller spikelets, more numerous florets, and shorter awns. Based on variations in spikelet size and awn length, the species has been divided into several varieties. These are weakly separable but tendencies may be noted in Missouri plants. Generally, typical plants, var. *octoflora,* are those with the more open panicles and longer awns, passing into var. *tenella* (Willd.) Fern. with slender panicles and shorter awns, and lastly var. *glauca* (Nutt.) Fern., with the most compact panicles and generally awnless spikelets.

Distribution: Widespread throughout the United States.

Missouri. Fields and waste ground, on dry, thin soils, occurring most commonly as var. *tenella,* throughout the state. Var. *octoflora,* and those plants with the awnless tendency, var. *glauca,* are found primarily in the southern counties. Flowering in May-June.

3. **Festuca sciurea** Nutt. Fig. 19.

Annual, similar in habit to species 1 and 2; leaf blades involute; panicles contracted; spikelets about 5-flowered; glumes dissimilar, the 1st 2 mm. long, the 2nd about 4 mm. long; lemmas pubescent, 3 mm. long, with a delicate awn about 10 mm. in length. This species differs from *F. myuros* by its more equal glumes, and from *F. octoflora* by distinctly longer awns. (*F. Elliotea* [Raf.] Fern.)

Distribution: Southeastern and Atlantic Coast region, west to Oklahoma and Texas.

Missouri. Fields and waste areas, scattered, occurring primarily in the southern counties. Flowering in April-May.

4. **Festuca elatior** L. MEADOW FESCUE. Fig. 20.

Perennial, forming loose to dense tufts; culms, erect, to 1 m. tall or more; foliage glabrous; leaf blades 5 mm. wide or more; auricles glabrous to ciliate, sometimes only on 1 side of sheath summit; panicles somewhat narrow and contracted to spreading, 5-25 cm. long with branches mostly floriferous; spikelets elongate, about 10 mm. long usually more than 5-flowered; glumes unequal with scarious margins; lemmas glabrous, 5-6 mm. long, awnless, or rarely with short awn. Plants which form dense tufts and are distinguished also by more spreading panicles and minutely ciliate auricles are referred to var. *arundinacea* (Schreb.) Wimmer (*F. arundinacea* Screb.).

Distribution: Widely distributed in the United States, becoming self-established in some regions; introduced from the Old World as a hay and pasture species. Several strains or selections have been developed or discovered in this country including Alta Fescue and Kentucky 31, both in the *arundinacea* complex.

Missouri. Fields and waste areas, scattered but not abundant. Flowering in May-June.

5. **Festuca ovina** L. SHEEP'S FESCUE. Fig. 21.

Perennial, forming dense tufts, lacking rhizomes; culms wiry, usually not more than 50 cm. tall; lower sheaths light colored, intact, not becoming fibrous as in species 6; leaf blades string-like, involute; panicles narrow, rather dense; spikelets oblong, about 5-flowered, 5-8 mm. long; glumes firm, sharp-pointed; lemmas 4-5 mm. long, aristate, or short awned. Coarse plants with hard, tough leaves have been designated as var. *duriuscula* (L.) Koch., commonly known as Hard Fescue.

Distribution: Northern and western United States and in some eastern areas, occasionally self-established; introduced from Europe as a forage species.

Missouri. Rare, reported from Jackson, Boone, and St. Louis counties. Flowering in June-July.

6. **Festuca rubra** L. RED FESCUE. Fig. 22.

Perennial, forming leafy tufts or loose sod; short rhizomes sometimes present; culms erect to decumbent near base, creeping, less than 1 m. tall; foliage mostly glabrous, the lower sheaths characteristically reddish, becoming stringy, fibrous;

FIG. 20.—*Festuca elatior.* Plant, × ½; spikelet and floret, × 5.

FIG. 21.—*Festuca ovina.* Panicle, × ½; floret, × 5.

FIG. 22.—*Festuca rubra.* Plant, × ½; spikelet and floret, × 5.

lower blades involute or narrow, about 1 mm. wide, some upper leaves flat and wider; panicles narrow, with short side branches; spikelets elongate or oblong, usually more than 5-flowered, 10-15 mm. long; glumes dissimilar, the 1st narrow, sharp-pointed, the 2nd wider and longer with scarious margins; lemmas glabrous, 5-6 mm. long with narrow scarious edges, awnless, or with an awn 1-3 mm. long. Plants distinguished by the absence of rhizomes and usually forming thick tufts are designated as var. *commutata* Gaudin, commonly known as Chewings Fescue. Numerous other distinctions and strains are recognized, based on foliage and spikelet characters, some of these of commercial importance.

Distribution: Cultivated in the northern parts of the United States, sometimes self-established; introduced from Europe as forage and turf species.

Missouri. Open or shaded ground, used in lawn mixtures and occasionally spreading, not common as an escape. Flowering in May-June.

7. **Festuca obtusa** Spreng. NODDING FESCUE. Fig. 23.

Perennial, solitary or loosely tufted; culms to 1 m. tall; foliage generally glabrous, or with slight pubescence on the lower sheaths; leaf blades thin, lax, 3-10 mm. wide; panicles diffuse, with few spikelets toward the ends of spreading branches; spikelets elliptic, few-flowered, about 4-7 mm. long; glumes dissimilar, the 1st awl-shaped, 3 mm. long, the 2nd wider and somewhat longer; lemmas glabrous or nearly so, about 3.5-4 mm. long, awnless. (*F. nutans* Spreng.)

Distribution: Eastern United States to the Middle West.

Missouri. Damp, shaded ground, alluvial bottoms, and calcareous slopes, generally distributed. Flowering in May-June.

8. **Festuca paradoxa** Desv. Fig. 24.

Perennial, similar to species 7, but generally coarser; panicles somewhat more compact, the branches stiffer, more ascending; spikelets ovate, few-flowered, 5-7.5 mm. long; lemmas glabrous, plump, averaging about 4.5 mm. long, awnless. This species is distinguished from the preceding by the more congested panicles and shorter branches, and the heavy, plump, slightly larger spikelets. (*F. Shortii* Kunth.)

Distribution: Eastern United States to the Middle West.

Missouri. Prairies, open woods, and bluffs, generally distributed. Flowering in late spring and early summer, generally later than the preceding species, also occupying more open sites.

FIG. 23.—*Festuca obtusa.* Panicle, × ½; floret, × 5.

FIG. 24.—*Festuca paradoxa.* Panicle, × ½; floret, × 5.

4. PUCCINELLIA Parl.

Annuals or perennials; panicles contracted, or diffuse with spreading branches; spikelets several-flowered, separating above the persistent glumes; glumes somewhat unequal, shorter than the lemmas; lemmas faintly nerved, blunt, or merely acute, the apex thin, scarious or sometimes lacerated, awnless.

1. **Puccinellia distans** (L.) Parl. WEEPING ALKALI GRASS. Fig. 25.

Perennial, forming tufts; culms erect to decumbent, to 1 m. tall; foliage glabrous, the leaf blades about 2 mm. wide, involute when dried; panicles 5-15 cm. long, with spreading to drooping branches; spikelets about 5-flowered, 4-5 mm. long; glumes thin-margined, the 1st about 1 mm. long, the 2nd somewhat longer; lemmas obscurely nerved, about 2 mm. long, with broad apex, the margin hyaline; palea equaling lemma.

Distribution: Western and northern United States and adjacent Canada; also Eurasia.

Missouri. Rare and little known, collected on waste ground, St. Louis County (Muhlenbach 70).

2. **Puccinellia Nuttalliana** (Schult.) Hitchc. Fig. 26.

Perennial, forming tufts; culms erect, to 1 m. tall; leaf blades narrow, involute; panicles with short spreading or ascending branches; spikelets about 5 mm. long; glumes slightly unequal, 1-2 mm. long; lemmas 2-2.5 mm. long, with irregular, somewhat narrowing apex. This species is similar to the preceding but is distinguishable by the less drooping panicle branches and somewhat larger spikelets. (*P. airoides* [Nutt.] Wats. & Coult.)

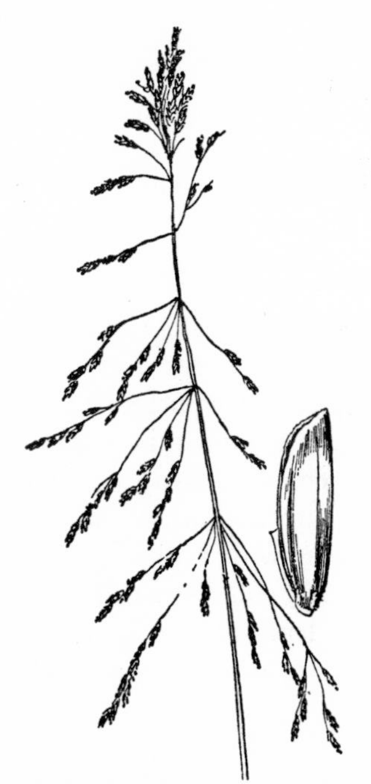

FIG. 25.—*Puccinellia distans.* Panicle, × ½; floret, × 10.

FIG. 26.—*Puccinellia Nuttalliana.* Panicle, × 1; floret, × 10.

Distribution: Western United States and adjacent Canada, east to Wisconsin, Kansas, and New Mexico; elsewhere introduced and local as in *Missouri,* waste ground, St. Louis County (Muhlenbach 1179).

5. GLYCERIA R. Br. MANNA GRASS

Perennials; panicles contracted, or open with spreading or drooping branches; spikelets several-flowered, separating above the persistent glumes; glumes unequal, shorter than the lowermost lemma; lemmas conspicuously nerved, obtuse to acute, the apex usually thin and scarious, awnless (in the preceding genus, *Puccinellia,* the lemmas are faintly nerved); palea nearly equal to or exceeding lemma.

KEY TO MISSOURI SPECIES

1. Spikelets narrow or elongate, several times longer than wide, 10-40 mm. long..............2
1. Spikelets ovate, only 2-3 times as long as wide, 3-7 mm. long..3
   2. Spikelets loosely flowered, with tapering lemmas, the palea noticeably longer with 2-toothed apex..1. *G. acutiflora*
   2. Spikelets with overlapping florets, more compact and cylindrical; lemmas oblong, the palea shorter, with simple apex..2. *G. septentrionalis*
3. Lemmas oblong, more than 2 mm. long, thin-textured; rare species from Butler and Scott counties..3. *G. pallida*
3. Lemmas oval-shaped, less than 2 mm. long, firm; common species............4. *G. striata*

1. **Glyceria acutiflora** Torr. Fig. 27.

Plants with weak, decumbent stems, rooting at the nodes, to 1 m. in length; foliage glabrous, the leaf blades about 5 mm. wide, with prominent, whitish ligules 4-6 mm. long; panicles slender with short, appressed branches; spikelets few, elongate, 2-4 cm. long; glumes pointed, the 1st 1-2 mm. long, the 2nd about twice as long; lemmas acuminate, 7-9 mm. long; palea with a 2-toothed apex, exceeding the lemma.

Distribution: Northeastern United States, west to Missouri, south to Tennessee.

Missouri. Swampy meadows, sloughs, sinks, central and southern Ozarks, north to Laclede and Dent counties. Flowering in June-July.

2. **Glyceria septentrionalis** Hitchc. FLOATING MANNA GRASS. Fig. 28.

Plants coarser than the preceding species, with weak, soft stems and decumbent habit, rooting at the nodes; foliage glabrous, the leaf blades flat, as much as 1.5 cm. wide; ligule thin, whitish, conspicuous; panicles narrow, branches appressed upward; spikelets linear, 1-2.5 cm. long; glumes thin-margined, obtuse, the 1st 2-3 mm. long, the 2nd 3-4 mm. long; lemmas mostly distinctly nerved, slightly scabrous or pubescent, 3.5-4 mm. long, with a blunt, scarious apex; palea equal to or slightly longer than the lemma. Plants with typically large spikelets, to 2.5 cm. long, and scabrous lemmas are var. *septentrionalis.* Those with generally smaller spikelets and merely pubescent lemmas are designated as var. *arkansana* (Fern.) Steyermark & Kucera (G. *arkansana* Fern, Rhodora, 31:49. 1929).

Distribution: Eastern United States to the Middle West, south to Texas.

Missouri. Sloughs, wet woods, upland sinks, meadows, scattered, but most common in the eastern counties. Var. *arkansana* has been reported from Ripley,

Butler, Wayne, Stoddard, and Dunklin counties in the southeast. Flowering in June-July.

3. **Glyceria pallida** (Torr.) Trin. Fig. 29.

Plants thin-stemmed, somewhat decumbent, rooting at the nodes, less than 1 m. tall; leaf blades flat, thin, 3-7 mm. wide; ligule thin, white, conspicuous; panicles light green, with weak, spreading branches; spikelets oblong, about 5-7 mm. long; glumes thin-margined, obtuse; lemmas conspicuously nerved, about 3 mm. long, with an obtuse, scarious apex; palea about the same length.

Distribution: Northeast and mid-Atlantic region, west to Wisconsin, and *Missouri,* where local in sloughs and wet woods, Butler and Scott counties. Flowering in early summer.

FIG. 27.—*Glyceria acutiflora.* Panicle, × 1; floret, × 10.

FIG. 28.—*Glyceria septentrionalis.* Panicle, × 1; floret, × 10.

FIG. 29.—*Glyceria pallida.* Plant, × 1; floret, × 10.

4. **Glyceria striata** (Lam.) Hitchc. Fig. 30.

Plants forming clumps; stems erect, to 1 m. or taller; foliage glabrous, the leaf blades 3-7 mm. wide with a conspicuous, whitish ligule; panicles diffuse, with slender, drooping branches; spikelets ovoid, about 3 mm. long; glumes thin, rounded, the 1st less than 1 mm. long, the 2nd slightly longer; lemmas coarsely nerved, 2 mm. long, rounded at apex, with thin, scarious margins; palea nearly equal to the lemma. (*G. nervata* Trin.)

Distribution: Widespread throughout the United States.

Missouri. Stream, springs, wet woods and meadows, generally distributed. This is our most common species. Flowering in June-July.

6. POA L. BLUEGRASS

Annuals or perennials; panicles narrow, compact, or diffusely spreading, the branches sometimes in whorls; spikelets several-flowered, separating above the persistent glumes; glumes subequal, somewhat keeled; lemmas mostly 5-nerved, keeled, sometimes scarious at the apex, with cobwebby pubescence at the base (except in *P. annua*); palea distinctly shorter than the lemma. A distinctive character is the keeled and boat-shaped tip of the leaf blades.

This is a wide-ranging genus with numerous species, many of which occupy cooler regions, in alpine habitats and the high latitudes.

KEY TO MISSOURI SPECIES

1. Plants annual, usually low and not exceeding 25-30 cm. (if found submerged in spring branches, see species 1 with perennial tendency)........2
1. Perennial, often taller, not occurring submerged in springs........3
   2. Culms decumbent near base, forming small tufts; cobwebby pubescence at base of lemmas absent........1. *P. annua*
   2. Culms upright; cobwebby pubescence present at base of lemmas........ ....2. *P. Chapmaniana*
3. Culms strongly flattened, forming loose sod........3. *P. compressa*
3. Culms rounded........4

FIG. 30.—*Glyceria striata.* Plant, × ½; spikelet, × 5; floret, × 10.

4. Rhizomes present; our most common species..4. *P. pratensis*
4. Rhizomes absent..5
5. Culms bulbous at base; spikelets forming bristly terminal clusters of bulblets..5. *P. bulbosa*
5. Culms not bulbous; spikelets producing normal florets..6
6. Panicles diffuse with slender, spreading branches; spikelets mostly sparse, distant 7
6. Panicles more compact; branches short or ascending; spikelets numerous, close......8
7. Panicles elongate with numerous close whorls of branches, progressively shorter upwards; spikelets about 4 mm. long...6. *P. sylvestris*
7. Panicles loose, sparsely branched; spikelets 5-6 mm. long...........................7. *P. Wolfii*
8. Panicles with ascending or spreading branches, 25-30 cm. in length....8. *P. palustris*
8. Panicles smaller, compact, about 10 cm. long, sometimes longer..........9. *P. trivialis*

1. **Poa annua** L. ANNUAL BLUEGRASS. Fig. 31.

Annual, forming soft, leafy tufts; culms somewhat decumbent at base, 15-30 cm. tall; leaf blades flat, about 3 mm. wide; panicle upright with few short branches; spikelets few-flowered, ovate-oblong, 3-5 mm. long; glumes unequal, 1-3 mm. long, scarious and indistinctly nerved, lemmas 5-nerved, pubescent on the back but lacking cobwebby base, 2.5-3 mm. long. This species is distinguished from the following, our only other annual *Poa,* by the lack of cobwebby pubescence at base of the lemmas, and generally coarser habit. Plants in aquatic situations with creeping habit, rooting at the nodes, have been referred to var. *reptans* Haussk. These are mostly perennial. Similar forms also partly or completely submerged with greatly elongated culms and loose panicles are designated as var. *aquatica* Aschers. In Missouri, the former is more common; however, the distinctions as provided by Hegi (1891) are poorly defined.

Distribution: Widely scattered throughout the United States; adventive from Europe.

Missouri. Open ground, fields, pastures, generally distributed. The creeping, aquatic forms occur in spring habitats, mostly from scattered localities in the Ozark counties. Flowering in May-June.

2. **Poa Chapmaniana** Scribn. ANNUAL BLUEGRASS. Fig. 32.

Annual, differing from species 1 in general appearance, chiefly by the slighter habit, finer foliage, and more compact panicles; spikelets oblong, few-flowered, about 4 mm. long; glumes unequal, 1-3 mm. long, scarious on the margins; lemmas 3-nerved with cobwebby pubescence at base and broad, scarious margins.

Distribution: Eastern and southern United States, west to Texas and Nebraska.

Missouri. Fallow areas, fields, alluvial ground, generally distributed, but most common in the southern counties. Flowering in spring.

3. **Poa compressa** L. CANADA BLUEGRASS. Fig. 33.

Perennial, forming loose sod, from rhizomes; culms 20-70 cm. tall; sheaths and lower culms strongly flattened; ligule collar-shaped 1-1.5 mm. long; leaf blades glabrous, 2-3 mm. wide, keeled, with boat-shaped tip; panicles mostly narrow, compact, with short, ascending branches of crowded spikelets; spikelets few-flowered, 4-5 mm. long; glumes 2-3 mm. long; lemmas mostly glabrous, only slightly cobwebby at base, 2-2.5 mm. long, with scarious apex.

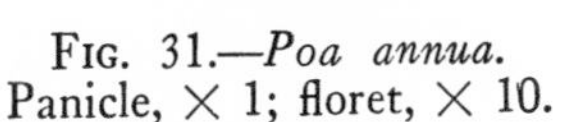

FIG. 31.—*Poa annua.* Panicle, × 1; floret, × 10.

FIG. 32.—*Poa Chapmaniana.* Panicle, × 1; floret, × 10.

FIG. 33.—*Poa compressa.* Panicle, × 1; floret, × 10.

Distribution: Widely scattered, but more common in the northern United States; introduced from Europe.

Missouri. Open ground, fields, prairie meadows, dry woods, generally distributed. Flowering in May-June.

4. **Poa pratensis** L. KENTUCKY BLUEGRASS. Fig. 34.

Perennial, forming dense sod, from rhizomes; culms to 1 m. tall, but usually shorter; sheaths somewhat rounded, not flattened as in the preceding species; ligule collar-shaped, less than 1 mm. long; leaf blades glabrous, 2-4 mm. wide, with boat-shaped tip; panicles pyramidal, with distinct whorls of branches; spikelets ovate, few-flowered, 4-5 mm. long; glumes unequal 2-3 mm. long; lemmas distinctly 5-nerved, about 3 mm. long, with conspicuous, cobwebby pubescence at base. This species produces a more compact sod than the preceding because of shorter internodes of the rhizomes, and is also distinguishable by the more open, pyramidal panicles and the rounded sheaths.

Distribution: Widespread in the United States, less common in the South; introduced from Europe by the early settlers.

Missouri. Pastures, lawns, roadsides, open woods, generally distributed, our most common bluegrass. Flowering in May-June.

5. **Poa bulbosa** L. BULBOUS BLUEGRASS. Fig. 35.

Perennial, forming tufts; culms bulbous at base, 20-50 cm. tall; leaf blades about 2 mm. wide, with inrolled margins; panicle contracted, bristly in appearance; spikelets in aggregate clusters, producing blackish bulblets 2 mm. long,

FIG. 34.—*Poa pratensis*. Plant, × ½; spikelet, × 5; floret, × 10.

subtended by narrow bracts with elongate tips.

Distribution: Widely scattered in the United States, not common; introduced from Europe.

Missouri. Local, collected on open ground, Christian County (Palmer 59430).

6. **Poa sylvestris** Gray. Fig. 36.

Perennial, forming small, loose tufts; culms 30-80 cm. tall; foliage glabrous, the leaf blades 3-5 mm. wide, somewhat lax; ligules conspicuous; panicles diffuse, pyramid-shaped, the branches slender in several whorls; spikelets several-flowered, about 4 mm. long; glumes 2-4 mm. long with scarious margins; lemmas distinctly 5-nerved, 3 mm. long, slightly pubescent on the back and cobwebby at base.

Distribution: Eastern and southern United States, to the Middle West.

Missouri. Moist woods, lower slopes, ravines, generally distributed. Flowering in May-June.

7. **Poa Wolfii** Scribn. Fig. 37.

Perennial, forming leafy tufts; culms erect, to about 80 cm. tall; leaf blades about 2 mm. wide; panicles open, with few spikelets, the branches spreading, usually in 2's along the main axis; spikelets several-flowered, 5-6 mm. long; glumes scarious-margined; lemmas 5-nerved, about 4 mm. long, cobwebby at base. This species is distinguished from the preceding which it resembles by its sparser branching and larger and fewer spikelets.

FIG. 35.—*Poa bulbosa,* × 1.

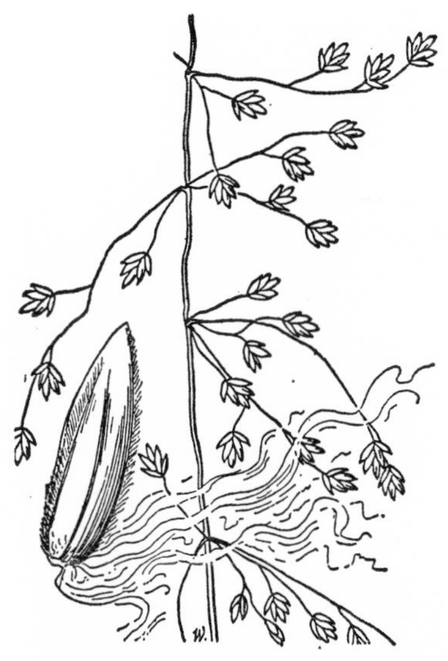

FIG. 36.—*Poa sylvestris.* Panicle, × 1; floret, × 10.

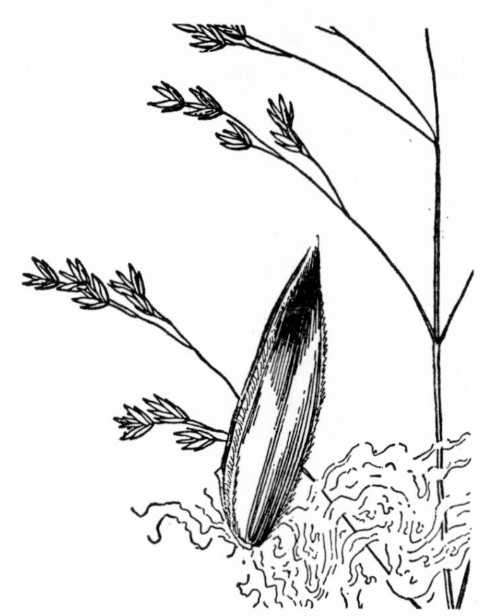

FIG. 37.—*Poa Wolfii*. Panicle, × 1; floret, × 10.

Distribution: North-central United States, south to Indiana and Nebraska.
Missouri. Moist woods, ravines, generally distributed. Flowering in May-June.

8. **Poa palustris** L. FOWL MEADOW-GRASS. Fig. 38.

Perennial, forming loose tufts; culms coarse, rooting from lower nodes, to 1 m. or taller; foliage glabrous, the leaf blades 2-4 mm. wide, with conspicuous ligule 3-5 mm. long; panicles elongate-pyramidal with whorled branches of crowded spikelets; spikelets 3-4 mm. long; glumes somewhat purplish, 2-3 mm. long; lemmas purplish, 2-3 mm. long, with scarious margins, cobwebby at base.

Distribution: Widespread in the western United States, east to New England, south to Virginia.

Missouri. Rare and little known, reported from Jackson and St. Louis counties. Flowering in early summer.

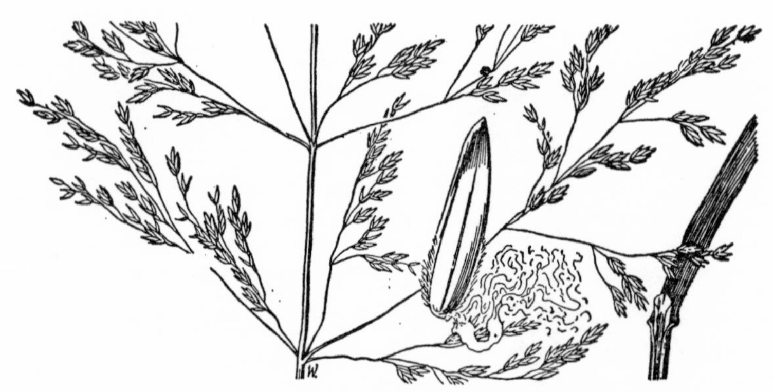

FIG. 38.—*Poa palustris*. Panicle, × 1; floret, × 10.

FIG. 39.—*Poa trivialis.* Panicle, × 1; floret, × 10.

9. **Poa trivialis** L. ROUGH BLUEGRASS. Fig. 39.

Perennial, forming sod, stoloniferous; culms to 1 m. tall, usually less robust than species 8; foliage light green, the sheaths scabrous or rough; leaf blades about 3 mm. wide; ligules elongate; panicles rather small, compact, 5-10 cm. long, with whorled branching, the main stalk rough; spikelets few-flowered, 3-4 mm. long; glumes 2-3 mm. long; lemmas purplish, about 3 mm. long, scarious-margined, cobwebby at base. This species is distinguishable generally from the other bluegrasses by the distinctly rough surface of the sheaths and main flowering stalk.

Distribution: Widely scattered primarily in the northern United States; adventive from Europe.

Missouri. Local, collected from Newton County (Palmer 59826). Flowering in June-July.

7. ERAGROSTIS Beauv. LOVEGRASS

Annuals or perennials; panicles narrow, compact or diffuse, with spreading or reflexed branching; spikelets 2-many-flowered, separating above the persistent glumes; glumes subequal; lemmas 3-nerved, sometimes keeled, acute or acuminate; palea mostly ciliate on margins, shorter than or about equaling lemma. A distinctive character is the ligule, consisting entirely of hairs.

Fourteen species are reported in Missouri, several of these adventive from Europe and Africa.

KEY TO MISSOURI SPECIES

1. Annuals, creeping or upright, but usually less than 50 cm. tall....2
1. Perennials, upright, frequently more than 50 cm. tall....10
   2. Plant low, spreading, rooting at the nodes....3
   2. Plants upright....4
3. Plants with perfect flowers (bisexual); panicles elongate; common species....1. *E. hypnoides*
3. Plants dioecious (staminate and pistillate individuals); panicles ovoid, about as broad as long; rare or infrequent species....2. *E. reptans*

4. Glands along leaf margins toward the base of leaf blades, usually also on the sheaths and nodes; spikelets elongate, imbricated, usually more than 10-flowered....5
4. Glands not present; spikelets 2-10 flowered....6
5. Spikelets as much as 3 mm. wide, somewhat flattened; common species....3. *E. cilianensis*
5. Spikelets narrower, usually less than 2 mm. wide; infrequent species....4. *E. poaeoides*
6. Spikelets loose, 2-5-flowered, less than 3-4 mm. long....7
6. Spikelets imbricate, more than 5-flowered, 5 mm. or longer....8
7. Panicles diffuse, spreading, spikelets single at ends of long, delicate branches; sheaths pilose....5. *E. capillaris*
7. Panicles more compact, with shorter, ascending branches; sheaths glabrous, or only pilose at the summit....6. *E. Frankii*
8. Spikelets delicate, about 1 mm. wide and 5 mm. long....8. *E. pilosa*
8. Spikelets coarser, exceeding 1 mm. in width, and mostly longer than 5 mm....7. *E. pectincea*
9. Spikelets 6-8-flowered, or more, usually more than 5 mm. long....10
9. Spikelets 2-6-flowered, 3-5 mm. long....11
10. Panicles tawny, somewhat flexuous at maturity; leaves long, involute, arching from basal clumps; introduced species from Africa, reported from Howell County....9. *E. curvula*
10. Panicles distinctly purple, showy, with stiff, spreading branches, the axils conspicuously tufted; leaves flat, pilose at summit of the sheath; common native species....10. *E. spectabilis*
11. Spikelets about 1 mm. wide, gray or slate colored; sheaths glabrous except hairy at the summit....11. *E. intermedia*
11. Spikelets 1-2 mm. wide, sometimes with a faint purplish cast; sheaths glabrous to pilose....12
12. Sheaths usually with scattered hairs; glumes acuminate about 2 mm. long; nerves of the lemma obscure....12. *E. hirsuta*
12. Sheaths glabrous or nearly so; glumes acuminate mostly longer, up to 3 mm.; nerves of the lemma conspicuous....13. *E. trichodes*

1. **Eragrostis hypnoides** (Lam.) B. S. P. Fig. 40.

Annual; culms low, creeping, rooting at the nodes; foliage glabrous to sparsely pubescent, the leaf blades short, about 2 mm. wide; panicles diffuse to somewhat compact, 2-5 cm. long; spikelets linear-oblong, mostly many-flowered (10 or more florets), 5-10 mm. long; florets perfect; lemmas prominently 3-nerved, glabrous, thin, about 1.5 mm. long.

Distribution: Widely scattered throughout the United States; also southern Canada.

Missouri. Alluvial banks, fields, low ground, on sandy soils, generally distributed. Flowering in July-August.

2. **Eragrostis reptans** (Michx.) Nees. Fig. 41.

Annual, with creeping habit, similar to species 1, but plants dioecious; pistillate panicles ovoid, composed of capitate clusters, the staminate ones less dense, 1-2 cm. long; pistillate spikelets narrow, linear, somewhat curving; staminate spikelets broader, elliptic, compressed; lemmas prominently 3-nerved, sparsely pubescent, thin, 2-3 mm. long. In addition to unisexual spikelets, this species can be distinguished from the preceding by the longer, pubescent florets.

Distribution: Central United States, from South Dakota to Ohio, south to Gulf region.

Missouri. Rare, reported on sandy ground from Jackson and Livingston counties. Flowering in July-August.

FIG. 40.—*Eragrostis hypnoides.* Plant, × ½; floret, × 10.

FIG. 41.—*Eragrostis reptans.* Pistillate (♀) and staminate (♂) plants, × ½; floret, × 10.

FIG. 42.—*Eragrostis cilianensis*. Plant, × ½; spikelet, × 5; floret, × 10.

3. **Eragrostis cilianensis** (All.) Lutati. STINKGRASS. Fig. 42.

Annual, forming leafy tufts, decumbent near base; culms mostly less than 50 cm. tall; leaf blades 2-6 mm. wide, pilose at summit of sheath; foliage with glandular dots usually along lower margins of leaves, also on sheaths and nodes; panicles somewhat compact, oblong, upright, 5-15 cm. long; spikelets linear-oblong, flattened, usually more than 10-flowered, about 3 mm. wide and 5-10 mm. long or more; florets strongly imbricated; lemmas with 3 conspicuous nerves, thin, 2-2.5 mm. long; grain roundish, loose within the floret. (*E. megastachya* Link.)

Distribution: Widespread in the United States; adventive from the Old World.

Missouri. Open ground, fields, waste areas, generally distributed. Flowering in June-July.

4. **Eragrostis poaeoides** Beauv. ex. Roem. & Schult. Fig. 43.

Annual, generally similar to species 3 but with slighter habit, more delicate leaves, and narrower panicles; glandular dots usually present on lower margins of leaves, sometimes sparingly so, also on keels of lemmas; spikelets linear, about 2 mm. wide or less, 5-10 mm. long; lemmas thin, about 1.5-2 mm. long; grain round, loose within the floret. (*E. minor* Host.)

Distribution: Eastern and central United States, west to Kansas and Texas; adventive from Europe.

Missouri. Open ground, fields, waste areas, infrequent and scattered, reported from Clay, Jackson, Christian, Stone, and Howell counties. Flowering in June-July.

5. **Eragrostis capillaris** (L.) Nees. LACEGRASS. Fig. 44.

Annual, forming tufts; culms usually simple, unbranched, erect, 20-60 cm. tall; sheaths sparsely long-pilose; leaf blades 2-3 mm. wide; panicles broad, diffuse, more than one-half the length of entire plant; spikelets 2-3 flowered, about 2 mm. long, from long spreading pedicels; glumes pointed, about 1 mm. long; lemmas

FIG. 43.—*Eragrostis poaeoides*. Panicle, × 1; floret, × 10.

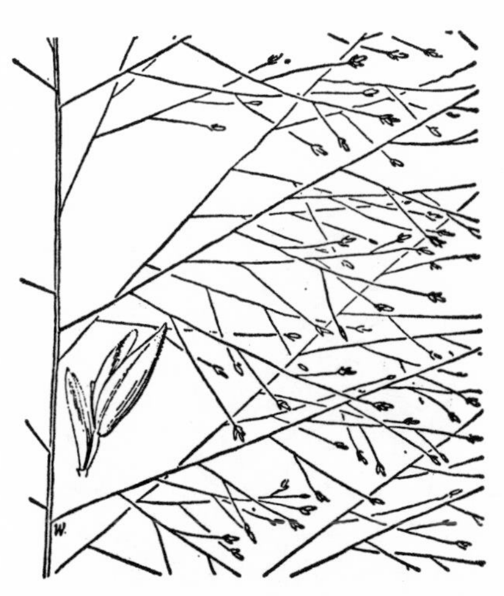

FIG. 44.—*Eragrostis capillaris*. Panicle, × 1; floret, × 10.

indistinctly nerved, glabrous, slate-colored, about 1 mm. long; grain plump, with a readily visible, longitudinal groove.

Distribution: Eastern and central United States, west to Kansas, Oklahoma, and Texas.

Missouri. Fields, waste areas, open woods, on dry or sandy soils, generally distributed. Flowering in July-August.

6. **Eragrostis Frankii** C. A. Meyer. Fig. 45.

Annual, forming tufts; culms branching at the nodes, somewhat decumbent below; sheaths mostly glabrous, long-pilose at summit; leaves 1-3 mm. wide, panicles elliptic, less than one-half the length of entire plant; spikelets 2-5 flowered, 2-3 mm. long, from short, delicate pedicels, giving inflorescence somewhat compact appearance; glumes pointed, about 1-1.5 mm. long; lemmas indistinctly nerved, glabrous, slate-colored, usually more than 1 mm. long; grain plump, not grooved. This species is easily distinguished from the preceding by the more compact panicles, short pedicels of the spikelets and somewhat larger florets.

Distribution: Eastern and central United States, west to Kansas and Oklahoma.

Missouri. Fields, waste areas, sandy alluvium, generally distributed. Flowering in summer.

7. **Eragrostis pectinacea** (Michx.) Nees. Fig. 46.

Annual, forming dense tufts, branching from the lower nodes, spreading or decumbent at the base; culms to about 50 cm. tall; sheaths long-pilose at the summit; leaf blades 2 mm. wide; panicles open, one-half or less as long as the entire plant; spikelets linear-elongate, 5 or more flowered, 5-7 mm. long, 1 mm. or more in width; lemmas thin, drab colored with a purplish cast, about 1.5 mm. long; grain oblong. (Including Missouri specimens identified as *E. diffusa* Buckl.)

Distribution: Primarily in the eastern and central United States, becoming widely scattered in the West.

FIG. 45.—*Eragrostis Frankii.* Panicle, × 1; floret, × 10.

FIG. 46.—*Eragrostis pectinacea.* Panicle, × 1; floret, × 10.

Missouri. Open ground, waste areas, sandy banks, generally distributed. Flowering in July-August.

Remarks: *E. diffusa* Buckl. has been reported for two counties in Missouri. Our specimens, however, are close to the description for *E. pectinacea* to which this species is closely related. Gleason (1952) included both as *E. pectinacea* as did Shinners (1956) for north Texas grasses.

8. **Eragrostis pilosa** (L.) Beauv. Fig. 47.

Annual, forming tufts, branching from the lower nodes, and somewhat decumbent near the base, resembling species 7, but mostly of slighter habit and with smaller panicles; spikelets linear-elongate, 5-10 flowered, about 1 mm. wide or less; lemmas about 1.5 mm. long. This species is distinguished from the preceding by the narrower, more delicate spikelets, although the separation is seldom clearly defined.

Distribution: Eastern and south-central United States; introduced from Europe.

Missouri. Open ground, waste areas, generally distributed. Flowering in July-August.

Remarks: *Eragrostis arida* Hitchc., a southwestern species, has been reported previously for several counties in Missouri. The original description by Hitchcock is of an annual plant with slender branching culms, somewhat decumbent at base, 20-40 cm. tall, with glabrous sheaths pilose at the summit, leaf blades 1-2 mm. wide, panicles open, one-third to one-half the length of the plant, spikelets oblong to linear, 8-15 flowered, 1.5-2 mm. wide, 5-10 mm. long (Wash. Acad. Sci. Jour. 23: p. 449, 1933). It is separated from *E. pilosa* by the slightly larger spikelets; however, no comparison is made with *E. pectinacea.* Certain specimens from Missouri identified as *E. arida,* upon further examination, appear to be or closely ap-

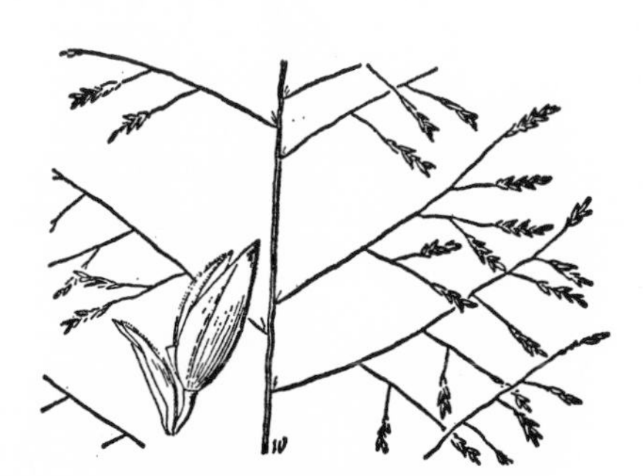

FIG. 47.—*Eragrostis pilosa.* Panicle, × 1; floret, and palea, × 10.

FIG. 48.—*Eragrostis curvula.* Panicle, × 1; floret, × 10.

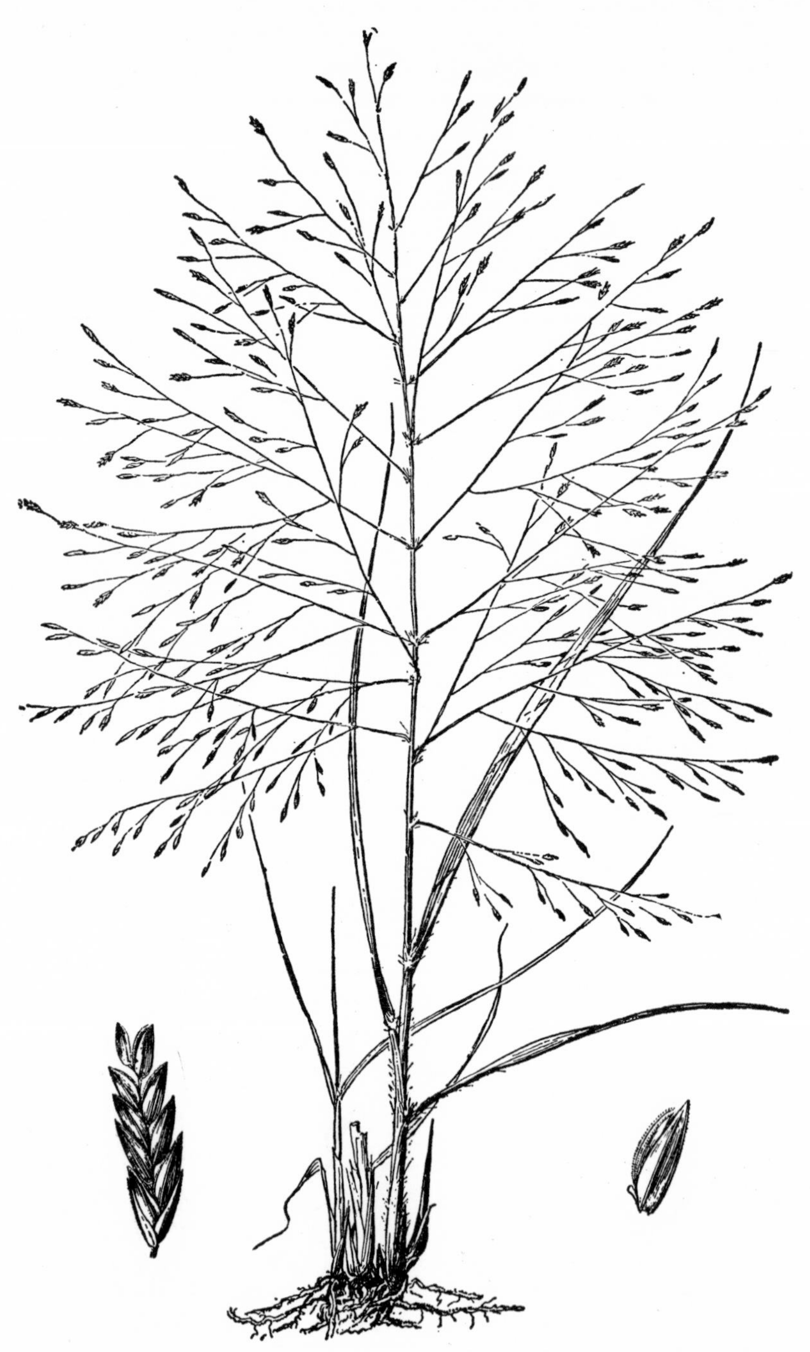

FIG. 49.—*Eragrostis spectabilis*. Plant, × ½; spikelet, × 5; floret, × 10.

proach *E. pectinacea.* In view of the apparent difficulty of separation, as well as the fact that *E. arida* is centered in the Southwest, from Texas westward, it is suggested that true *arida* probably does not occur in Missouri.

9. **Eragrostis curvula** (Shrad.) Nees. WEEPING LOVEGRASS. Fig. 48.

Perennial, forming dense leafy clumps; culms to 1 m. or more tall; leaf blades narrow, inrolled, tapering to long, string-like tips; panicles somewhat nodding, the branches pilose in the axils; spikelets appressed along the branches, linear, somewhat cylindrical, 6 or more flowered, about 1 cm. long; glumes deciduous; lemmas thin, conspicuously nerved, light green, about 3 mm. long.

Distribution: Scattered in the southern United States; introduced from South Africa in 1927.

Missouri. Local, collected on dry, sandy ground, Howell County (Kucera 501). Flowering in July-August.

10. **Eragrostis spectabilis** (Pursh.) Steud. PURPLE LOVEGRASS. Fig. 49.

Perennial, forming dense tufts; culms 30-60 cm. tall; sheaths mostly glabrous, sometimes sparsely hirsute, long-pilose at the summit; leaf blades somewhat stiff, 3-5 mm. wide; panicles upright, with stiffly spreading branches, hairy in the axils, breaking at maturity to form a tumbleweed, conspicuously purplish; spikelets oblong, imbricated, 6-12-flowered, 5-6 mm. long; lemmas noticeably nerved, 1.5-2 mm. long; palea ciliate on the edges; grain roundish.

Distribution: Eastern and central United States, west to Minnesota and the Southwest.

Missouri. Open ground, old fields, prairies, generally distributed. Flowering in July-September.

11. **Eragrostis intermedia** Hitchc. Fig. 50.

Perennial, forming coarse tufts, with hard bases; culms wiry, 30-70 cm. or more tall; sheaths long pilose at summit; leaf blades narrow, with inrolled margins; panicle mostly diffuse, the branches whorled and spreading, sparsely hairy in the axils; spikelets several-flowered, slate-colored, about 1 mm. wide, 5 mm. long or less; lemmas obscurely nerved, glabrous, about 2 mm. long; grain oblong.

Distribution: Scattered in the south-central and southern United States.

Missouri. Infrequent and scattered, open ground, fields, Jackson, Jasper, Newton, Christian, and Texas counties. Flowering in midsummer.

12. **Eragrostis hirsuta** (Michx.) Nees. Fig. 51.

Perennial, forming tufts, with hard, coarse bases; culms to 1 m. or more tall; sheaths hirsute, or sparsely so to nearly glabrous; leaf blades 4-8 mm. wide; panicles diffuse, spreading, large, about one-half the entire length of plant; spikelets 2-4 flowered, somewhat purplish, 1-2 mm. wide, about 3 mm. long; glumes sharp pointed; lemmas obscurely nerved, glabrous, about 2 mm. long; grain oblong.

Distribution: Eastern and central United States, west to Oklahoma and Texas.

Missouri. Open ground, waste areas, on dry sandy or stony soils, through the southern section, south of a line from Barton to Scott counties. Flowering in July-August.

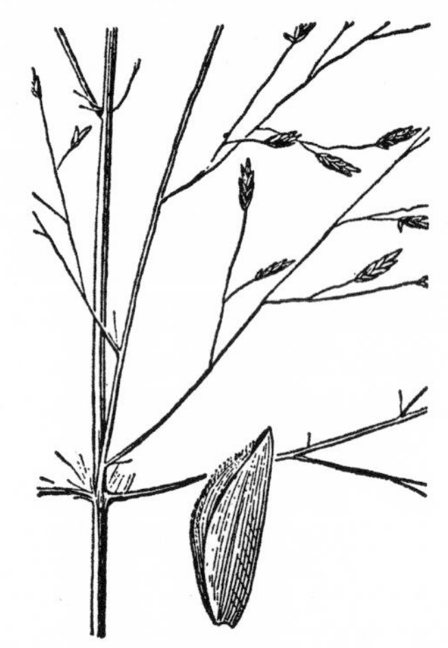

FIG. 50.—*Eragrostis intermedia.* Panicle, × 1; floret, × 10.

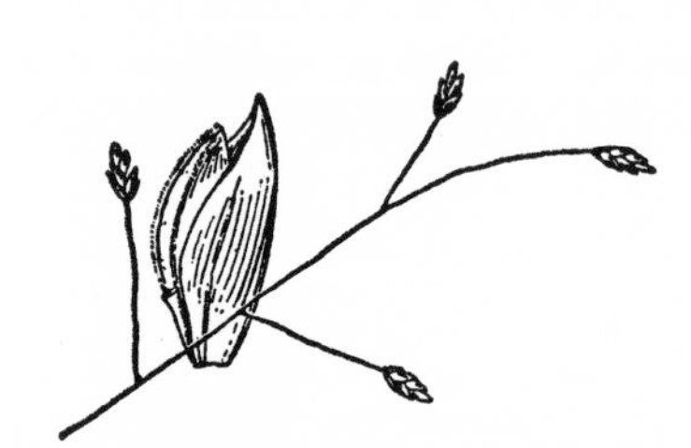

FIG. 51.—*Eragrostis hirsuta.* Panicle, × 1; floret, × 10.

13. **Eragrostis trichodes** (Nutt.) Wood. Fig. 52.

Perennial, in small tufts, less coarse than species 12; sheaths mostly glabrous; leaf blades long, string-like; panicles diffuse, with flexuous, spreading branches; spikelets about 5-flowered, 4-6 mm. long; lemmas conspicuously nerved, thin, glabrous, 2-3 mm. long; grain dark, round-elliptic. This species is separated from the preceding by the glabrous sheaths, more delicate branching of the panicles and the larger, conspicuously-nerved lemmas.

Distribution: Central United States, from Illinois to Colorado, south to Texas.

Missouri. Infrequent and scattered, open ground, on dry, sandy soils, Jackson, Carroll, St. Louis, Ste. Genevieve, Dent, and Ozark counties. Flowering in late summer.

8. DIARRHENA Beauv.

Perennials; panicles narrow, with few, ascending branches; spikelets few-flowered, remote, scattered along the slender axis, separating above the persistent

FIG. 52.—*Eragrostis trichodes.* Panicle, × 1; floret, × 10.

FIG. 53.—*Diarrhena americana.* Plant, × ½; spikelet and floret, × 5.

glumes; glumes unequal; lemmas 3-nerved, with a stiff, pointed apex; palea shorter than the lemma; grain plump, somewhat beaked.

1. **Diarrhena americana** Beauv. Fig. 53.

Plants forming extensive clumps, spreading by rhizomes; culms leafy, reclining to erect, 50-100 cm. tall; leaf blades dark, shiny green with a conspicuous midvein, elongate, 10-20 mm. wide, tapering toward the base; panicles wand-like, slender, with several, short, closely ascending branches; spikelets 3-5-flowered, shattering readily; florets plump; glumes unequal, the 1st 1-nerved, the 2nd 3-nerved; lemmas prominently 3-nerved, oblong to obovate, 4-10 mm. long, acuminate or abruptly pointed. Plants with more elongate lemmas, 7-10 mm. long, with an acuminate tip represent the typical variety (var. *americana*). Those with distinctly obovate lemmas, 4-7 mm. long, the apex short and abruptly beaked are separated as var. *obovata* Gl.

Distribution: Eastern and central United States, west to South Dakota and Texas.

Missouri. Damp woods, shaded limestone slopes, generally distributed as var.

FIG. 54.—*Distichlis spicata.* Plant, × 1; floret, × 5.

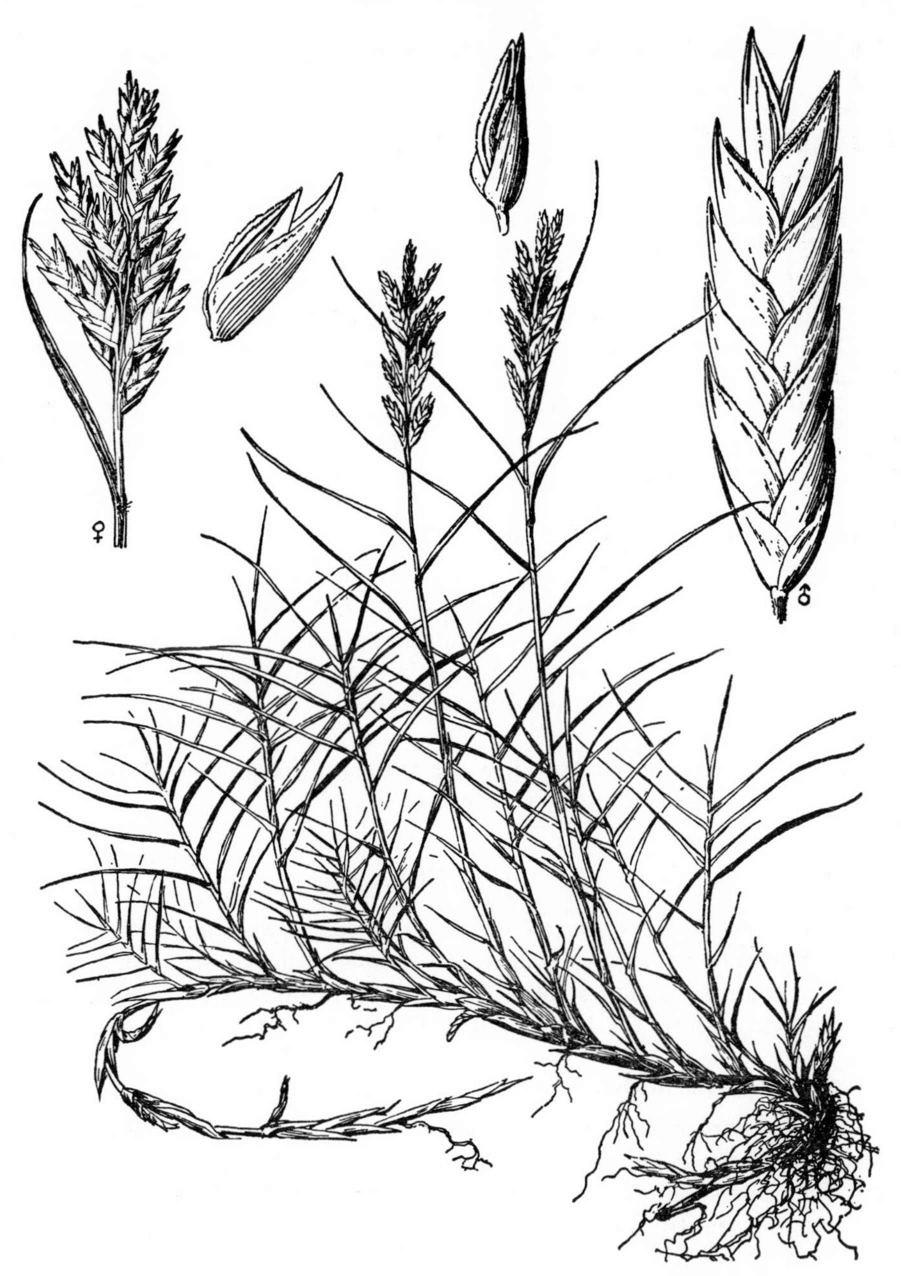

Fig. 55.—*Distichlis stricta.* Staminate plant, × ½; staminate spikelet and floret, × 5; pistillate panicle, × 1; pistillate floret, × 5.

obovata, except in the extreme southeastern counties. The typical variety has been reported only from Christian, Ozark, Stone, and Taney counties. Flowering in July-August.

9. DISTICHLIS Raf. Salt-grass

Perennials, dioecious; panicles dense, with short, contracted branches; spikelets several to many-flowered, compressed-keeled, separating above the persistent glumes; lemmas closely overlapping, faintly-nerved, acute, those of the pistillate spikelets firmer than the staminate ones.

1. **Distichlis spicata** (L.) Greene. Fig. 54.

Plants forming dense colonies, rhizomatous; culms leafy, erect, 10-50 cm. tall; sheaths overlapping, glabrous at the summit; leaf blades 2-ranked, short, stiff, with inrolled margins; panicles dense, 2-6 cm. long, among the upper leaves; spikelets about 7-8 mm. long, the pistillate ones 5-6 flowered, the staminate about 10-flowered, both from short, ascending branches, or nearly sessile; glumes keeled, 2-4 mm. long; lemmas 3-5 mm. long; palea nearly equal to the lemma, smooth-margined.

Distribution: Coastal marshes of the United States, also locally in *Missouri*, salt spring, Saline County (Steyermark 21581), the only known station for this species in the interior. Flowering in summer.

2. **Distichlis stricta** (Torr.) Rydb. Fig. 55.

Plants similar in general habit to species 1; sheaths pilose at summit; leaf blades inrolled, tapering; panicles dense; spikelets keeled, generally more elongate than the preceding, to 15 mm. long with florets usually more numerous; lemmas also larger, 5-7 mm. long; palea somewhat lacerate on the margins.

Distribution: Western and central United States, east to Minnesota and Texas.

Missouri. Rare and scattered, waste areas, on dry ground, Buchanan, Jackson, and St. Louis counties. Flowering in summer.

10. UNIOLA L.

Perennials; panicles contracted to somewhat spreading; spikelets several-flowered, usually compressed, sometimes conspicuously so, separating above the persistent glumes; glumes similar, firm, keeled; lemmas with numerous nerves, sharply-keeled, acute, the lower ones sterile.

1. **Uniola latifolia** Michx. WIDE-LEAF UNIOLA. Fig. 56.

Plants few together or in loose clumps, developing from short rhizomes; culms erect, to 1 m. or taller, sheaths glabrous; ligule membraneous, less than 1 mm. long; leaf blades with numerous veins, conspicuously broad, sometimes as much as 2 cm. wide, tapering to base; panicles nodding, with flexuous branches; spikelets about 10-flowered, conspicuously flattened, about 15 mm. wide, 15-30 mm. long, turning brown; glumes narrow, linear-lanceolate, about 6 mm. long; lowermost lemma sterile, also linear-lanceolate; fertile lemmas larger, ovate-lanceolate, about 10-12 mm. long; palea about two-thirds as long as lemma; grain dark, elliptic, 5 mm. long.

Distribution: Southern and central United States, west to Texas and Kansas, north to the Ohio Valley.

Missouri. Moist limestone slopes, alluvial bottoms, creek banks, generally distributed, but probably absent in the extreme northwestern counties. Flowering in summer.

FIG. 56.—*Uniola latifolia*. Plant, × ½; spikelet and floret, × 3.

FIG. 57.—*Uniola laxa.* Plant, × 1; floret, × 5.

2. **Uniola laxa** (L.) B. S. P. Fig. 57.

Plants sparsely tufted, from short rhizomes; culms erect, 50-100 cm. tall; leaf blades 3-5 mm. wide, tapering to long, fine tip; panicles narrow, with short branches; spikelets 4-5 mm. long, not strongly compressed as in species 1; glumes narrow, pointed, 1-2 mm. long; lower lemma sterile, slightly longer than the glumes; fertile lemmas about 4 mm. long; palea about one-half as long as lemma; grain blackish, 2 mm. long.

Distribution: Eastern and southern United States, west to Texas and Oklahoma, north to New York.

Missouri. Local, damp swales, Ripley County (Steyermark 66921). Flowering in summer.

11. DACTYLIS L.

Perennials; panicles consisting of 1-sided clusters of spikelets toward ends of branches; spikelets few-flowered, compressed-keeled, separating above the persistent glumes; glumes unequal, keeled; lemmas flattened, strongly keeled, awnless, or with short, awn-like tip.

1. **Dactylis glomerata** L. ORCHARD GRASS. Fig. 58.

Plants forming dense, leafy tufts; culms erect, to 1 m. or taller; sheaths retrorsely scabrous; ligule conspicuous, thin, whitish, about 5 mm. long; leaf blades as much as 10 mm. wide; panicles erect, with short, somewhat stiff, ascending or spreading branches; spikelets crowded in 1-sided glomerules at the ends of the branches; glumes lanceolate, with cilia on the conspicuous keel; lemmas flattened, the keel mostly ciliate, 5-6 mm. long, sharp-tipped or sometimes with a short awn 1-2 mm. long. Plants lacking cilia on the keel of the lemma are sometimes separated as var. *detonsa* Fries. A dwarf cultigen with silver-striped leaf

FIG. 58.—*Dactylis glomerata.* Plant, × ½; spikelet and floret, × 5.

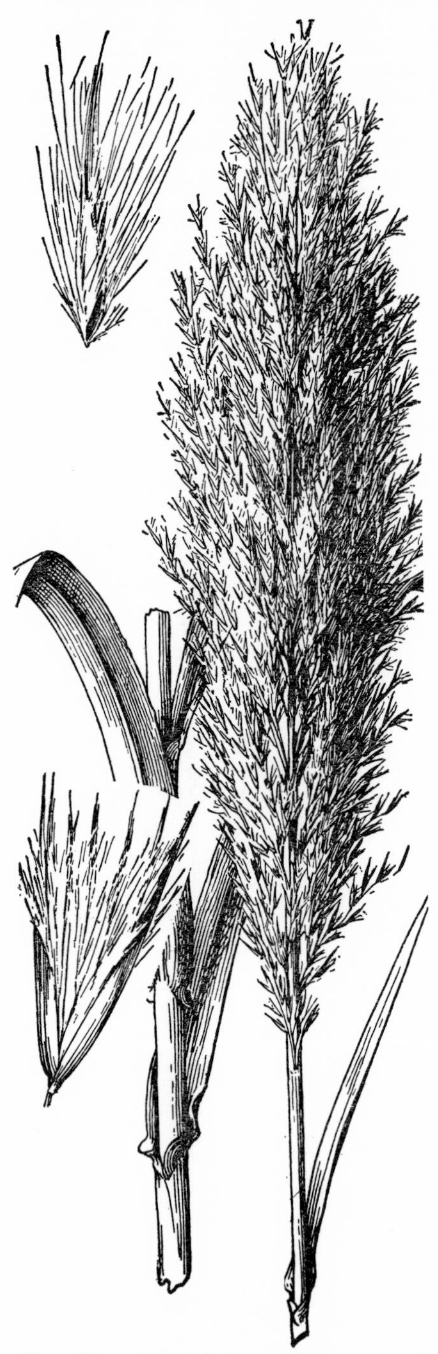

FIG. 59.—*Arundo donax*. Plant, × ⅓; spikelet and floret, × 3.

blades is designated as var. *variegata,* having no specific authorship. Numerous strains and ecological types also occur (Stapeldon, 1938).

Distribution: Widely distributed in the United States, most common in the East; introduced as a forage species from Europe, occasionally self-established.

Missouri. Open ground, fields, generally distributed. Var. *detonsa* is scattered and infrequent. Flowering in May-June.

12. ARUNDO L.

Tall, leafy-stemmed perennials, spreading by thick, coarse rhizomes; panicles terminal, large, showy; spikelets several-flowered, soft-fluffy, separating above the persistent glumes; glumes mostly similar, elongate, about equal to the uppermost florets; lemmas conspicuously pilose, short-awned.

1. **Arundo donax** L. GIANT REED. Fig. 59.

Plants coarse, forming large clumps; culms hard, 1-3 cm. thick, 5-6 m. tall, with hollow internodes, somewhat bamboo-like in general appearance; leaf blades numerous, about 5 cm. wide, mostly 2-ranked; panicles erect, dense-wooly, large, as much as 40-50 cm. long; spikelets about 10 mm. long, with elongate, tapering glumes and lemmas, the latter pilose, short awned.

Distribution: Widely planted in the southern United States, as an ornamental and for erosion control; introduced from the Old World tropics.

Missouri. Infrequent, used as an ornamental, reported as an escape in Newton, Boone, and Dunklin counties. Flowering in late summer.

13. PHRAGMITES Trin.

Tall, cane-like perennials, spreading by rhizomes; panicles large, showy, with silky appearance; spikelets several-flowered, long-villous, separating above the persistent glumes; glumes dissimilar, lanceolate; lemmas long-pointed, all reaching about the same level, the upper ones being progressively shorter; palea much shorter than its lemma; rachilla long-pilose.

1. **Phragmites communis** Trin. var. **Berlanderi** (Fourn.) Fern. COMMON REED. Fig. 60.

Plants robust, forming extensive clumps or colonies; culms erect, 2-3 m. tall; leaf blades numerous, elongate, 2-3 cm. wide or more; panicles dense, plume-like, with stiffly ascending branches; spikelets about 10 mm. long; rachilla with numerous pilose hairs exceeding the florets; glumes unequal, the 1st about one-half as long as the 2nd; lemmas narrow, long-pointed, the lower ones about 10 mm. long, becoming shorter upward.

Distribution: World-wide, one of the most broadly distributed species; western and northern United States, absent in the Southeast.

Missouri. Sloughs, low prairies, river banks, in the north and west-central counties. Flowering in late summer.

14. MELICA L.

Perennials; panicles mostly diffuse, with spreading branches; spikelets few-flowered, separating above the persistent glumes, or sometimes falling entire;

FIG. 60.—*Phragmites communis*. Plant, × ⅓; spikelet and floret, × 3.

FIG. 61.—*Melica nitens*. Plant, × 1; floret, × 5.

glumes subequal, thin-papery, scarious; lemmas several-nerved, thin-margined, awnless, or with a short awn from the 2-lobed apex; upper lemmas much reduced, sterile. A diagnostic character is the closed sheaths.

1. **Melica nitens** Nutt. MELIC GRASS. Fig. 61.

Plants forming loose, sparse clumps; culms erect, 50-80 cm. tall; foliage mostly glabrous, the leaf blades thin, 5-7 mm. wide, long-tapering; panicles with spreading branches in 2's and 3's, these of varying length; spikelets pendulous, 2-3-flowered, about 10 mm. long; glumes somewhat equal, papery, with broad apex, the 2nd almost equal to spikelet length; fertile lower lemmas conspicuously nerved, with wide, scarious margins, about 7 mm. long; the upper lemmas much reduced, about 2-3 mm. long, sterile, with rounded apex, not protruding beyond the apex of fertile lemmas. (Including Missouri specimens identified as *M. mutica* Walt.)

Distribution: Eastern and central United States, west to Wisconsin and Texas.

Missouri. Wooded slopes, limestone ledges, generally distributed. Flowering in May-June.

Remarks: *M. mutica* Walt. previously has been reported for Missouri. All our specimens, however, are *M. nitens*. According to Boyle (1945) *M. mutica* is more southeastern and does not occur in Missouri, although it is found in Arkansas and Tennessee.

15. TRIDENS Roem. & Schult.

Perennials; panicles dense, spike-like to diffusely branched; spikelets several-flowered, separating above the persistent glumes; glumes equal, mostly thin; lemmas with 3 nerves, these usually extending beyond the apex as minute teeth or awns; palea about equal to lemma, fringed on lower margins. (*Triodia* R. Br.)

KEY TO MISSOURI SPECIES

1. Panicles diffuse, with spreading branches..........2
1. Panicles strict, dense, or narrow..........3
    2. Panicle branches flexuous, floriferous only on outer two-thirds; spikelets fertile; common species..........1. *T. flavus*

FIG. 62.—*Tridens flavus*. Plant, × ½; spikelet and floret, × 5.

2. Panicle branches somewhat stiff, floriferous nearly to base; spikelets sterile; local species from Boone County..........2. *T. oklahomensis*
3. Panicles thin, with relatively few spikelets, exposing most of the central axis..........3. *T. elongatus*
3. Panicle dense, spike-like, with numerous spikelets..........4. *T. strictus*

1. **Tridens flavus** (L.) Hitchc. PURPLETOP. Fig. 62.

Plants forming tufts; culms erect, to 1 m. tall, or more; sheaths smooth, conspicuously flattened toward base; leaf blades elongate, 3-8 mm. wide, with prominent central mid-nerve; panicles open, with spreading, dark-viscid branches; spikelets several-flowered, 6-10 mm. long, mostly purplish or rarely yellow; glumes scarious, less than one-half as long as entire spikelet, about 3 mm. long, with short, abrupt tip; lemmas 4-5 mm. long, the 3 nerves villous toward base, each terminating beyond the dentate apex as a short tip. Plants with the purplish spikelets represent the common form, to which forma *cuprea* (Jacq.) Fosberg is sometimes applied. Accordingly, the typical designation, forma *flavus,* refers to the rare or infrequent, yellow-spikelet form. Plants with more sparsely-flowered panicles than var. *flavus* and the branches conspicuously hairy at the base are designated as var. *Chapmanii* (Small) Shinners (*T. Chapmanii* [Small] Chase).

Distribution: Eastern and southern United States, west to Nebraska and Texas.

Missouri. Waste ground, old fields, open woods, generally distributed. The yellow-spikelet form has been collected from Ripley county (Steyermark 82568), the var. *Chapmanii* from Shannon County (Bush 5126).

2. **Tridens oklahomensis** (Feath.) Feath. Fig. 63.

Plants tall, erect, similar in general habit to species 1, but usually somewhat more robust; panicles more compact, bearing spikelets nearly to the base of the branches; spikelets several-flowered, about 8 mm. long, *sterile,* somewhat purplish but distinctly less viscid than those of the preceding species; glumes nearly equal, one-half or more as long as the entire spikelet; lemmas about 4 mm. long, villous on the 3 nerves. This taxon is shown tentatively as a hybrid of species 1 and 4, but is maintained here pending additional study (Rhodora 59: 1957).

Distribution: Type locality, Stillwater, Oklahoma (Featherly, in Rhodora, 1938), since collected in Boone County, *Missouri* (Kucera 2501). Flowering in late summer, but not producing seed.

3. **Tridens elongatus** (Buckl.) Nash. Fig. 64.

Plants forming clumps; culms erect, 40-70 cm. tall; sheaths rough, scabrous; leaf blades about 3 mm. wide, long-tapering; panicles slender, erect, with a few, short, ascending branches; spikelets few in number, 6-8 mm. long, purplish-tinged; glumes conspicuously nerved, the 1st acuminate, the 2nd less pointed, both about 6 mm. long; lemmas 5-6 mm. long, the 3 nerves somewhat villous, not excurrent as short awns.

Distribution: Southwestern United States, north to Colorado and Missouri.

Missouri. Dry prairies, limestone glades, in the west-central and southwestern counties. Flowering in late summer.

FIG. 63.—*Tridens oklahomensis.* Panicle, × 1; floret, × 5.

FIG. 64.—*Tridens elongatus.* Panicle, × 1; two views of floret, × 5.

4. **Tridens strictus** (Nutt.) Nash. Fig. 65.

Plants forming clumps; culms erect, about 1 m. tall; sheaths glabrous, compressed below; leaf blades elongate 4-8 mm. wide; panicles dense, spike-like, 1-2 cm. thick, 8-15 cm. long; spikelets crowded, somewhat flattened, about 5 mm. long; glumes linear-elongate, about as long to somewhat longer than the entire spikelet; lemmas 3 mm. long, the 3 nerves villous on lower part, the central nerve protruding beyond apex as minute tip.

Distribution: Southeastern United States, west to Missouri and Texas.

Missouri. Open ground, roadsides, upland prairies, mostly in the southern counties, south of a line from Barton through Laclede counties and eastward, observed as a recent adventive in Boone County and established in several locations. Flowering in late summer.

16. TRIPLASIS Beauv.

Annuals or perennials; panicles narrow, included in the sheaths, to exserted and spreading; spikelets few-flowered, separation above the persistent glumes; glumes about equal; lemmas 3-nerved, villous, with short awn from the 2-lobed apex; palea densely villous on the upper margins.

1. **Triplasis purpurea** (Walt.) Chapm. SANDGRASS. Fig. 66.

Annual, forming tufts; culms slender, erect, 20-80 cm. tall; sheaths somewhat inflated; nodes bearded; leaf blades short, stiff, about 2 mm. wide; panicles

FIG. 65.—*Tridens strictus*. Panicle, × 1; two views of floret, × 5.

FIG. 66.—*Triplasis purpurea*. Plant, × ½; spikelet, floret, and cleistogamous spikelet, × 5.

sparsely branched, exserted and spreading, also reduced, from lower sheaths; spikelets few-flowered, about 6 mm. long, purplish; glumes thin, lanceolate, about 3 mm. long; lemmas 3-4 mm. long, the 3 nerves conspicuously villous, with short awn about 1 mm. long; grain brownish, elliptic, 2 mm. long.

Distribution: Eastern and southern coastal regions of the United States, also Great Lakes area and westward to Colorado and Texas.

Missouri. Dry sands, alluvial flats, Jackson, Osage, Clark, St. Louis, Jefferson, Ozark, and Dunklin counties. Flowering in summer.

TRIBE III. HORDEAE

17. AGROPYRON Gaertn. WHEATGRASS

Annuals or perennials; spikes stiff, narrow, or occasionally bristly, the rachis mostly continuous, or sometimes breaking at the joints; spikelets several-flowered, flattened, sessile, arranged singly and flatwise at each node of the rachis; at maturity, spikelets separating above the persistent glumes, or falling entire with disarticulated rachis joints; glumes equal, well-developed, subulate or awned; lemmas awnless or sometimes awned; palea equal to lemma.

1. **Agropyron repens** (L.) Beauv. QUACKGRASS. Fig. 67.

Perennial, forming a tough sod, spreading by long, yellowish rhizomes; culms erect, to about 1 m. tall; leaf blades thin, somewhat lax, 5-10 mm. wide, with conspicuous mid-vein; auricles present; spikes erect, 5-15 cm. long; spikelets 3-8-flowered, 10-20 mm. long; glumes generally lanceolate, scarious-margined or margins inrolled, somewhat variable in length, 8-15 mm. long, subulate-tipped or merely short-awned; lemmas about 10 mm. or somewhat longer, awnless, or with awns of variable length but these are usually less than 10 mm. long. Those plants distinguished mainly by the glumes being narrow, with inrolled margins, are separated by some authors as var. *subulatum* (Screb.) Reichevb., other specimens with awned lemmas as var. *subulatum* forma *Vaillantianum* (Wulf & Schreb.) Fern. In general, no distinctive separations occur in Missouri plants although tendencies are exhibited.

Distribution: Widely distributed, but most common and probably native in the northern United States, absent from the Southeast and lower Mississippi Valley; native also to parts of Europe and Asia.

Missouri. Open ground, fields, waste areas, scattered, but most abundant in the northern counties. Quackgrass is commonly an aggressive weed. Flowering in May-June.

2. **Agropyron Smithii** Rydb. WHEATGRASS. Fig. 68.

Perennial, forming a sod, spreading by rhizomes; culms to about 30 cm. or somewhat taller; foliage mostly glabrous, conspicuously bluish-green; leaf blades narrow, 2-5 mm. wide, somewhat stiff, with scabrous, inrolled margins; auricles prominent; spikes stiff, pale or bluish-green, 5-15 mm. long; spikelets usually more than 5-flowered, 15-20 mm. long; glumes rigid, lanceolate, with long-tapering tip, about 10 mm. long or more; lemmas 10-15 mm. long, pointed, or

FIG. 67.—*Agropyron repens*. Plant, × ½; spikelet and floret, × 3.

with short awns about 1 mm. long. This species is distinguished from the preceding by the bluish-green or glaucous foliage, stiff, involute leaf blades, the narrower, tapering glumes, and the brownish rhizomes, which in the latter are characteristically yellowish.

Distribution: Wide-ranging, in the western two-thirds of the United States, east to Ohio and Kentucky.

Missouri. Open ground, fields, prairies, generally distributed but not abundant. Flowering in May-June, somewhat earlier than quackgrass.

FIG. 68.—*Agropyron Smithii*, × 1.

FIG. 69.—*Agropyron trachycaulum*, × 1.

3. **Agropyron trachycaulum** (Link) Malte. SLENDER WHEATGRASS. Fig. 69.

Perennial, forming tufts, lacking rhizomes, thus differing from species 1 and 2; culms to 1 m. tall; leaf blades flat, mostly glabrous, 2-8 mm. wide; auricles mostly present, or sometimes one or both absent; spikes as much as 20 cm. in length; spikelets becoming distant or remote on the lower rachis, usually less than 5-flowered; glumes variable in length, 7-15 mm. long, long-tapering to subulate-awned; lemmas about 10 mm. long, awnless, or with variable awn to 10 mm. in length. Plants essentially awnless, or awns less than 5 mm. long represent the typical variety (var. *trachycaulum*). Plants distinguished by conspicuously long awns exceeding the length of the lemmas are referred to two varieties. Those with generally large spikelets, the glumes mostly 12 mm. or longer, are designated as var. *unilaterale* (Cassidy) Malte., and other specimens with shorter glumes as var. *glaucum* (Pease & Moose) Malte. The latter two varieties constitute *A. subsecundum* [Link] Hitchc. of the *Manual of Grasses* (Hitchc. 1951).

Distribution: Wide-ranging in the western and northern United States, absent in the lower Mississippi Valley and southeastward.

Missouri. Fields and waste ground, infrequent and widely scattered. The awned form of var. *glaucum* has been collected from Jacksaon and Pike counties. Flowering in late June-July.

18. TRITICUM L. WHEAT

Annuals; spikes stiff, thick, the rachis continuous, or in some species brittle and fragmenting at maturity; spikelets several-flowered, sessile, arranged singly at each joint of the rachis; glumes rigid, broad, with several distinct nerves, toothed at apex; lemmas broad, thick, the keel displaced to one side, awned or awnless.

The wheats are of Eurasian origin, and include wild and domesticated species. The more primitive species are characterized by weak, fragmenting spikes whereas later forms developing under domestication are firm and non-fragmenting. The origin of common wheat, *T. aestivum* L., gradually is becoming known. Its ancestry includes the wild eikorn group of wheats. McFadden and Sears (1946) demonstrated that a wild grass, *Aegilops squarrosa* L., is one of the sources of derivation. More recently Sarker and Stebbins (1956) concluded that *Aegilops speltoides* Tausch. is also involved in the ancestry of modern wheat.

1. **Triticum aestivum** L. COMMON WHEAT. Fig. 70.

Plants relatively coarse, erect, to 1 m. or more in height; leaf blades wide, flat; auricles conspicuous; spikes erect, thick; spikelets plump, the lemmas awnless, or with long, scabrous awns in the bearded varieties.

Occasionally volunteering in open ground and along roadsides where grain is scattered, but not persisting.

19. AEGILOPS L.

Annuals; spikes jointed, cylindrical, falling entire and usually breaking into sections; spikelets several-flowered, single, arranged flatwise and recessed in the concavity of the rachis; glumes oriented toward the outer side of the spikelets, the adjacent margins overlapping, firm, broad, toothed at apex; lemmas broadened upward, truncate, usually awned.

1. **Aegilops cylindrica** Host. JOINTED GOATGRASS. Fig. 71.

Plants forming leafy tufts; culms erect, about 50 cm. tall; leaf blades 2-4 mm. wide; spikes numerous, about 4 mm. thick, 5-10 cm. long, or more; rachis joint broadened upward; spikelets 8-10 mm. long; glumes stiff, conspicuously nerved, about 10 mm. long, with keel to one side and terminating in lateral awn, if bidentate at apex, the awn central; lemmas thickened, broadened toward apex, those of the upper spikelets with progressively longer awns, as much as 4-5 cm. long.

Distribution: Widely distributed in the United States, occurring in wheatlands and pastures; adventive from Europe. The long, scabrous awns may cause injury to grazing animals.

Missouri. Fields and waste areas, widely scattered, and locally abundant in some areas. Flowering in early summer.

FIG. 70.—*Triticum aestivum.* Plant with awned spikes (bearded wheat) and a nearly awnless spike (beardless wheat), × ½; spikelet and floret, × 3.

FIG. 71.—*Aegilops cylindrica*, × ½.

20. SECALE L. Rye

Annuals or short-lived perennials; spikes terminal, bristly; spikelets mostly 2-flowered, arranged singly and flatwise at each node of the rachis; glumes small, narrow, 1-nerved or nerveless, persistent, the florets falling separately; lemmas narrow, tapering to long, ascending awn.

This genus, like wheat, is thought to have originated in Eurasia, and includes several wild as well as cultivated species. The common rye, *S. cereale* L., is well known, cultivated primarily in cooler regions. It is more winter-hardy than wheat.

FIG. 72.—*Secale cereale*. Plant, × ½; spikelet, × 3; floret, × 5.

1. **Secale cereale** L. Common Rye. Fig. 72.

Plants erect, similar in general appearance to wheat, but easily distinguished by the more flexible spikes and narrow, tapering glumes and lemmas.

Occasionally volunteering in the uncultivated state, but not persisting.

21. ELYMUS L. Wild Rye

Annuals or perennials; spikes stiff or nodding, narrow or bristly, the rachis continuous in most species, or sometimes fragmenting; spikelets 1-several-flowered, sessile, 2 (sometimes 1 or 3) at each node of the rachis; at maturity, spikelets mostly separating above the persistent glumes; glumes well-developed or sometimes bristle-like, awned or awnless; lemmas firm, pointed or awned; palea enveloped by the inrolled margins of the lemma.

Key to Missouri Species

1. Awns of mature spikelets flexuous, curling, and spreading........2
1. Awns of mature spikelets straight, pointing upward, or absent........3
   2. Spikes diffuse; glumes less than one-half mm. wide, bristle-like; rare species........1. *E. interruptus*
   2. Spikes thick, dense; glumes about 1 mm. wide; common species of prairies, damp ground........2. *E. canadensis*
3. Glumes noticeably bowed and rounded at base, mostly more than 1 mm. in width, awned or merely subulate-tipped........5. *E. virginicus*
3. Glumes scarcely bowed and rounded at base, 1 mm. or less in width, distinctly awned........4
   4. Spikelets noticeably pubescent (except in *f. arkansanus*); upper side of leaves soft-downy to touch........4. *E. villosus*
   4. Spikelets glabrous; leaves not soft-downy on upper surface........5
5. Spikes somewhat flexuous or nodding; glumes distant and divergent; common species of alluvial woods and riverbanks........3. *E. riparius*
5. Spikes strict, upright; glumes close together and parallel; restricted species of dry limestone localities in southwest Missouri........6. *E. glaucus*

1. **Elymus interruptus** Buckl. Fig. 73.

Perennial, forming tufts; culms erect, about 1 m. tall; principal leaf blades generally glabrous, or scabrous above, 5-10 mm. wide; spikes diffuse, somewhat flexuous, 5-15 cm. long, the rachis joints thin, flat, about 7 mm. long; spikelets with long, wide-spreading awns; glumes bristle-like, divergent; lemmas about 10 mm. long, the scabrous awns horizontally-spreading, several times longer than the body.

Distribution: North-central United States and western Great Lakes region; also southwestern, in New Mexico and Texas; sporadic and not common.

Missouri. Rare, Gentry, Lafayette, and Barry counties. Flowering in midsummer.

Remarks: This species has been interpreted as a hybrid of *Elymus canadensis* L. and *Hystrix patula* Moench. based on intermediate characters of the spikelets. However, it is outside the natural range of the latter species in the southwestern part of its distribution. Church (1950) indicated that the problem dealing with origin of *E. interruptus,* especially in the northern part of its range, is not a simple one. It was suggested that the bristle-like character of the glumes may arise in *Elymus* populations independent of *Hystrix.*

FIG. 73.—*Elymus interruptus,* × 1.

2. **Elymus canadensis** L. CANADA WILD RYE. Fig. 74.

Perennial, forming tufts; culms mostly stout, 1-1.5 m. tall; leaf blades green to bluish-green, glabrous to somewhat scabrous, 1-2 cm. wide; auricles conspicuous; spikes curving or nodding, bristly, 10-25 cm. long, the rachis joints elongating toward base; glumes conspicuously nerved, more than 1 mm. wide, awned; lemmas 10-15 mm. long, with spreading or divergent awn 20-30 mm. in length; palea nearly equal to body of lemma, thus differing from species 3 with palea much shorter than lemma. Plants usually coarse-robust, distinguished by distinctly glaucous or bluish-green foliage and large spikes to 25 cm. long or more, have been separated as forma *glaucifolius* (Muhl.) Fern. This robust, glaucous condition is particularly distinctive in some Missouri plants (including *E. robustus* Scribn. & Small).

Distribution: Widespread in the United States but absent in the Southeast from Alabama to South Carolina.

Missouri. Prairies, roadsides, swales, limestone slopes, generally distributed. Plants with glaucous condition occur with the typical form. Flowering early in July-August.

3. **Elymus riparius** Wieg. Fig. 75.

Perennial; culms to 1 m. or taller; leaf blades thin, long-tapering to fine tip, 5-15 mm. wide; auricles present; spikes generally nodding, 5-20 cm. long, the rachis somewhat flexuous, consisting of joints 4-5 mm. long; glumes linear,

FIG. 74.—*Elymus canadensis*. Plant, × ½; spikelet and floret, × 5.

conspicuously nerved, straight-awned; lemmas glabrous, about 10 mm. long, exceeding the palea, the awn straight, 10-30 mm. long; this species is distinguished from species 4 by its generally smooth spikes, and from species 2 by the unequal lemma and palea, and the straight, non-spreading awns.

Distribution: Eastern and central United States, west to Nebraska and Kansas.

Missouri. Rich or moist woods, north-facing limestone slopes and alluvial banks, generally distributed. Flowering in midsummer.

4. **Elymus villosus** Muhl. Fig. 76.

Perennial, forming small tufts; culms slender, 50-100 cm. tall; leaf blades soft-pubescent on upper surface, 5-15 mm. wide; auricles conspicuous; spikes generally nodding, 5-10 cm. long; the rachis hairy, consisting of numerous short joints 2-3 mm. in length; glumes setaceous, conspicuously nerved with straight awns; lemmas pubescent, sometimes glabrous or nearly so, about 7-8 mm. long,

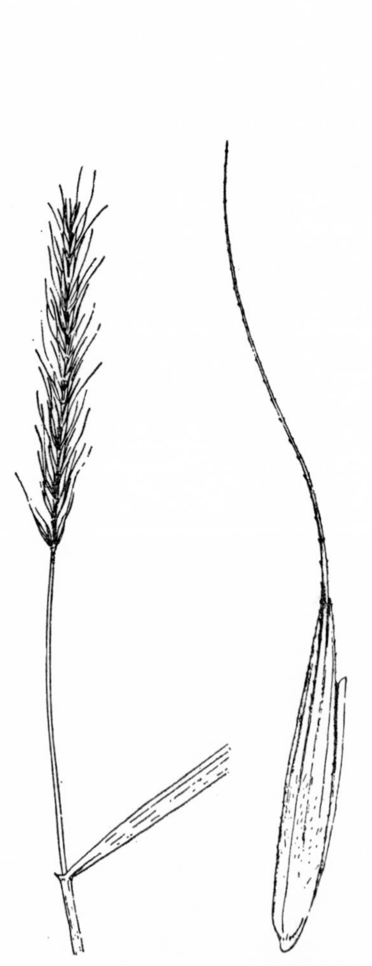

FIG. 75.—*Elymus riparius*. Panicle, × ½; floret, × 5.

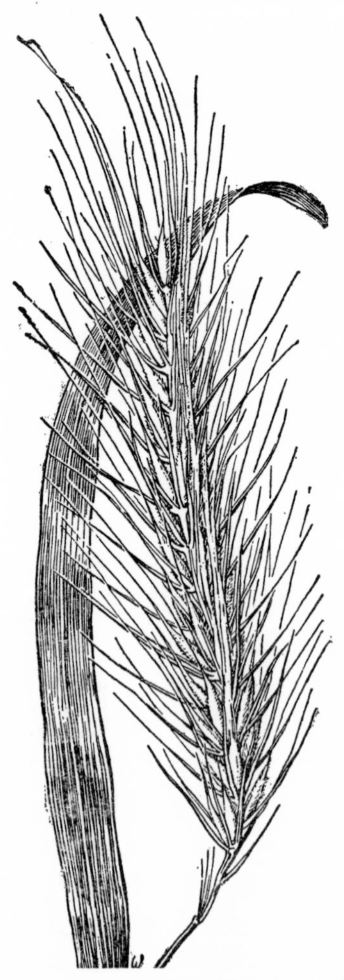

FIG. 76.—*Elymus villosus*, × 1½.

with straight awn 10-30 mm. in length. Plants with glabrous spikelets have been recognized by some authors as forma *arkansanus* (Scribn. & Ball) Fern. As applied to Missouri plants the separation is minor, although some specimens occur which exhibit a glabrous tendency. (*E. striatus* of Am. Authors.)

Distribution: Eastern and central United States, west of North Dakota, Wyoming, and Texas.

Missouri. Usually rich or moist woods, low ground, creek banks, and limestone slopes, generally distributed. Plants with a tendency for smooth or scabrous spikelets occur only infrequently and are integrated completely with the typical form. Flowering in midsummer.

5. **Elymus virginicus** L. VIRGINIA WILD RYE. Fig. 77.

Perennial, forming tufts, culms erect, 50-100 cm. or more tall; leaf blades generally smooth to scabrous 5-15 mm. wide; auricles small or imperfectly developed; spikes generally erect, 5-15 cm. long, exserted or sometimes partially enclosed in the upper spathe-like sheaths; glumes more than 1 mm. wide, bowed and rounded at the smooth and yellowish base; lemmas smooth to hirsute with straight awns 1-3 cm. long, or awnless. This is a variable species including distinctive forms as well as intergradations. The interpretation of Missouri

FIG. 77.—*Elymus virginicus* var. *virginicus*. Panicle, × ½; spikelet, × 5.

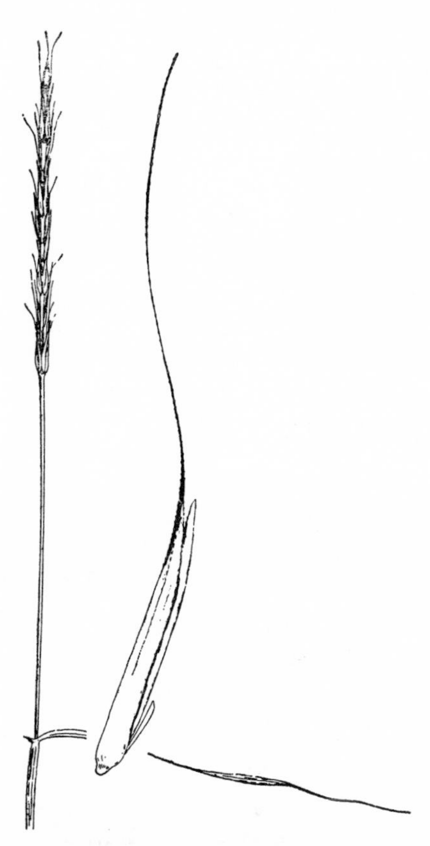

FIG. 78.—*Elymus glaucus*. Panicle, × ½; floret, × 5.

material is based on a synthesis of earlier treatments and recognizes the following intraspecific groups: Plants with spikes wholly or partially inserted in the upper sheaths, the spikelets awned and essentially glabrous, are distinguished as typical. These are designated as var. *virginicus*. Similar plants but differing by the hirsute spikelets are referred to forma *hirsutiglumis* (Scribn.) Fern. Plants with well-exserted spikes, the spikelets also awned and glabrous are determined as var. *glabriflorus* (Vasey) Bush, those with pubescent spikelets as forma *australis* (Scribn. & Ball) Fern. The variety *jejunus* (Ramalay) Bush is similar, but characterized by smaller spikes with strict appearance, a distinction not too well-defined since intermediate characters between it and var. *virginicus* as well as var. *glabriflorus* are frequent. Plants with essentially awnless glumes and lemmas are separated as var. *submuticus* Hook.

Distribution: Widespread in the United States from the Atlantic region west to Arizona and the Pacific Northwest.

Missouri. Wooded areas, prairie openings, moist banks, and stream bottoms, generally distributed, with the exception of var. *submuticus* which is scattered and less common. Flowering in late June-July.

6. **Elymus glaucus** Buckl. Fig. 78.

Perennial, forming small tufts; culms to 1 m. tall; leaf blades mostly smooth or soft, minutely-pubescent on the upper surface, 5-10 mm. wide; spikes long-exserted, erect, narrow, 5-10 cm. long, the rachis smooth, consisting of relatively few joints, each about 5 mm. long; glumes widening above the base, and tapering to a short awn about one-half the length of the body, the abaxial pair close and parallel; lemmas 8-9 mm. long with awn 10-20 mm. in length; palea equal to the body of the lemma. (*E. Mackenzii* Bush.)

Distribution: Western United States primarily, extending east to Missouri, Iowa, and Michigan.

Missouri. Dry prairies, limestone bluffs, Ozark, Taney, Stone, Barry, McDonald, Newton, Jasper, and Barton counties in the southwestern section Flowering in late June-July.

Remarks: *E. Macounii* Vasey is listed for Missouri in some manuals. According to Stebbins *et al.* (1946) it is a hybrid of *Agropyron trachycaulum* (Link) Malte and *Hordeum jubatum* L. The hybrid is sterile. A particular feature is the ready disarticulation of the rachis, a characteristic of *H. jubatum.* Collections by Bush (Eagle Rock, Missouri) appear to be *E. glaucus.*

22. SITANION Raf.

Perennials; spikes broad, with spreading awns, bristly, at maturity the rachis separating readily at the nodes; spikelets few-flowered, 2 at each node of the rachis, both falling entire with the rachis joint; glumes bristle-like, terminating in 1-several, elongate, spreading awns of varying length; lemmas firm, with long central awn, and also shorter lateral awns; palea equal to body of lemma.

1. **Sitanion Hystrix** (Nutt.) J. G. Smith. SQUIRRELTAIL. Fig. 79.

Plants erect, to about 50 cm. tall; leaf blades mostly glabrous to slightly pubescent, 1-4 mm. wide, occasionally with inrolled margins; spikes diffuse, bristly, 5-10 cm. long; spikelets 2-flowered; glumes scabrous, bristle-like, less than 0.5 mm. wide; lemmas scabrous, somewhat wider, about 10 mm. long, with spreading awns to 10 cm. in length.

Distribution: Western United States, east to *Missouri,* where apparently adventive and little known, reported on dry, waste ground, Jackson County.

FIG. 79.—*Sitanion Hystrix.* Plant, × ½; spikelet and floret, × 3.

FIG. 80.—*Hystrix patula*. Plant, × ½; spikelet and floret, × 3.

23. HYSTRIX Moench.

Perennials; spike diffuse, bristly, with continuous rachis; spikelets 2-4 flowered, 2-4 (sometimes 1) at each node of the rachis; at maturity, spikelets separating above the persistent glumes; glumes obsolete or reduced, bristle-like; lemmas firm, involute, with long straight awn; palea equal to body of lemma.

1. **Hystrix patula** Moench. BOTTLE-BRUSH GRASS. Fig. 80.

Plants solitary or few together in sparse clumps; culms erect, 50-150 cm. tall; leaf blades mostly glabrous, flat, 7-15 mm. wide; spikes somewhat flexuous, 5-15 cm. long; spikelets mostly 2 at each node; the awns horizontally spreading; glumes variable, obsolete to long-setaceous; lemmas typically glabrous, or sometimes pubescent, about 10 mm. long, with straight, scabrous awn 10-40 mm. long. Plants with pubescent lemmas have been separated as forma *Bigeloviana* (Fern.) Gl. The distinction in Missouri plants is fairly well-defined.

Distribution: Eastern and central United States, west to North Dakota and Kansas.

Missouri. Woods and rocky slopes, generally distributed. Plants with pubescent lemmas occur with the typical form, but are less common. Flowering in late June-July.

24. HORDEUM L. BARLEY

Annuals or perennials; spike bristly, the rachis continuous or in some species breaking readily at maturity; spikelets mostly 1-flowered usually in 3's at each node of the rachis, all falling attached together with the rachis section; only central spikelet of each group of 3, fertile and sessile, the 2 lateral spikelets sterile and pedicelled, or all spikelets sessile and fertile; glumes narrow, awned, or bristle-like; perfect lemma firm, rounded on back, long-awned, those of the sterile spikelets reduced; rachilla extended behind palea.

This genus consists of both New and Old World species, the latter group including the common or cultivated barley, *H. vulgare* L.

KEY TO MISSOURI SPECIES

1. Rachis mostly continuous, not fragmenting; all spikelets fertile, sessile, awned or awnless..........3. *H. vulgare*
1. Rachis fragmenting at maturity; only central spikelet fertile, sessile, the 2 laterals sterile and pedicellate..........2
    2. Spikes bushy, somewhat nodding; awns several times larger than the florets..........1. *H. jubatum*
    2. Spikes narrow, strict; awns about equal to florets..........2. *H. pusillum*

1. **Hordeum jubatum** L. FOXTAIL BARLEY. Fig. 81.

Perennial, forming small tufts, culms erect, 25-50 cm. tall; upper sheaths spathe-like, enclosing the base of the spike; leaf blades scabrous, 2-5 mm. wide, tapering to fine tip; spikes somewhat nodding, pale-green becoming tawny, 5-10 cm. long, about as wide, the rachis separating readily; spikelets in 3's, the central one sessile, with fertile lemma 6-8 mm. long, the awns as much as 50 mm. or even longer, the 2 lateral spikelets on short stalks, the lemmas reduced but long-awned; glumes narrow, with long, slender awn.

Distribution: Wide-ranging, north and central United States, absent in the Southeast.

Missouri. Open ground, fields, waste areas, scattered and most common in the northern and western counties, rare or absent in the Ozarks. Flowering in June-July.

2. **Hordeum pusillum** Nutt. LITTLE BARLEY. Fig. 82.

Annual; culms erect, 15-40 cm. tall; sheath glabrous to short-pilose, the uppermost sometimes inflated and including the base of the spike; leaf blades scabrous, 2-5 mm. wide; spikes erect, strict, narrow, about 1.5 cm. wide, 3-7 cm. long, breaking readily at maturity; spikelets in 3's, the central one sessile, with fertile lemma 8-12 mm. long, the awns of similar length, the 2 lateral spikelets on short stalks, smaller, also awned; outer glume of each lateral spikelet bristle-like, the inner one and those of the central spikelet broadened above the base and terminating in straight awn.

Distribution: Widespread in the United States, most common westward.

Missouri. Open ground, fields, waste areas, on dry soils, generally distributed. Flowering in May-June.

3. **Hordeum vulgare** L. COMMON BARLEY. Fig. 83.

Coarse annual with wide, flat leaves and conspicuous, curved auricles; spikes stiff, erect, dense with continuous rachis, thus differing from the 2 preceding native species which fragment readily; the 3 spikelets at each node sessile, well-developed, producing full grains. Plants with awnless spikelets, the lemmas with tri-lobed apex, are designated as var. *trifurcatum* (Schleht) Alefeld.

Cultivated barley is occasionally spontaneous in waste ground, but is never persistent. Specimens with trifurcate lemmas have been reported only rarely in Missouri.

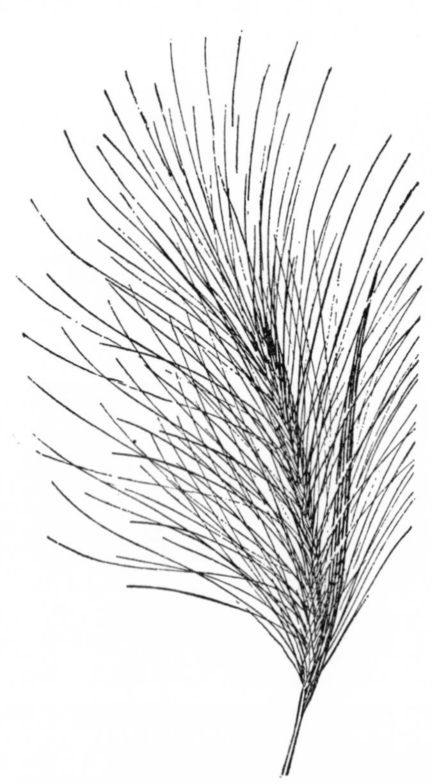

FIG. 81.—*Hordeum jubatum*, × 1.

FIG. 82.—*Hordeum pusillum*, × 1.

FIG. 83.—*Hordeum vulgare.* Plant, × ½; group of spikelets and florets, × 3; spike of beardless barley, × ½.

FIG. 84.—*Lolium multiflorum*. Plant, × ½; spikelet, × 3; floret, × 5.

25. LOLIUM L. RYEGRASS

Annuals or perennials; spike flattened, with continuous rachis; spikelets several-flowered, 1 at each node, oriented edgewise to the rachis; at maturity, spikelets separating above the persistent glumes; 1st glume inner side of spikelets toward rachis, usually absent except in the terminal spikelet; outer glume present; lemmas awned or awnless.

The ryegrasses are of European origin. These have been introduced into the United States for forage and turf use, frequently becoming self-established in cultivated areas.

1. **Lolium multiflorum** Lam. ITALIAN RYEGRASS. Fig. 84.

Annuals or short-lived perennials; culms erect to 1 m. tall or more; foliage dark green, glabrous, the leaf blades about 4 mm. wide; auricles conspicuous; spikes erect, from leafy stalks; spikelets 8-15 flowered, sometimes more, 10-15 mm. or longer; single glume of variable length; lower lemma about 8 mm. long, usually with delicate awn. Plants of smaller stature and generally fewer spikelets are sometimes separated as var. *diminutum* Hutel.

This species differs from species 2 by the presence of awns; however, it is closely related and not entirely distinct. Various intergrading forms occur. The so-called domestic ryegrass is designated as *L. multiflorum* x *perenne*, and resembles Italian ryegrass.

Missouri. Scattered, open ground and waste areas near cultivation. Flowering in late spring.

2. **Lolium perenne** L. PERENNIAL RYEGRASS. Fig. 85.

Perennial, but not long-lived; culms about 50 cm. tall, generally shorter and of slighter habit than species 1; foliage dark green, glabrous; auricles present, or occasionally 1 or both absent; spikes stiff, erect, 10-15 cm. or longer; spikelets 5-10-flowered, about 10 mm. long; lemmas 5-6 mm. long, awnless.

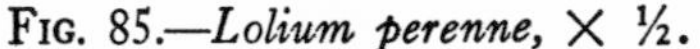

FIG. 85.—*Lolium perenne*, × ½.

FIG. 86.—*Lolium temulentum*, × ½.

Missouri. Open ground, alluvial fields, waste places, general and more common than the Italian ryegrass. Flowering in spring, somewhat earlier than the preceding species.

3. **Lolium temulentum** L. POISON DARNEL. Fig. 86.

Annual; culms coarse, erect, 50-125 cm. tall; leaf blades mostly glabrous, 3-6 mm. wide; spikes stiff, erect, 15-20 cm. long or more; spikelets 4-8-flowered, as much as 20 mm. long, the plump florets sometimes exceeded by the straight, rigid, acuminate glume; lemmas awned.

This species is reported to have toxic properties attributed to a narcotic alkaloid present in the grain.

Missouri. Rare, reported from Jackson, McDonald, and Platte counties. Flowering in May-June.

TRIBE IV. AVENEAE

26. KOELERIA Pers.

Annuals or perennials, panicles narrow, spike-like; spikelets 2-several-flowered, separating above the persistent glumes; glumes somewhat unequal, firm, keeled, the 2nd about equal to uppermost floret; lemmas glabrous, firm, awnless; palea thin, about equal to lemma; rachilla prolonged behind the upper floret as a short stipe.

1. **Koeleria cristata** (L.) Pers. JUNEGRASS. Fig. 87.

Perennial, forming tufts; culms erect, to 50 cm. or taller; lower sheaths pubescent, becoming glabrous above; ligule collar-shaped, less than 1 mm. long; leaf blades narrow, about 2 mm. wide, involute when dry; panicles spike-like, 5-10 cm. long, with short, condensed branches; spikelets 2-flowered, 4-5 mm. long; glumes scabrous on keel, the 2nd longer, and only slightly shorter than the closely imbricated florets; lemmas scabrous, about 3 mm. long.

Distribution: Widespread in the United States, but absent in the mid-Atlantic region and Southeast; native also to southern Europe and temperate Asia.

Missouri. Prairies, open woods, glades, generally distributed. Flowering in May-June.

27. SPHENOPHOLIS Scribn.

Perennials; panicles compact, spike-like, or somewhat diffuse, with spreading branches; spikelets generally 2-flowered, separating below the glumes and falling entire (in the preceding genus, *Koeleria,* the separation is above the glumes); glumes dissimilar, the 1st narrow or awl-shaped, the 2nd broader, mostly obovate; lemmas firm, keeled near apex, rounded below, awnless; palea thin, about equal to lemma.

KEY TO MISSOURI SPECIES

1. Panicles narrow, compact, distinctly spike-like; 2nd glume obovate, almost as broad as long............1. *S. obtusata*
1. Panicles somewhat spreading or diffuse, not compact; 2nd glume longer than broad......2
   2. Panicles profusely-flowered; 1st glume very narrow, awl-shaped, shorter than 2nd glume............2. *S. intermedia*
   2. Panicles sparsely-flowered; 1st glume oblong, about equal to 2nd glume............3. *S. nitida*

1. **Sphenopholis obtusata** (Michx.) Scribn. PRAIRIE WEDGEGRASS. Fig. 88.

Plants forming small tufts; culms leafy, erect, to 1 m. tall; foliage glabrous to somewhat pubescent, the leaf blades 3-4 mm. wide; ligule about 1.5 mm. long, with lacerated margin; panicles erect, dense, spike-like, sometimes with short-lobes; spikelets 2-flowered, 2-3 mm. long; 1st glume narrow, oblong, the 2nd conspicuously obovate with rounded apex, almost as broad as long; lower lemma about 2-2.5 mm. long. Plants with lobing effect of the panicles have been recognized by some authors as var. *lobata* (Trin.) Scribn., those with pubescent foliage as var. *pubescens* (Scribn. & Merr.) Scribn. Although these tendencies may be noted in some Missouri specimens, on the whole the divisions are not well-defined.

Distribution: Widespread throughout the United States and adjacent Canada, south to Mexico.

FIG. 87.—*Koeleria cristata*. Plant, × ½; glumes and floret, × 10.

FIG. 88.—*Sphenopholis obtusata*. Plant, × ½; glumes and floret, × 10.

Missouri. Prairies, dry woods, rocky slopes, generally distributed. Flowering in May-June.

2. **Sphenopholis intermedia** (Rydb.) Rydb. SLENDER WEDGEGRASS. Fig. 89.

Plants generally resembling species 1 in habit, but panicles less compact, more branching, somewhat nodding or flexuous; spikelets about 3-4 mm. long; 1st glume very narrow, almost awl-shaped, the 2nd somewhat obovate, but distinctly longer than broad; lemmas generally longer, averaging 2.5-2.7 mm.

Distribution: Widely distributed in the United States and adjacent Canada.

Missouri. Shaded slopes and low woods, generally distributed, occupying more moist locations than the preceding. Flowering in May-June.

3. **Sphenopholis nitida** (Biehler) Scribn. Fig. 90.

Plants tufted; culms slender, erect, 40-80 cm. tall; foliage somewhat pubescent, the leaf blades 2-4 mm. wide; panicles diffuse, sparsely-flowered, with spreading branches; spikelets about 3.5 mm. long; glumes nearly equal in length, the 1st narrow-oblong, the 2nd obovate, but longer than broad; lemmas about 2.5-2.7 mm. long. This species is easily distinguished from either of the two preceding ones by the diffuse panicles and sparsely-flowered branches.

Distribution: Eastern and central United States, west to Missouri and Texas, local elsewhere.

Missouri. Open woods, barren slopes, on dry, rocky soils, in the southern counties, the least common of our species and not known north of the Missouri River. Flowering in May-June.

FIG. 89.—*Sphenopholis intermedia.* Panicle, × 1; glumes and floret, × 10.

FIG. 90.—*Sphenopholis nitida.* Panicle, × 1; glumes and floret, × 10.

28. TRISETUM Pers.

Perennials; panicles diffuse to somewhat dense; spikelets 2-several-flowered, separating above the persistent glumes (except in *T. pensylvanicum* with disarticulation below the glumes); glumes dissimilar, thin, papery; lemmas also thin, papery, with tuft of hairs at base, awnless, or with curving awn attached below the split apex.

1. **Trisetum flavescens** (L.) Beauv. YELLOW FALSE OATS. Fig. 91.

Plants slender, erect, to 1 m. tall; foliage generally glabrous, or lower sheaths pubescent; leaf blades 2-5 mm. wide; panicles somewhat congested, with short, close branches; spikelets 3-4-flowered, about 5 mm. long, excluding awns; glumes dissimilar, the 1st narrow-lanceolate, the 2nd longer and broader; lemmas 4-5 mm. long, with scarious margins and bent awn 8-10 mm. long.

Distribution: Widely scattered in the United States; adventive from Europe.

Missouri. Rare and probably not established, collected in Jackson County (Bush in 1891). No other collections are known. Flowering in May-June.

2. **Trisetum pensylvanicum** (L.) Beauv. Fig. 92.

Plants slender, erect, or somewhat decumbent near base, 50-80 cm. tall; foliage mostly glabrous, the leaf blades 2-6 mm. wide; panicles narrow, the short branches loosely ascending; spikelets 2-flowered, 5-7 mm. long; glumes keeled, thin-textured, about 4-5 mm. long, the 1st oblong, abruptly acute, the 2nd slightly longer and obovate; lemmas about 4 mm. long, the lower one usually awnless, the upper one with straight awn 4-5 mm. long.

Distribution: Southeastern United States and Coastal Plain, inland to Ohio, also *Missouri,* where local, collected on swampy ground of spring branch on Crowley's Ridge, Stoddard County (Steyermark 78285).

FIG. 91.—*Trisetum flavescens.* Panicle, × 1; floret, × 5.

FIG. 92.—*Trisetum pensylvanicum.* Panicle, × 1; glumes and floret, × 5.

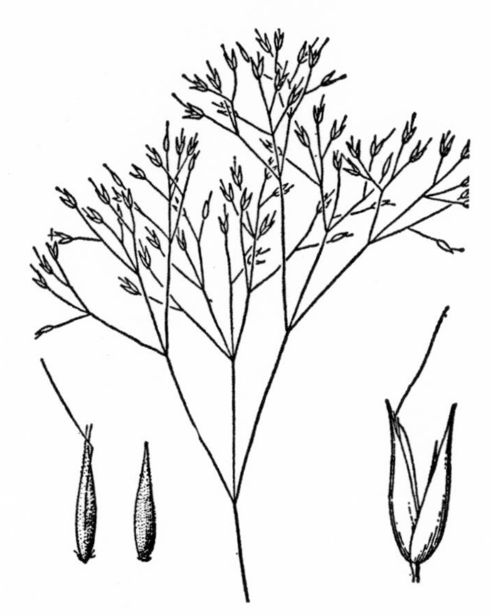

FIG. 93.—*Aira elegans.* Panicle, × 1; spikelet and florets, × 10.

29. AIRA L. HAIRGRASS

Small annuals; panicles delicate, narrow to diffuse; spikelets 2-flowered, separating above the persistent glumes, the latter exceeding the florets; lemmas firm, the lower one usually awnless, the upper one awned from below the middle.

1. **Aira elegans** Willd ex. Gaudin. Fig. 93.

Plants forming small tufts; culms erect, about 30 cm. tall at most; foliage generally glabrous, the leaf blades narrow, 1-2 mm. wide, becoming involute; panicles diffuse, delicately branched; spikelets from the ends of the branches, 2-2.5 mm. long; glumes exceeding the 2 florets; lemmas with minute tuft of hairs at base, the upper one with bent awn 2-3 mm. long.

Distribution: Southeastern and mid-Atlantic states, west to Arkansas and Missouri; also Far West.

Missouri. Recently discovered, open ground, on dry soils, St. Louis, and Oregon counties. Flowering in May.

30. AVENA L. OATS

Annuals; panicles large, with spreading branches; spikelets 2-3-flowered, separating above the persistent glumes; glumes equal, conspicuously nerved, papery, exceeding the florets; lemmas hard, smooth or hairy, awnless, or with conspicuous awn attached from near or below middle.

All species are of Old World origin, including the cultivated oats, *Avena sativa* L., widely used for grain, forage, and food.

1. **Avena fatua** L. WILD OATS. Fig. 94.

Plants leafy, erect, to about 1 m. tall or more; foliage mostly glabrous, the leaf blades flat, as much as 1 cm. wide; panicles flexuous, spreading; spikelets mostly 3-flowered; glumes equal, 2.5-3 cm. long, exceeding or overtopping the

FIG. 94.—*Avena fatua*. Plant, × ½; spikelet and floret, × 2.

florets; lemmas with stiff, brownish pubescence, 1.5-2 cm. long, the apex 2-cleft, with bent awn to 4 cm. long, twisted in the lower part.

Distribution: Most common in the western United States, and utilized to some extent as range forage, scattered elsewhere; introduced from Europe.

Missouri. Infrequent and scattered, waste ground, Jackson, Boone, and St. Louis counties. Flowering in May-June.

2. **Avena sativa** L. CULTIVATED OATS. Fig. 95.

Plants leafy, erect, to 1 m. or more in height; leaf blades smooth, with scabrous margins, 5-15 mm. wide; ligule membraneous, about 3 mm. long; panicles large, 1-3 cm. long, the branches somewhat lax and spreading; spikelets 2-flowered; glumes about 2.5 cm. long, exceeding the florets; lemmas and rachilla smooth; awns lacking, or sometimes short, simple awn present from back of lemma.

Distribution: Widely cultivated for grain, mostly in the northern and central United States, used as forage in the South, occasionally spontaneous; probably native to Asia.

Missouri. Scattered, fields, waste areas, feed lots, not persistent. Flowering in May-June.

Remarks: So-called False Wild Oats or "fatuoids" occur which resemble the wild oats, *A. fatua.* The degree of similarity varies, with transitional characters of awn, pubescence, and articulation being observed. Two ideas are held as to the origin of these fatuoids, as discussed by Huskins (1946): (1) mutations occurring in *A. sativa,* and (2) natural crossing of *A. sativa* and *A. fatua.* While the latter does occur, the mutation theory appears more tenable. It is thought that the appearance of fatuoids results from the loss of inhibitory controls in *A. sativa* which normally suppress the "fatuoid factor" that is present. The various fatuoid types which have been observed are distinguishable generally from the cultivated oats by the presence of one or several awns per spikelet, these being bent and twisted, increasing pubescence of the lemmas, and the greater tendency for floret separation. All these characteristics or tendencies are emphasized in wild oats, suggesting possibly an ancestral derivation of *A. sativa* from *A. fatua.*

31. ARRHENATHERUM Beauv.

Perennials; panicles mostly narrow, with short, flexuous branches; spikelets 2-flowered, the lower floret usually staminate, the upper one perfect; glumes thin, persistent, the florets falling separately; lemmas thin, the lower dorsally awned, the upper awnless, or with minute awn; rachilla extended behind 2nd floret.

1. **Arrhenatherum elatius** (L.) Presl. TALL OATGRASS. Fig. 96.

Plants forming leafy tufts; culms erect, to 1 m. tall or more; foliage glabrous, the leaf blades 5-10 mm. wide; panicles shiny, 10-25 cm. long, with short, spreading branches; spikelets about 8 mm. long; glumes unequal, the 2nd longer, nearly reaching upper floret; lemmas about 7 mm. long, bearded at base, the lower one (staminate) with twisted, bent awn 10 mm. or longer attached from below middle, the upper lemma (perfect) minutely awned, attached slightly below apex.

FIG. 95.—*Avena sativa.* Spikelet, × 2.

FIG. 96.—*Arrhenatherum elatius.* Plant, × ½; spikelet and upper floret, × 5.

FIG. 97.—*Holcus lanatus.* Plant, × ½; spikelet, florets, and mature fertile floret, × 5.

FIG. 98.—*Danthonia spicata.* Plant, × ½; spikelet, floret, and cleistogene, × 5.

Distribution: Widely distributed in the United States; introduced from Europe early in the nineteenth century as a forage species.

Missouri. Little known, open ground, Jasper, Boone, and Pike counties. Flowering in June-July.

32. HOLCUS L.

Perennials; panicles narrow, contracted, rather dense; spikelets 2-flowered, separating below the glumes and falling entire; glumes nearly equal and overtopping the florets; lower lemma perfect, awnless, the upper staminate and short-awned.

1. **Holcus lanatus** L. Velvetgrass. Fig. 97.

Plants leafy, erect or somewhat decumbent near base, rooting at the lower nodes, 50-100 cm. tall; sheaths generally soft-pubescent; leaf blades as much as 1 cm. wide; panicles contracted spike-like, 5-15 cm. long; spikelets about 4 mm. long; glumes overtopping the florets; lemmas about 2 mm. long, the lower one awnless, the upper with short, curved awn about 1 mm. long, attached below apex.

Distribution: Widely scattered in the United States; adventive from Europe.

Missouri. Little known, open ground, Jackson, Vernon, and Jasper counties. Flowering in May-June.

33. DANTHONIA Lam. & D. C.

Perennials; panicles narrow, contracted to somewhat spreading; spikelets several-flowered, separating above the persistent glumes; glumes nearly equal, elongate, mostly overtopping the florets; lemmas bidentate, awned from between the teeth, the latter sometimes extending into simple awns; cleistogamous flowers produced from the lower sheaths.

1. **Danthonia spicata** (L.) Beauv. Poverty Oatgrass. Fig. 98.

Plants forming dense, basal clumps of curled leaves; culms erect, to about 50 cm. tall; sheaths and leaf blades glabrous to sparsely pilose, the latter narrow, 1-3 mm. wide, tapering to involute tip; ligule consisting of pilose hairs; panicles narrow, sparsely flowered; glumes thin, elongate-acuminate, about 10 mm. long or more, overtopping the several florets; lemmas pilose, about 2.5-3 mm. long, cleft at apex, with bent awn about 5-8 mm. long, twisted in lower part.

Distribution: Eastern and central United States, less common westward.

Missouri. Dry woods, glades, prairies, on thin or rocky soils, generally distributed, common in the Ozark region. Flowering in May-June.

TRIBE V. AGROSTIDEAE

34. CALAMAGROSTIS Adans.

Perennials; panicles contracted to spreading; spikelets 1-flowered, separating above the persistent glumes; glumes acute or narrow-pointed, nearly equaling or slightly exceeding the floret; lemma with basal tuft of soft, ascending hairs, dorsally awned; palea only slightly shorter than lemma; rachilla usually extended behind the floret as a hairy bristle.

KEY TO MISSOURI SPECIES

1. Panicles compact, mostly spike-like, with short branches; awn of lemma straight, slender.......2. *C. inexpansa*
1. Panicles somewhat open, the branches spreading; awn of lemma straight or bent.........2
   2. Awn straight, simple; species of damp prairies, generally distributed in the northern counties.......1. *C. canadensis*
   2. Awn bent, twisted below; rare species of dry bluffs.......3. *C. insperata*

1. **Calamagrostis canadensis** (Michx.) Beauv. BLUEJOINT. Fig. 99.

Plants forming clumps, spreading by rhizomes; culms erect, to 1.5 m. tall, sometimes more; sheaths smooth, slightly keeled; ligule conspicuous, with irregular margin; leaf blades scabrous on the edges, otherwise glabrous, about 5 mm. wide, or more; panicles pyramidal, the branches somewhat flexuous, in distinct whorls, spikelets purplish, about 2-5 mm. long; glumes similar; lemma conspicuously nerved, 2-3 mm. long, somewhat shorter than glumes, with copious tuft of white hairs at base, and slender, straight awn from the middle of the back. Plants with generally small spikelets about 2-3 mm. long are sometimes designated as var. *Macouniana* (Vasey) Stebbins. According to some authors the separation is scarcely distinct.

Distribution: Wide-ranging across the northern United States and adjacent Canada, south to Missouri, also higher elevations in the Southwest.

Missouri. Wet lowlands, prairie swales, sloughs, most common in the northern counties, infrequent south of the Missouri River reported from Jackson, Lafayette, St. Louis, and Cape Girardeau counties. Plants with the small spikelet tendency, var. *Macouniana,* are more prevalent than the typical variety. Flowering in May-June.

2. **Calamagrostis inexpansa** Gray var. *brevior* (Vasey) Stebbins. Fig. 100.

Plants forming clumps, rhizomatous; culms 50-100 cm. tall; sheaths glabrous; ligule conspicuous, about 5 mm. long; leaf blades scabrous on the margins, about 4 mm. wide; panicles narrow, compact; glumes nearly equal, 3-4 mm. long, slightly longer than the floret; lemma inconspicuously nerved, tufted at base, with straight awn from the back. This species is easily distinguished from the preceding by its strict, spike-like panicles.

Distribution: Northern United States and adjacent Canada, south to Missouri and Indiana, also higher elevations in the Southwest.

Missouri. Prairies and swales, infrequent and scattered, Jackson, Barton, Jasper, and Texas counties. Flowering in June-July.

FIG. 99.—*Calamagrostis canadensis*. Plant, × ½; glumes and floret, × 10.

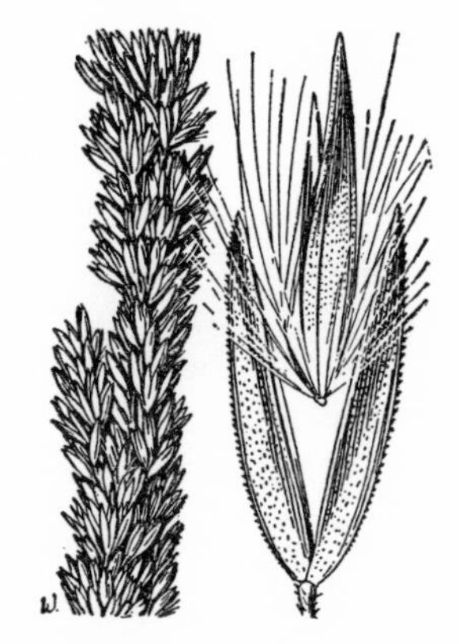

FIG. 100.—*Calamagrostis inexpansa*. Panicle, × 1; glumes and floret, × 10.

3. **Calamagrostis insperata** Swallen. Fig. 101.

Plants rhizomatous; culms about 1 m. tall; sheaths glabrous; ligule conspicuous; leaf blades 4-8 mm. wide, long-tapering; panicles with spreading, flexuous branches in several whorls; spikelets about 5 mm. long; glumes nearly equal, the 1st somewhat longer than the 2nd, both exceeding the floret; lemma with tufts of short hairs from the sides, not reaching the apex, with bent, twisted awn from near base.

Distribution: Known originally only from Ohio; recently found in *Missouri* on cherty limestone, Ozark and Douglas counties (Steyermark 20043, 23350). For an interesting report of this rare species in Missouri, see Van Schaack (1954).

35. CALAMOVILFA Hack.

Perennials; panicles with close, ascending branches to somewhat spreading; spikelets 1-flowered, separating above the unequal, persistent glumes; lemmas with tuft of hairs at base, awnless; palea about equal to lemma; rachilla not extended behind the floret.

1. **Calamovilfa longifolia** (Hook.) Scribn. SAND REEDGRASS. Fig. 102.

Plants forming clumps or mats, spreading by rhizomes; culms leafy, erect to 1.5 m. tall; sheaths glabrous, except for pilose hairs at summit, overlapping on the lower culm; ligule consisting of hairs, 1-2 mm. long, leaf blades elongate, 3-7 mm. wide, involute toward tip; panicles somewhat stiff, with ascending branches; spikelets about 5-7.5 mm. long; glumes somewhat dissimilar, the 1st ovate, 4-6 mm. long, the 2nd longer, acuminate, about level with top of floret; lemma with dense tufts of hairs at base, awnless; palea nearly equaling lemma.

Distribution: North-central United States and lower Canada, south to Colorado and Missouri.

Missouri. Sandy, open ground, reported from Clay, Jackson, Jefferson, and St. Louis counties. Flowering in July.

36. AGROSTIS L.

Annuals or perennials; panicles narrow, compact to diffuse, spreading; spikelets 1-flowered, separating above the persistent glumes; glumes mostly equal, acuminate, equaling or overtopping the floret; lemma awnless, or with delicate awn attached below apex; palea thin, equal to lemma, or much reduced or absent. (Including *Apera* Adans.)

KEY TO MISSOURI SPECIES

1. Palea present, conspicuous; introduced forage and lawn species, occasionally establishing in pastures, fields, and waste ground 2
1. Palea minute or lacking; native prairie and woodland species 5
    2. Perennials spreading by stolons or rhizomes; lemmas awnless 3
    2. Annuals; lemmas with delicate, hair-like awn 4
3. Ligule longer than broad; naturalized forage species, becoming common .... 1. *A. alba*
3. Ligule shorter than broad; used as a fine turf, infrequently spreading .... 2. *A. tenuis*
    4. Panicles contracted, with short branches .... 3. *A. interrupta*
    4. Panicles open, branches spreading .... 4. *A. spica-venti*
5. Lemmas awned; delicate annual of open ground, prairies, and glades .... 5. *A. Elliottiana*
5. Lemmas awnless; perennials of open ground, prairies, or woodland 6

FIG. 101.—*Calamagrostis insperata.* Panicle, × 1; glumes and floret, × 10.

FIG. 102.—*Calamovilfa longifolia.* Plant, × ½; spikelet and floret, × 5.

6. Spikelets 2 mm. or longer; panicles diffuse; summer flowering species........................ ....7. *A. perennans*
6. Spikelets less than 2 mm. long, clustered toward ends of branches, spring flowering species..6. *A. hiemalis*

1. **Agrostis alba** L. REDTOP. Fig. 103.

Perennial, forming sod, spreading by rhizomes; culms erect or somewhat decumbent near base, to 1 m. tall; leaf blades about 3-5 mm. wide, sometimes more, with long taper; ligule conspicuous, longer than broad, 3-4 mm. long, truncate; panicles erect, pyramidal, with distinct whorls of spreading branches; spikelets crowded, reddish or purplish, about 2-3 mm. long; glumes spreading at maturity, overtopping the lemma; lemma thin, 2 mm. or less in length; palea shorter than lemma.

Distribution: Widespread in the United States, naturalizing especially in the cooler regions; introduced as a forage species from Europe.

Missouri. Fields and waste ground, usually on moist soils, generally distributed. Flowering in June.

Remarks: This species has been designated as *A. gigantea* Roth var. *dispar* (Michx.) Philipson in the monograph of British species (Philipson, 1938). More recently, Gleason (1952) has treated it as *A. stolonifera* L. var. *major* (Gaud.) Farw. The *Manual of Grasses* (Hitchc., 1951) is followed here, in which the more widely used *alba* is retained.

2. **Agrostis tenuis** Sibth. COLONIAL BENT, RHODE ISLAND BENT. Fig. 104.

Perennial, forming tufts or sod, from rhizomes or sometimes stoloniferous; culms of slighter habit than species 1; leaf blades narrow, 2-4 mm. wide; ligule 1-2 mm. long, mostly shorter than broad; panicles pyramidal, diffuse, with slender, whorled branches; spikelets not crowded, purplish, 2-3 mm. long; glumes exceeding the florets; lemma about 2 mm. long; palea shorter than lemma. Plants with awned lemmas have been treated as forma *aristata* Parnell (Druce).

Distribution: Scattered in the northern parts of the United States, primarily in the northeast and Pacific coast regions; introduced from Europe as a fine turf and forage species.

Missouri. Utilized in turf mixtures and occasionally self-established, but not common. Flowering in June-July.

3. **Agrostis interrupta** L. Fig. 105.

Annual, forming small tufts; culms branching, about 50 cm. tall; sheaths glabrous; ligule conspicuous; leaf blades flat, 2-5 mm. wide; panicles interrupted, spike-like, with short, ascending branches, floriferous to the base; spikelets crowded, about 2 mm. long; glumes unequal, the 2nd somewhat longer and equaling the floret; lemma with a delicate awn to 10 mm. long attached below the apex; palea equal to the lemma. (*Apera interrupta* [L.] Beauv.)

Distribution: Widely scattered in the United States; adventive from Europe.

Missouri. Local, reported on waste ground, St. Louis County.

4. **Agrostis spica-venti** L. Fig. 106.

Annual, resembling species 3 in general habit, but the panicles more open, with spreading branches; spikelets about 2 mm. long; glumes unequal, about

Fig. 103.—*Agrostis alba.* Plant, × ½; 2 spikelets and floret, × 5.

FIG. 104.—*Agrostis tenuis*. Panicle, × 1; glumes, floret, and ligule, × 5.

FIG. 105.—*Agrostis interrupta*. Panicle, × ½; glumes and floret, × 5.

FIG. 106.—*Agrostis spica-venti*. Plant, × ½; glumes and floret, × 5.

FIG. 107.—*Agrostis Elliottiana*. Panicle, × 1; glumes and floret, × 5.

equaling the floret; lemma with a delicate awn about 10 mm. long. (*Apera spica venti* [L.] Beauv.)

Distribution: Widely scattered in the United States; adventive from Europe. *Missouri.* Local, reported on waste ground, Jackson County.

5. **Agrostis Elliottiana** Schult. Fig. 107.

Annual, forming small tufts; culms erect, mostly less than 50 cm. tall; leaf blades narrow, short, about 1 mm. wide; ligule conspicuous, tapering to a point, several times longer than broad; panicles diffuse, delicate, more than one-half the length of entire plant; spikelets about 2 mm. long; glumes nearly equal, exceeding

FIG. 108.—*Agrostis hiemalis.* Plant, × ½; glumes and floret, × 5.

the floret; lemma conspicuously nerved, with a flexuous, thread-like awn to 10 mm. long; palea absent.

Distribution: Eastern and southern United States, west to Kansas and Texas.

Missouri. Glades, prairies, rocky slopes, fields, primarily in the central and southern counties, absent in the North. Flowering in May-June.

6. **Agrostis hiemalis** (Walt.) B. S. P. HAIRGRASS. Fig. 108.

Perennial, forming dense tufts; culms slender, erect, 50-100 cm. tall; leaf blades narrow, 1-2 mm. wide; ligule conspicuous, with a lacerated margin; panicles diffuse, with delicate, spreading branches in several whorls; spikelets minute, about 1.5 mm. long, crowded toward ends of the branches; glumes somewhat unequal, acuminate, exceeding the floret; lemma awnless, about 1 mm. long, or shorter; palea absent.

Distribution: Eastern and northern United States, west to Oklahoma and Kansas.

Missouri. Fields, prairies, thin woods, generally distributed. Flowering in May-June.

Remarks: The closely related, later-blooming *A. scabra* Willd. is a coarser plant with larger spikelets about 2 mm. long. Although previously recorded for Missouri, it is apparently not present in our flora. Specimens do occur, however, which approach the dimensions of *A. scabra,* as provided in the *Manual of Grasses* (Hitchc. 1951). Gleason (1952) refers to these plants as *A. hiemalis* var. *tenuis* (Tuckerm.) Gl.

7. **Agrostis perennans** (Walt.) Tuckerm. Fig. 109.

Perennial, forming sparse tufts; culms erect to weak-stemmed, decumbent, about 50 cm. or taller; leaf blades lax, 1-4 mm. wide; ligule blunt, 1-4 mm. long; panicles diffuse, with slender, forking branches; spikelets 2-3 mm. long; glumes unequal, acuminate, the 1st somewhat longer, both exceeding the floret; lemma about 1.5-2 mm. long, awnless; palea absent. Weak-stemmed, decumbent plants with thin, lax leaves, are sometimes designated as var. *aestivalis* Vasey. These possibly are a habitat form.

FIG. 109.—*Agrostis perennans.* Panicle, × 1; glumes and floret, × 5.

Distribution: Eastern and central United States, west to Nebraska and Texas.

Missouri. Upland woods, shaded slopes, alluvial banks, generally distributed. The weak, decumbent form, var. *aestivalis,* occurs in damp, shaded habitats throughout. Flowering in July.

37. CINNA L.

Perennials; panicles contracted or somewhat open with spreading branches; spikelets 1-flowered, separating below the glumes and falling entire; glumes mostly equal, narrow, acuminate; floret on short stipe; lemma minutely awned from just below bidentate apex; palea shorter than lemma.

1. **Cinna arundinacea** L. WOODREED. Fig. 110.

Plants solitary or few together in a loose tuft; culms with bulbous bases, erect, to 1 m. or taller; sheaths glabrous; ligule conspicuous, with lacerated margin; leaf blades mostly glabrous, 5-10 mm. wide; panicles somewhat lax, with close branches of numerous spikelets; spikelets compressed, 4-6 mm. long; glumes 3.5-6 mm. long, the 1st 1-nerved, the 2nd 3-nerved; lemma 3-4 mm. long, with minute awn, less than 1 mm. long from between teeth of the split apex; palea 1-nerved. Weakly distinguishable plants with short, narrow panicles are sometimes designated as var. *inexpansa* Fern & Grisc.

Distribution: Eastern and central United States, west to South Dakota and Texas.

Missouri. Swampy ground, alluvial woods, moist ravines, generally distributed. Flowering in July-August.

38. ALOPECURUS L.

Annuals or perennials; panicles mostly dense, cylindrical, spike-like; spikelets 1-flowered, separating below the glumes and falling entire; glumes mostly equal, compressed; lemma with slender dorsal awn from near or below middle; palea absent.

KEY TO MISSOURI SPECIES

1. Panicles elongate, spike-like, less than 5 mm. thick; perennial species of aquatic habitats........1. *A. aequalis*
1. Panicles spike-like, 5-10 mm. thick; annuals or perennials of damp ground, fields........2
   2. Panicles cylindrical, 5-7 mm. thick; common native species........2. *A. carolinianus*
   2. Panicles 7-10 mm. thick; introduced species, not common........3. *A. pratensis*

1. **Alopecurus aequalis** Sobol. SHORT-AWN FOXTAIL. Fig. 111.

Aquatic perennial; culms erect to spreading-decumbent, to 50 cm. or more in length; sheaths glabrous; ligules conspicuous, papery; leaf blades 2-5 mm. wide, lax, long-tapering; panicles narrow, spike-like, 3-4 mm. thick; spikelets light green, about 2-5 mm. long; glumes silky-pubescent, 2 mm. long; lemma with straight awn, reaching or only slightly exceeding the apex. *A. geniculatus* L., the Water Foxtail, is quite similar, and possibly might be confused with *A. aequalis;* however, the former does not occur in Missouri, and can be distinguished by the longer awns which distinctly exceed the floret.

FIG. 110.—*Cinna arundinacea.* Plant, × ½; glumes and floret, × 10.

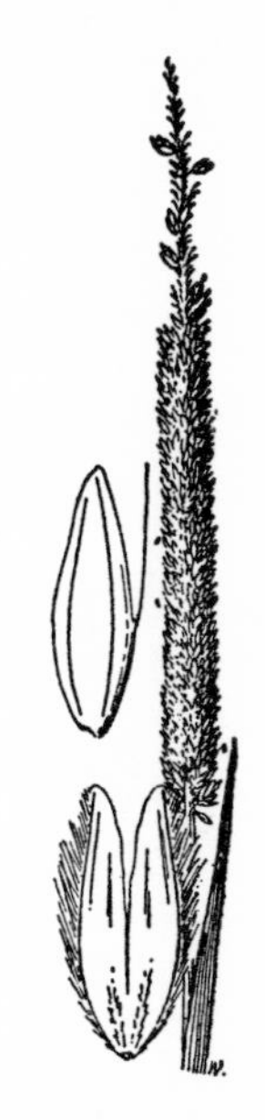

FIG. 111.—*Alopecurus aequalis.* Panicle, × 1; glumes and floret, × 10.

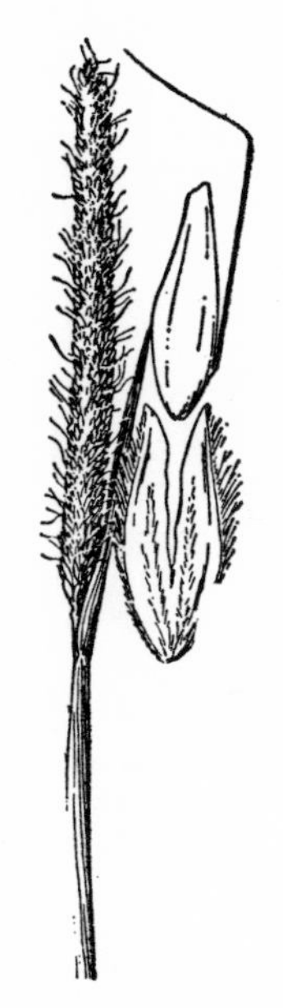

FIG. 112.—*Alopecurus carolinianus.* Plant, × 1; glumes and floret, × 10.

Distribution: Northern United States, south to Ohio, Missouri, and Arizona.
Missouri. Sinks, ponds, sloughs, in shallow water or swampy ground, scattered, primarily in the southern counties. Flowering in May-June.

2. **Alopecurus carolinianus** Walt. Fig. 112.

Annual, forming tufts; culms branching from the base, erect to somewhat decumbent, to about 50 cm. tall; upper sheaths mostly inflated, or enlarged; ligule conspicuous; leaf blades 2-5 mm. wide, not much longer than the sheaths; panicles cylindrical, spike-like, about 5-7 mm. thick; spikelets 2-5 mm. long; glumes joined at base, pubescent, about reaching level of floret; lemma with bent awn exceeding the apex about 3 mm., thus giving inflorescence a bristly appearance.

Distribution: Widespread, represented in most regions of the United States.
Missouri. Fields, swales, and alluvial banks, damp ground, generally distributed. Flowering in April-May.

3. **Alopecurus pratensis** L. MEADOW FOXTAIL. Fig. 113.

Perennial, forming loose tufts; culms erect to somewhat decumbent, to 50 cm. or taller; leaf blades as much as 10 mm. wide, long-tapering, panicles dense, spike-like, 7-10 mm. thick; spikelets about 5 mm. long; glumes jointed at base, long-ciliate, about reaching level of floret; lemma with bent awn attached near base and exserted beyond apex about 5 mm.

Distribution: Primarily in the northern and central areas of the United States; introduced as a forage species from the Old World about 1850.

FIG. 113.—*Alopecurus pratensis.* Plant, × ½; glumes and floret, × 10.

Missouri. Rare, reported from Boone and St. Louis counties. Flowering in April-May.

39. PHLEUM L. TIMOTHY

Annuals or perennials; panicles dense, cylindrical, spike-like; spikelets 1-flowered, separating above the persistent glumes; glumes equal, keeled, pointed or somewhat awn-like, exceeding the floret; lemma awnless, with broad apex; palea shorter than lemma.

1. **Phleum pratense** L. Fig. 114.

Perennial, forming clumps; culms with bulbous bases, erect, to 1 m. tall; sheaths glabrous; ligule conspicuous, about 2-3 mm. long; leaf blades 4-10 mm. wide; panicles spike-like, 5-8 mm. thick, as much as 15 cm. long; spikelets compacted, 3-3.5 mm. long; glumes stiffly ciliate on keel, with short, awn-like tip 1 mm. long; lemma thin, 1-2 mm. long, awnless.

Distribution: Widespread forage species naturalized in the United States; introduced from Europe in the 1700's.

Missouri. Fields, pastures, waste ground, generally distributed. Flowering in late May-June.

40. MUHLENBERGIA Schreb.

Annuals or perennials; panicles condensed or spike-like to broad, diffuse; spikelets 1-flowered, separating above the persistent glumes; glumes variable, from minute or lacking to overtopping the floret, awned or awnless; lemma 3-nerved, awned from the apex or awnless; palea present, about equal to the lemma.

FIG. 114.—*Phleum pratense.* Plant, × ½; glumes and floret, × 10.

Eleven species are reported from Missouri, all perennial, most of these having rhizomes.

KEY TO MISSOURI SPECIES

1. Panicles broad, diffuse, with spreading branches, mostly sparsely flowered......2
1. Panicles dense, or at least narrow with closely ascending branches......3
   2. Rhizomes present; lemma awnless; plants of moist ground......1. *M. asperifolia*
   2. Rhizomes lacking; lemma long-awned; plants of dry sands......2. *M. capillaris*
3. Rhizomes present......4
3. Rhizomes absent......10
   4. Panicles dense, with thick lobing; glumes elongate-tapering, both much exceeding the floret......3. *M. racemosa*
   4. Panicles close but not usually dense, the lobes or side branches slender, ascending; both glumes exceeding the floret, or only the 2nd glume sometimes longer......5
5. Lemma awnless; glumes narrowing rather abruptly from about the middle; one of our most common species of upland woods and rocky slopes......4. *M. sobolifera*
5. Lemma awned, or if awnless the glumes with a gradual taper starting from near base; species of low, moist ground, except *M. tenuifolia* with an awned lemma occurring on drier soils in upland woods......6
   6. Lemma mostly awned......7
   6. Lemma awnless or merely sharp-tipped......9
7. Glumes with a gradual taper, thin, with a broad hyaline margin to apex......7. *M. sylvatica*
7. Glumes with an abrupt taper, the apex an awn-like projection of the mid-nerve......8
   8. Glumes nearly equal; culms mostly simple, few-leaved; species of dry woods habitat......5. *M. tenuifolia*
   8. Glumes unequal; culms much-branched, with numerous leaves; species of low ground......6. *M. brachyphylla*
9. Plants branching from the middle and upper nodes, spreading or reclining, with bushy, top-heavy appearance, rooting at the lower nodes......8. *M. frondosa*
9. Plants simple or sparsely branched......9. *M. mexicana*
   10. Glumes present; plants with a hard, bulb-like base, native to limestone bluffs and dry prairie glades......10. *M. cuspidata*
   10. Glumes minute or obsolete; plants not bulbous at the base, occurring in fields, lawns, mostly in damp, shaded habitats......11. *M. Schreberi*

1. **Muhlenbergia asperifolia** (Nees. & Mey.) Parodi. SCRATCHGRASS. Fig. 115.

Plants tufted, rhizomatous; culms branching from the base, erect or somewhat decumbent, to 50 cm. tall; sheaths crowded, flattened; leaf blades harsh, narrow, 1-2 mm. wide; panicles diffuse, with spreading branches; spikelets 1.5-2

FIG. 115.—*Muhlenbergia asperifolia.* Plant, × 1; glumes and floret, × 10.

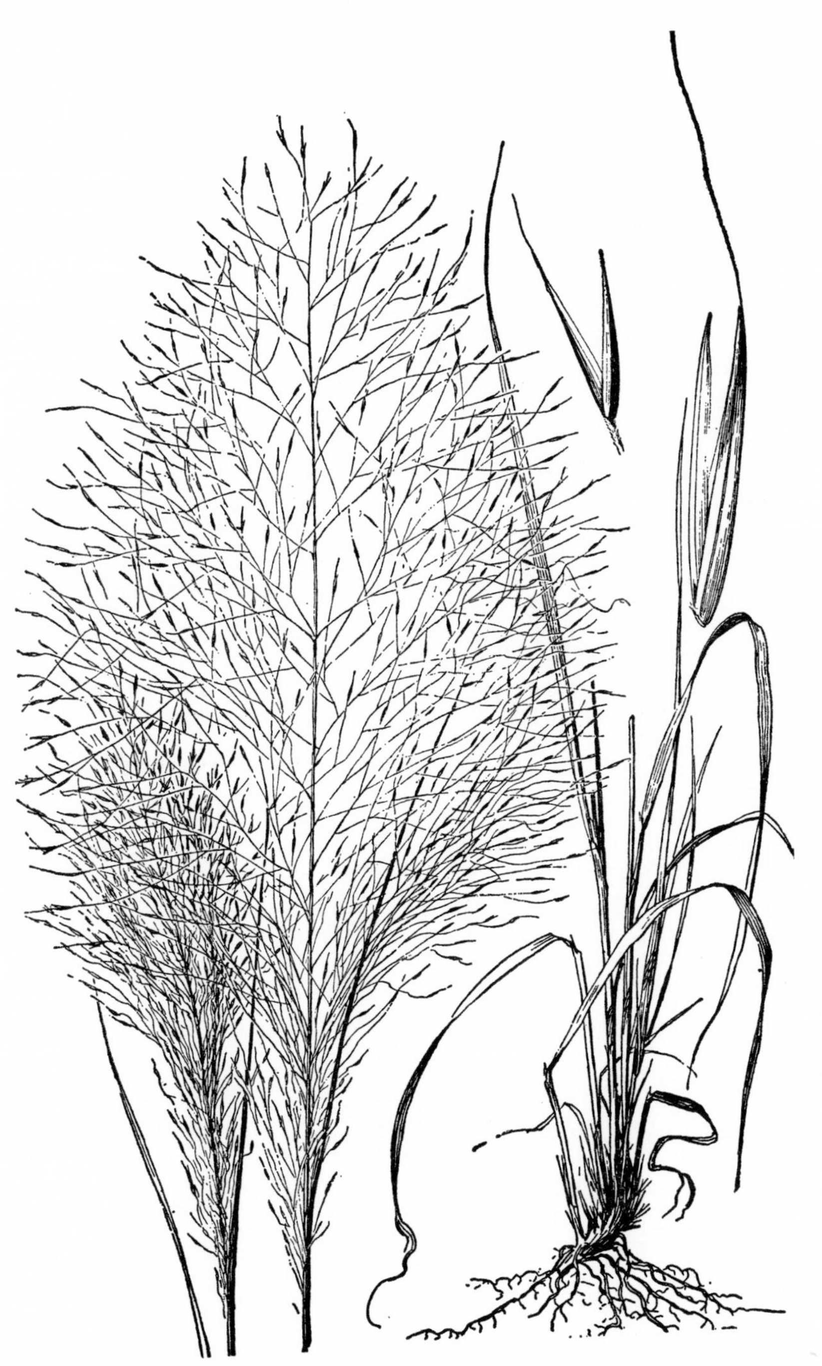

FIG. 116.—*Muhlenbergia capillaris*. Plant, × ½; glumes and floret, × 10.

mm. long, occasionally 2-flowered; glumes similar, narrow, shorter than to about equal to the floret; lemma 1-1.5 mm. long, awnless; palea similar to the lemma.

Distribution: Widespread in the western United States, east to Wisconsin and Indiana.

Missouri. Infrequent, moist, sandy ground, Holt, Jackson, and St. Louis counties. Flowering in late summer.

2. **Muhlenbergia capillaris** (Lam.) Trin. HAIRGRASS. Fig. 116.

Plants tufted, lacking rhizomes; culms stiff, erect, to 1 m. tall; leaf blades 1-4 mm. wide, becoming involute; ligule conspicuous, pointed; panicles showy, broad, purplish, with fine, spreading branches; spikelets about 4 mm. long; glumes dissimilar, the 1st shorter, both acute to short-awned; lemma 3-4 mm. long, with delicate awn several times as long; palea similar to lemma.

Distribution: Eastern and southern United States, west to Kansas and Texas.

Missouri. Cherty slopes, bluffs, sandy prairies, scattered, the Ozarks and southwestern counties. Flowering in July-August.

3. **Muhlenbergia racemosa** (Michx.) B. S. P. Fig. 117.

Plants rhizomatous; culms stiff, erect, branching, to 1 m. tall; sheaths keeled; leaf blades 2-6 mm. wide, long-tapering; panicles dense, spike-like, lobed; spikelets 4.5-7 mm. long; glumes linear, awn-like, exceeding the lemma; lemma tufted at base, awnless; palea similar to lemma.

Distribution: Widespread, northern United States and adjacent Canada, south to Maryland, Oklahoma, and New Mexico.

Missouri. Sloughs, alluvial bottoms, mostly damp soils, generally distributed. Flowering in late summer.

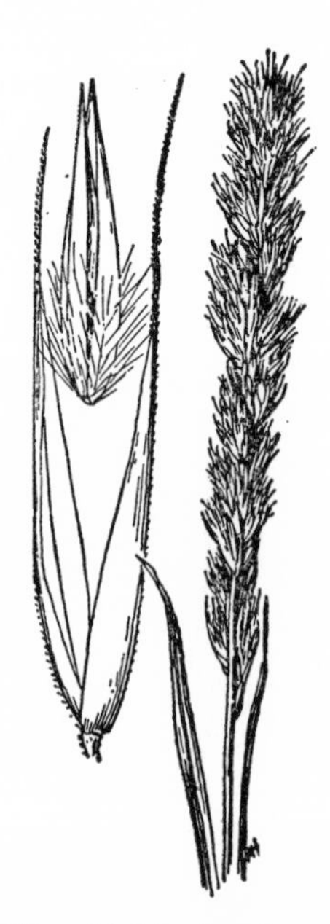

FIG. 117.—*Muhlenbergia racemosa.* Panicle, × 1; glumes and floret, × 10.

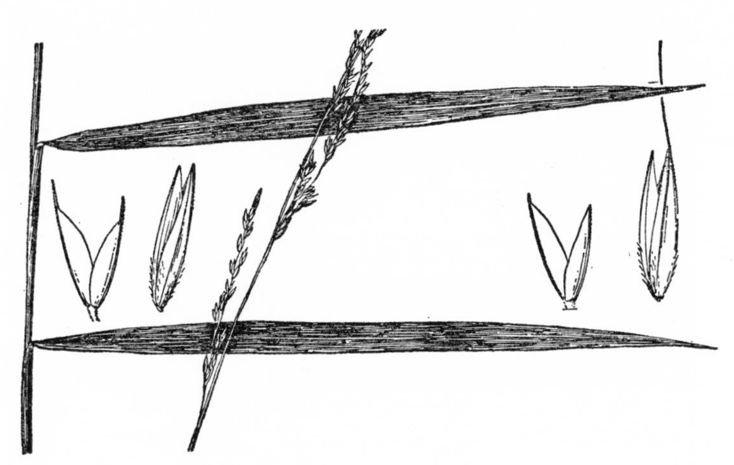

FIG. 118.—*Muhlenbergia sobolifera.* Plant, × 1; glumes and floret, × 10.

4. **Muhlenbergia sobolifera** (Muhl.) Trin. Fig. 118.

Plants forming sparse tufts, rhizomatous; culms slender, erect, sparsely branched, 30-90 cm. tall; leaf blades few, spreading, glabrous, 3-7 mm. wide; panicles narrow, with short, appressed branches; spikelets pale green, about 2 mm. long from short pedicels; glumes somewhat unequal, pale whitish, with green midrib, shorter than the lemma; lemma about 2 mm. long, typically awnless. Plants differing only by the presence of minute awn 1-2 mm. long have been separated as forma *setigera* (Scribn.) Deam. The distinction seems minor.

Distribution: Northeastern United States and mid-Atlantic region, west to Nebraska and Texas.

Missouri. Dry woods and rocky slopes, generally distributed, one of our most common species. The short-awned form has been reported from Christian County (Palmer 58256). Flowering in late summer.

5. **Muhlenbergia tenuiflora** (Willd.) B. S. P. Fig. 119.

Plants rhizomatous, taller and coarser than species 4, leaf blades few, spreading, 5-9 mm. wide; panicles narrow, with slender, appressed branches; spikelets 3-4 mm. long; glumes equal, sharp-pointed, shorter than the lemma; lemma averaging about 3 mm. long, with a long, slender awn.

Distribution: Eastern and central United States, west to Iowa and Oklahoma.

Missouri. Dry woods, calcareous slopes, creek bottoms, generally distributed. Flowering in late summer.

6. **Muhlenbergia brachyphylla** Bush. Fig. 120.

Plants rhizomatous; culms erect, to 1 m. tall, more branched, and leafier than species 5; sheaths glabrous, keeled, with a prominent mid-rib; leaf blades numerous, 2-5 mm. wide; panicles narrow, with short, ascending branches; spikelets 3-4 mm. long; glumes unequal, acute, shorter than the lemma, or awned and exceeding the latter; lemma 2.5-3 mm. long, pubescent near the base, with a slender awn. Those plants with the glumes prominently awned, thus exceeding the

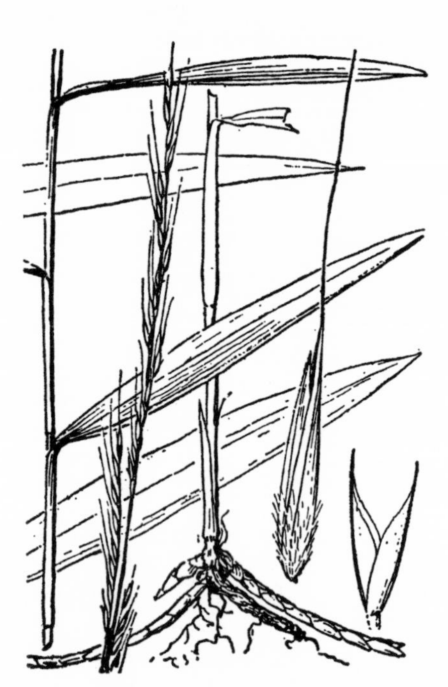

FIG. 119.—*Muhlenbergia tenuiflora.* Plant, × 1; glumes and floret, × 10.

FIG. 120.—*Muhlenbergia brachyphylla.* Plant, × 1; glumes and floret, × 10.

lemmas, but otherwise similar, have been separated as forma *aristata* Palmer & Steyermark.

Distribution: Central United States and mid-Atlantic region, south to Texas.

Missouri. Low woods, moist slopes, swales, spring branches, generally distributed. Plants with awned glumes have been reported from Pike County (Steyermark 82921). Flowering in late summer.

7. **Muhlenbergia sylvatica** Torr. Fig. 121.

Plants solitary or somewhat tufted, rhizomatous; culms sparsely branched, erect, to 1 m. tall; leaf blades thin, 2-7 mm. wide; panicles delicate, flexuous and narrow, with closely ascending branches; spikelets about 3 mm. long; glumes nearly equal, with scarious margins, tapering from near the base to an acute or awn-tipped apex; lemma 2.5-3 mm. long, pilose near the base, with a straight awn, 5-10 mm. long. Plants with awnless lemmas have been separated as forma *attenuata* Palmer & Steyermark.

Distribution: Eastern and central United States, west to South Dakota and Texas.

Missouri. Moist ravines, low calcareous slopes and creek bottoms, generally distributed. The awnless form is found occasionally. Flowering in July-August.

8. **Muhlenbergia frondosa** (Poir) Fern. Fig. 122.

Plants rhizomatous; culms rooting at the lower nodes, profusely branched, mostly from the upper nodes, top-heavy, eventually reclining or sprawling to 1

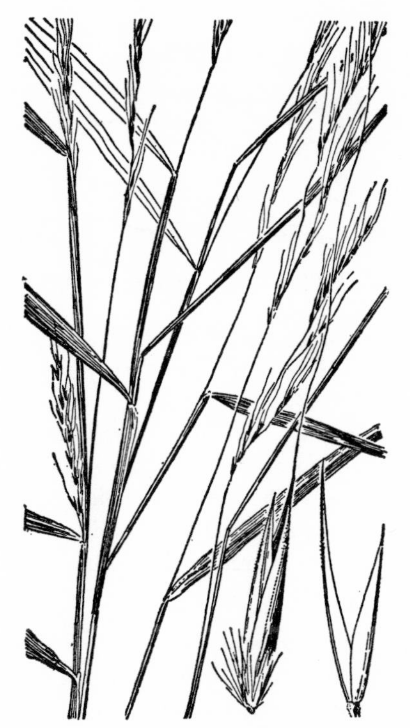

FIG. 121.—*Muhlenbergia sylvatica.* Plant, × 1; glumes and floret, × 10.

FIG. 122.—*Muhlenbergia frondosa.* Plant, × 1; glumes and floret, × 10.

m. long; internodes usually glabrous in the upper part; leaf blades numerous, usually short, 2-6 mm. wide; panicles narrow, condensed, with short, ascending branches, some terminal, others from the upper sheaths; spikelets mostly 2-3 mm. long, occasionally to 4 mm.; glumes nearly equal, awn-tipped, lemma pilose near the base, awnless, or with an awn to 10 mm. long. Plants with awned lemmas are sometimes distinguished as forma *commutata* (Scribn.) Fern.

Distribution: Eastern and central United States, west to North Dakota and Texas, absent in the Southeast.

Missouri. Low woods, alluvial banks, on moist ground, generally distributed. Plants with awned lemmas may be found occasionally. Flowering in late summer.

Remarks: This species was segregated from *M. mexicana* (L.) Trin. by Fernald (1943); thus earlier collections may be a composite of both species. See the following species for a comparison of these closely allied taxa.

9. **Muhlenbergia mexicana** (L.) Trin. Fig. 123.

Plants rhizomatous, similar to species 8, but usually not rooting at the lower nodes, and less branched and sprawling; internodes also somewhat puberulent in the upper part, but a weak character difference; panicles dense, spike-like, usually thicker and more compact than in the preceding; spikelets about 3 mm. long; glumes nearly equal, linear-attenuate; lemma pubescent at the base, awnless, or with an awn about 5 mm. long. Plants with awned lemmas are sometimes distinguished as forma *ambigua* (Torr.) Fern.

Distribution: Widespread in the United States, but absent in the Southeast.

FIG. 123.—*Muhlenbergia mexicana.* Plant, × 1; glumes and floret, × 10.

Missouri. Moist prairies and creek bottoms, generally distributed. The awned form is found occasionally, initially reported from Howell County (Steyermark 69076).

Remarks: Plants with essentially glabrous lemmas but otherwise weakly separated from the two preceding species are designated as *M. glabriflora* Scribn. Specimens thus determined are rare in Missouri, one such collection being from Barton County (Palmer 53237). The vagueness of specific characters in these closely related entities indicates a need for re-evaluating current treatments.

10. **Muhlenbergia cuspidata** (Torr.) Muhl. Fig. 124.

Plants distinctly tufted, lacking rhizomes; culms with small, hard, bulb-like bases, stiffly erect, 25-50 cm. tall; sheaths usually pilose; leaf blades narrow, 1-2 mm. wide, with involute margins; panicles slender with short, ascending branches; spikelets 2.5-3 mm. long; glumes awn-tipped, shorter than the floret; lemma awnless, narrowing to minute, cupidate tip.

Distribution: North-central United States, south to Kentucky and Arizona.

Missouri. Dry glades and bluffs, western counties and the Ozarks, also high loessial prairies of northwestern Missouri, Atchison, Holt, and Buchanan counties. Flowering in July-August.

11. **Muhlenbergia Schreberi** Gmel. Fig. 125.

Plants forming bunches, becoming mat-like; culms slender, much-branched, reclining, rooting at the lower nodes, at most about 50 cm. tall; sheaths compressed; leaf blades short, spreading, 3-4 mm. wide; panicles slender, flexuous; glumes whitish, truncate, minute, the 1st occasionally lacking, to 1.5 mm. long; lemma 2-3 mm. long, with a delicate awn about 3 mm. in length. Plants with minute glumes mostly less than 1 mm. long represent the typical variety (var. *Schreberi*). Those with the longer glumes, to 1.5 mm. long, and the lemma about 3 mm. long are separated as var. *curtisetosa* (Scribn.) Steyermark & Kucera (*M. curtisetosa* [Scribn.] Bush, Am. Midl. Nat. 6:35. 1919).

Distribution: Eastern and central United States, west to Nebraska and Texas.

Missouri. Alluvial woods, gravel bars, on damp ground, also shaded lawns, generally distributed. Plants with tendency for longer glumes, var. *curtisetosa,* are much less common. Flowering in late summer.

41. SPOROBOLUS R. Br. DROPSEED.

Annuals or perennials; panicles narrow, spike-like, occasionally inserted in the sheath, or broadly diffuse with spreading branches; spikelets 1-flowered,

FIG. 124.—*Muhlenbergia cuspidata.* Plant, × 1; glumes and floret, × 10.

FIG. 125.—*Muhlenbergia Schreberi.* Plant, × ½; glumes and floret, × 10.

separating above the persistent glumes; glumes usually unequal; lemma awnless; palea similar to the lemma, or in some species exceeding it.

KEY TO MISSOURI SPECIES

1. Panicles, when exserted, broad, with spreading branches (sometimes enclosed, or partly so, in sheath as in *S. cryptandrus,* the branches thus closely appressed); perennials......2
1. Panicles narrow or strict, not spreading even when exserted, frequently enclosed or partially inserted in the inflated sheath; annuals or perennials......5
   2. Spikelets 3 mm. long or more; glumes sharp-acuminate, with an awn-like apex; common prairie species......1. *S. heterolepis*
   2. Spikelets less than 3 mm. long (mostly 1.5-2.5 mm.); glumes acute, but not awn-tipped; either rare species or typically from dry bluffs and sandy alluvium......3
3. Spikelets few, toward the ends of somewhat stiffly spreading branches; rare in Missouri, confined to loessial prairies of Atchison County......2. *S. airoides*
3. Spikelets mostly aggregated, the panicles flexuous or drooping, or sometimes narrow, and included in the sheath......4
   4. Spikelets about 2 mm. long or more, the 1st glume about one-half as long as the 2nd; common species of dry prairies and sandy banks about the state......3. *S. cryptandrus*
   4. Spikelets about 1.5 mm. long, the 1st glume small, inconspicuous, and much shorter than 2nd glume; rare species, little known, reported initially from Jackson County......4. *S. pyramidatus*
5. Glumes nearly equal; annual species......6
5. Glumes dissimilar; perennial species......7
   6. Spikelets plump, the lemma and palea ovate to acute, glabrous......5. *S. neglectus*
   6. Spikelets narrow, the lemma and palea linear-elongate, pubescent......6. *S. vaginiflorus*
7. Panicles usually long-exserted; spikelets 2 mm. long at most; rare species of Asian origin, introduced in Dunklin County......7. *S. Poiretii*
7. Panicles usually partly inserted; spikelets 3-4 mm. long or more; native species......8
   8. Lemma obtuse, noticeably plump toward base, about equal to palea......8. *S. asper*
   8. Lemma sharp-tapering, slender, the palea usually exceeding it......9. *S. clandestinus*

1. **Sporobolus heterolepis** A. Gray. PRAIRIE DROPSEED. Fig. 126.

Perennial, densely tufted, with conspicuous basal foliage of arching leaves; flower stalks erect, to 1 m. tall; leaf blades fine, involute toward tip; panicles erect, longer than broad, with spreading branches; spikelets 4-6 mm. long; glumes unequal, acuminate, the 1st shorter than the floret, the 2nd exceeding it; lemma obtuse, somewhat shorter than palea; grain spherical and conspicuous.

Distribution: Mid-continent, from Canada to Texas, infrequent eastward to New England.

Missouri. Prairies, barrens, limestone bluffs, generally distributed. Flowering in July-August.

2. **Sporobolus airoides** (Torr.) Torr. ALKALI SACATON. Fig. 127.

Perennial, forming dense tufts; culms erect to 1 m. tall; sheaths sparsely pilose toward the summit; leaf blades narrow, involute; panicles diffuse, with broadly spreading branches; spikelets about 2 mm. long; glumes unequal, the 1st shorter, the 2nd about equal to the floret; lemma and palea similar in size and texture.

Distribution: Throughout the western United States, east to *Missouri,* where local in the dry hill prairies of Atchison County, and adventive in Jackson County. Flowering in midsummer.

FIG. 126.—*Sporobolus heterolepis*. Plant, × 1; spikelet and floret with caryopsis and split palea, × 10.

FIG. 127.—*Sporobolus airoides*. Plant, × ½; glumes and floret, × 10.

FIG. 128.—*Sporobolus cryptandrus*. Plant, × ½; glumes and floret, × 10.

3. **Sporobolus cryptandrus** (Torr.) A. Gray. SAND DROPSEED. Fig. 128.

Perennial, sparsely tufted; culms erect, to 1 m. tall; sheaths densely pilose toward the summit, somewhat overlapping on the lower part of the culm; ligule consisting of hairs, about 0.5 mm. long; leaf blades mostly involute, becoming string-like toward the tip; panicles usually narrow, with short, floriferous branches, sometimes partially included in the sheath; spikelets about 2-3 mm. long; glumes thin, unequal, the 1st about one-half as long as the 2nd, the latter about equal to the floret; lemma and palea thin, nearly equal.

Distribution: Widespread in the United States, less common or absent toward the Southeast.

Missouri. Loessial bluffs, dry prairies, sandy embankments, scattered and most prevalent from counties along the Missouri and Mississippi rivers. Flowering in July-August.

4. **Sporobolus pyramidatus** (Lam.) Hitchc. Fig. 129.

Perennial, forming tufts; culms spreading or decumbent, to about 50 cm. tall; panicles spreading, the branches whorled; spikelets small, about 1.5 mm. long; glumes strongly unequal, the 1st much shorter, the 2nd about equaling the floret. (*S. argutus* Kunth.)

Distribution: Southern and western United States, to Mexico, Central America and southward.

Missouri. Rare and little known, collected from Jackson County (Bush 510).

5. **Sporobolus neglectus** Nash. BALDGRASS, DROPSEED. Fig. 130.

Annual, forming loose tufts; culms decumbent and branching from base, to 50 cm. tall; sheaths inflated; leaf blades mostly glabrous to somewhat hairy, involute; panicles congested, 2-4 cm. long, inserted in sheaths; spikelets 2.5-3 mm. long, glumes about equal, shorter than the floret; lemma plump, glabrous; palea similar, split at maturity, exposing the ovoid grain. Plants which are generally glabrous represent the typical variety (var. *neglectus*). Those with pubescent foliage, but otherwise similar are separated as var. *ozarkanus* (Fern.) Steyermark & Kucera (*S. ozarkanus* Fern., Rhodora 35:109. 1933).

Distribution: Widespread in the eastern and central United States, scattered westward.

Missouri. Limestone glades, dry woods, sand bars, waste ground, generally distributed, known locally in the Ozark glades as "bald grass." Pubescent forms are most prevalent in the Ozarks. Flowering in July-August.

6. **Sporobolus vaginiflorus** (Torr.) Wood. Fig. 131.

Annual, tufted; culms spreading or decumbent near the base, branching, similar in general habit to species 5; panicles narrow, usually included in the inflated sheaths; differing mainly in the longer, more attenuate spikelets, 3-5 mm. long, and the pubescent lemma; palea about equal to the lemma, or exceeding the latter. Plants differing from the typical variety by the palea exceeding the lemma as a distinct beak are separated as var. *inaequalis* Fern.

Distribution: Eastern and central United States, west to Nebraska, Kansas, Oklahoma, and Arizona.

Missouri. Prairie glades, dry woods, waste areas, generally distributed. Var. *inaequalis* is scattered and less common. Flowering in July-August.

FIG. 129.—*Sporobolus pyramidatus.* Panicle, × 1; glumes and floret, × 10.

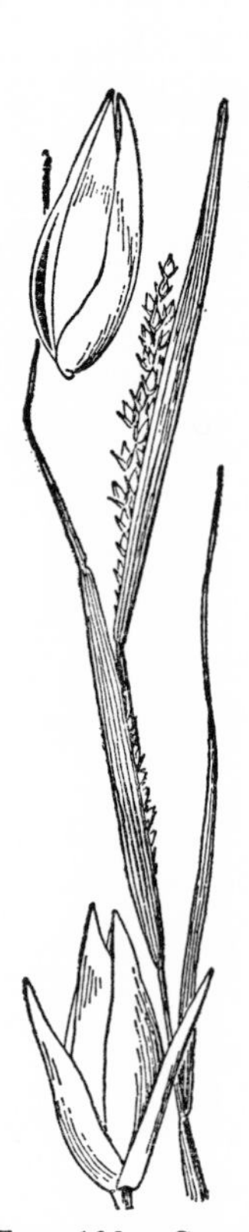

FIG. 130.—*Sporobolus neglectus.* Plant, × 1; spikelet and floret, × 10.

FIG. 131.—*Sporobolus vaginiflorus.* Plant, × 1; glumes and floret, × 10.

7. **Sporobolus Poiretii** (Roem. & Schult) Hitchc. SMUTGRASS. Fig. 132.

Perennial, forming sparse tufts, culms erect, to 1 m. tall; leaf blades 2-4 mm. wide, long-tapering; panicles mostly dense, slender, much elongated, with short, ascending branches; spikelets crowded, about 2 mm. long; glumes shorter than the floret; lemma and palea acute, nearly equal.

Distribution: Southeastern United States and mid-Atlantic area, west to Oklahoma and Texas.

Missouri. Rare and little known, collected in cotton fields, Dunklin County (Bush 1907).

8. **Sporobolus asper** (Michx.) Kunth. Fig. 133.

Perennial, generally tufted; culms erect, to 1 m. or taller; upper sheaths glabrous, inflated, wholly or partly including the panicle; leaf blades glabrous,

FIG. 132.—*Sporobolus Poiretii*. Plant, × ½; spikelet and floret, × 10.

FIG. 133.—*Sporobolus asper*. Plant, × 1; glumes and floret, × 10.

FIG. 134.—*Sporobolus clandestinus*. Plant, × 1; glumes and floret, × 10.

elongate, 2-3 mm. wide, becoming involute toward the tip; panicles light-colored to purplish, spike-like within the sheath; spikelets 3.5-7 mm. long; glumes unequal, obtuse, both shorter than the floret; lemma glabrous, 4-6 mm. long, keeled toward the apex; palea nearly equal to the lemma, and similarly keeled, splitting near the base as the plump grain matures. Plants usually less coarse than the typical variety, and with smaller spikelets 3.5-4 mm. long are occasionally designated as var. *Hookeri* (Trin.) Vasey. (*S. Drummondii* Vasey). Other plants with conspicuous pilosity of the sheaths may be referred to var. *pilosus* (Vasey) Hitchc. These separations seem valid for some Missouri specimens, although vague and unsatisfactory for others, particularly in attempting to assess the degree of pubescence.

Distribution: Widespread in the United States, but absent in the Southeast and Far West.

Missouri. Prairies, glades, dry woods, waste ground, generally distributed. Plants with varietal tendencies occur sporadically, but primarily in the Ozarks and southwestern counties. Flowering in late summer.

9. **Sporobolus clandestinus** (Bieler.) Hitchc. Fig. 134.

Perennial, mostly tufted; culms erect, to 1 m. tall; sheaths glabrous or sparsely pilose; leaf blades elongate, involute, with a string-like tip; panicles narrow, inserted or partly so; spikelets 5-7 mm. long; glumes subequal, acute, shorter than the floret; both lemma and palea pubescent, elongate, nearly equal, or the latter conspicuously longer. This species is easily distinguished from the preceding by the less robust habit, the lanceolate spikelets, and pubescent lemma. Plants in which the palea typically exceeds the lemma represent the typical variety (var. *clandestinus*). Those with nearly equal lemma and palea are separated as var. *canovirens* (Nash) Steyermark & Kucera (*S. canovirens* Nash, Briton, Man. 1042. 1901).

Distribution: Eastern and central United States, west to Kansas and Texas.

Missouri. Prairies, dry woods, on cherty or sandy soils, in the southern and eastern counties. Flowering in late summer.

42. HELEOCHLOA Host.

Annuals; panicles dense, cylindrical, spike-like; spikelets 1-flowered, separating above the persistent glumes; glumes flattened, about equal, shorter than the floret; lemma awnless; palea present, similar to lemma.

1. **Heleochloa schoenoides** (L.) Host. Fig. 135.

Plants tufted; culms leafy, decumbent near base, 15-40 cm. tall; sheaths enlarged, partially including the spike-like panicles; spikelets about 2.5-3 mm. long; glumes scabrous on keel; lemma 1-nerved, awnless; palea only slightly shorter than lemma; grain dark, obconical, about 1.5 mm. long.

Distribution: Sporadically distributed in the United States; adventive from Europe.

Missouri. Rare, waste ground, St. Louis and Franklin counties. Flowering in July-August.

FIG. 135.—*Heleochloa schoenoides.* Plant, × ½; spikelet and floret, × 5.

43. BRACHYELYTRUM Beauv.

Perennials; panicles slender, sparsely flowered; spikelets 1-flowered, separating readily above the persistent glumes; glumes unequal, reduced; lemma distinctly nerved, awned; palea tightly enclosed by lemma; rachilla a conspicuous extension behind the palea.

1. **Brachyelytrum erectum** (Schreb.) Beauv. Fig. 136.

Plants solitary or few in loose clumps, rhizomatous; culms leafy, erect, to 1 m. tall, sheaths somewhat pubescent; leaf blades thin, lax, as much as 1 cm. wide or more; panicles somewhat flexuous, very narrow, with short, close, ascending branches; spikelets about 10 mm. long; glumes reduced, acuminate, the 1st occasionally obsolete; lemma narrow, pubescent on the conspicuous nerves, and with distinct callus at base; awn of lemma straight, 10-30 mm. long.

Distribution: Eastern and central United States, west to Kansas and Oklahoma.

Missouri. Moist wooded slopes, ravines, mostly on calcareous soils, generally distributed. Flowering in June-July.

44. ORYZOPSIS Michx.

Perennials; panicles narrow, spike-like, or open with spreading branches; spikelets 1-flowered, separating above the persistent glumes; glumes nearly equal, enlarged; lemma hard, obscurely nerved, awned; palea enclosed by lemma.

1. **Oryzopsis racemosa** (Smith) Ricker. Fig. 137.

Plants forming tufts, rhizomatous; culms slender, erect, to 1 m. tall; leaf blades longer toward upper part of plant, soft-pubescent on the lower surface, as much as 1 cm. wide or more; panicles with few ascending or spreading branches; spikelets few, about 8 mm. long; glumes conspicuously nerved, awn-tipped, exceeding the floret; lemma hard, dark, pubescent, with inrolled margin; awn of

FIG. 136.—*Brachyelytrum erectum.* Plant, × ½; branchlet with glume of two spikelets, and floret, × 5.

FIG. 137.—*Oryzopsis racemosa.* Panicle, × ½; floret, × 5.

lemma straight, 10-20 mm. long, jointed, and breaking from body leaving a stipe about 1 mm. long at apex.

Distribution: Northern and central United States, south to Kentucky, west to South Dakota.

Missouri. Rare, reported from Clark and Shannon counties. Flowering in summer.

45. STIPA L.

Perennials; panicles narrow to somewhat spreading, spikelets 1-flowered, readily separating above the persistent glumes; glumes unequal, thin, enlarged; lemma elongate, hard, with sharp, hairy callus at base, terminating in a conspicuous, twisted awn.

1. **Stipa spartea** Trim. PORCUPINE-GRASS. Fig. 138.

Plants forming loose clumps; culms erect to about 1 m. tall; leaf blades narrow, becoming involute upon drying; ligule conspicuous, about 5 mm. long; panicles narrow, flexuous, sparsely branched; spikelets excluding the awns, large, as much as 4 cm. long; glumes thin, acuminate, somewhat unequal, both exceeding the floret; lemma narrow, cylindrical, about 2 cm. long, sharp-pointed, with a tuft of hairs at the base; awn of the lemma stiff, twisted, as much as *10-15 cm.* long or sometimes longer.

Distribution: Wide ranging, from the Great Lakes region to the Central Plains, south to Oklahoma and Arizona.

Missouri. Prairies, roadsides, rocky slopes, in the northern and western counties. Flowering in May-June.

FIG. 138.—*Stipa spartea.* Plant, × ½; glumes and floret, × 2.

46. ARISTIDA L. TRIPLE-AWN

Annuals or perennials; panicles mostly narrow and flexuous; spikelets 1-flowered, separating above the persistent glumes; glumes elongate, acuminate; lemma hard, linear-elongate, with a pointed callus at the base, and terminating in a 3-parted awn; palea tightly enclosed by the lemma.

KEY TO MISSOURI SPECIES

1. Sheaths conspicuously wooly-pubescent; southern and Coastal Plain species occurring locally on dry sands in southeastern Missouri.......1. *A. lanosa*
1. Sheaths smooth or merely sparsely hairy; scattered to generally distributed species 2
   2. Awns of the lemma nearly equal, spreading, flexuous, 30 mm. or more in length, not coiled or sharply twisted at the base.......2. *A. oligantha*
   2. Awns of the lemma shorter, either straight or coiled at the base, or the central awn sometimes nearly 30 mm. long, but conspicuously curved at the base and the lateral awns distinctly shorter, as in *A. ramosissima*.......3
3. Lateral awns distinctly shorter than the central awn, only one-fourth or less as long.......4
3. Lateral awns usually one-half to approximately equaling the central awn.......6
   4. Lemma mostly 15 mm. long or more, the central awn exceeding 20 mm., with a conspicuous loop at the base.......3. *A. ramosissima*
   4. Lemma not exceeding 10 mm. in length, the central awn usually much shorter than 20 mm.......5
5. Central awn distinctly coiled at the base.......4. *A. dichotoma*
5. Central awn not coiled, merely with sharp bend at the base.......5. *A. longespica*
   6. Central awn coiled at base.......6. *A. basiremea*
   6. Central awn straight or merely with sharp bend at base.......7
7. Central awn bent sharply at base, horizontally spreading.......5. *A. longespica*
7. Central awn straight or flexuous.......8
   8. Central awn mostly exceeding 20 mm.......9
   8. Central awn shorter than 20 mm.......10
9. Hard-based perennial; 1st glume exceeding 2nd.......7. *A. purpurescens*
9. Annual; 1st glume shorter than 2nd.......9. *A. intermedia*
   10. Callus densely bearded at base; central awn usually 10-15 mm. long.......8. *A. adscensionis*
   10. Callus sparsely bearded; central awn usually more than 15 mm. long.......9. *A. intermedia*

1. **Aristida lanosa** Muhl. Fig. 139.

Perennial, forming sparse tufts; culms erect, to 1 m. tall; sheaths conspicuously white-wooly; leaf blades elongate, 3-4 mm. wide; panicles narrow, with

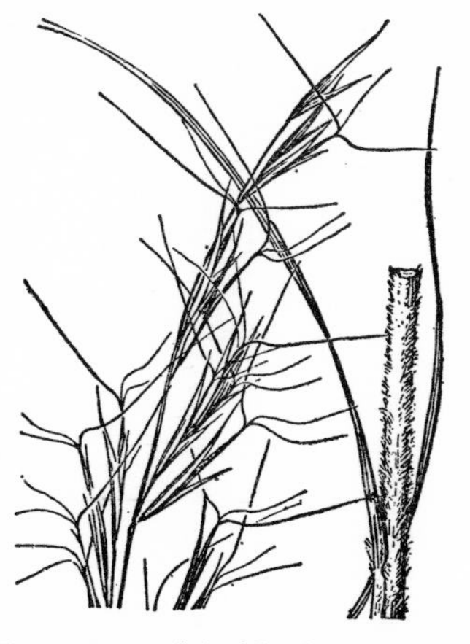

FIG. 139.—*Aristida lanosa*, × 1.

FIG. 140.—*Aristida oligantha.* Plant, × ½; glumes and floret, × 2.

short, ascending branches; spikelets about 10 mm. long; glumes unequal, the 1st slightly longer than the 2nd, both exceeding the floret; lemma about 8 mm. long, with spreading awns 2-3 times longer, the central awn somewhat exceeding the laterals.

Distribution: Southern United States and mid-Atlantic region, north to New Jersey, west to Missouri.

Missouri. Local, confined to sandy slopes of Crowley's Ridge, Stoddard, and Dunklin counties. Flowering in July.

2. **Aristida oligantha** Michix. Fig. 140.

Annual; culms slender, profusely branched, erect, to about 50 cm. tall; leaf blades very narrow, or string-like, 1 mm. wide; panicles loose, flexuous; spikelets 2-3 cm. long; glumes unequal, acuminate, the 1st slightly shorter; lemma 1-2 cm. long, the awns nearly equal, spreading, not coiled at base, sometimes as much as 4 cm. long or more. This species is easily distinguished from other Missouri species by the long, flexuous awns, all approximately equal.

Distribution: Eastern and central United States, west to South Dakota and Texas.

Missouri. Open ground and waste areas, on dry soils, generally distributed, one of our most common species. Flowering in July-August.

3. **Aristida ramosissima** Engelm. Fig. 141.

Annual; culms slender, branching from the nodes, erect, to about 50 cm. tall; leaf blades narrow, 1 mm. wide; panicles loose, flexuous, or simply branched and racemose, the spikelets then mostly single along the main axis; spikelets 1.5-2.5 cm. long; glumes unequal, acuminate, the 2nd longer, tapering to short awn about 3 mm. long, and exceeding floret; lemma 1.5-2 cm. long; central awn of lemma as much as 2 cm. in length, distinctly curved at base with quarter to full turn; lateral awns much shorter, at most about 5 mm. long.

Distribution: Central United States, from Iowa and Indiana southward to Gulf region.

Missouri. Sandy prairies, open ground, on dry soils, scattered and not common, occuring generally south of a line from Barton to St. Louis counties. Flowering in midsummer.

4. **Aristida dichotoma** Michx. POVERTY-GRASS. Fig. 142.

Annual, forming tufts; culms branching from lower nodes, mostly erect, to about 50 cm. tall; leaf blades narrow, 1 mm. wide, the margins inrolled; panicles sparsely-flowered, spikelets 6-12 mm. long; glumes nearly equal, or the 2nd longer and about equal to or exceeding the floret; lemma 5-8 mm. long; central awn of lemma exceeding 8 mm. coiled at base; lateral awns straight, much shorter, only about 2 mm. long. Plants with spikelets 6-8 mm. long and nearly equal glumes represent the typical variety (var. *dichotoma*). Those with larger spikelets to 12 mm. long and glumes more dissimilar are separated as var. *Curtisii* Gray. These divisions are not easily separable for some Missouri specimens with intermediate characteristics.

Distribution: Eastern and central United States, west to Wyoming, Colorado, and Texas.

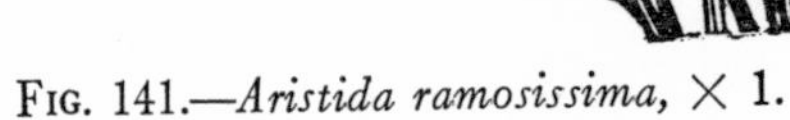
FIG. 141.—*Aristida ramosissima,* × 1.

FIG. 142.—*Aristida dichotoma,* × 1.

Missouri. Open ground, waste areas, thin woods, on dry, cherty or sandy soils, generally distributed. Plants with a tendency toward var. *Curtisii* are less common, and occur primarily in the central and southern counties. Flowering in July-August.

5. **Aristida longespica** Poir. Fig. 143.

Annual, forming tufts; culms slender, branching, resembling species 4 in general habit; panicles narrow, flexuous, sometimes with simple branching, the single spikelets sessile or short-pedicelled; spikelets about 5-6 mm. long; glumes nearly equal, shorter than to slightly exceeding the lemma; central awn of the lemma 7-15 mm. long, horizontally spreading, curved at the base; lateral awns straight, ascending, much shorter but variable, 1-6 mm. in length. Plants weakly separated by a tendency for longer lateral awns are sometimes designated as var. *geniculata* (Raf.) Fern. The separation is poorly defined in our plants.

Distribution: Eastern and central United States, west to Kansas and Texas.

Missouri. Upland prairies, fields, dry woods, in the southern and eastern counties, absent in the Northwest. Flowering in July-August.

6. **Aristida basiramea** Engelm. ex Vasey. Fig. 144.

Annual, forming tufts; culms branching from near the base, erect, to about 50 cm. tall; leaf blades about 1 mm. wide, becoming involute; panicles loose, sparsely flowered; spikelets 10-15 mm. long; glumes unequal, the 1st shorter than the floret, the 2nd exceeding it; lemma about 8-10 mm. long; central awn of lemma twisted or coiled at base, to 18-20 mm. in length; lateral awns straight, ascending, about 10 mm. long.

Distribution: North-central United States, south to Oklahoma, occurring also in New England.

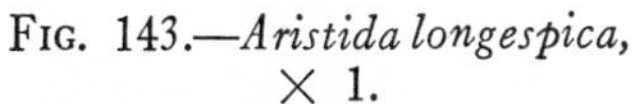

FIG. 143.—*Aristida longespica*, × 1.

FIG. 144.—*Aristida basiramea*, × 1.

Missouri. Fields and waste ground, scattered and infrequent in the central and southern counties. Flowering in July-August.

7. **Aristida purpurescens** Poir. Fig. 145.

Perennial, forming narrow tufts; culms erect, about 50 cm. tall; leaf blades 1-2 mm. wide, involute toward tip; panicles loose, flexuous, about one-half the length of entire plant; spikelets 10-12 mm. long; glumes unequal, the 1st exceeding the 2nd, both overtopping floret; lemma 5-8 mm. long; central awn of

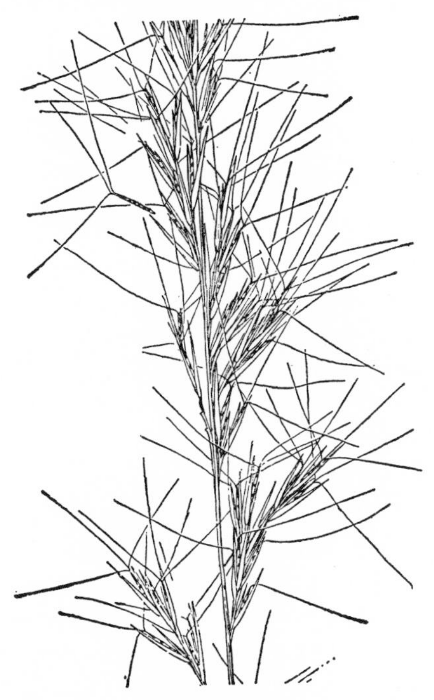

FIG. 145.—*Aristida purpurascens*, × 1.

FIG. 146.—*Aristida adscensionis*, × 1.

lemma spreading, ascending, 15-30 mm. long; lateral awns about three-fourths as long.

Distribution: Eastern and central United States, west to Kansas and Texas.

Missouri. Open ground, dry prairies, thin woods, on sandy or cherty soils, common in the Ozarks and southern counties, less frequent north of the Missouri River. Flowering in July-August.

8. **Aristida adscensionis** L. Fig. 146.

Annual, forming tufts; culms branching at base, erect to somewhat spreading, to about 70 cm. tall; leaf blades narrow, involute; panicles flexuous, mostly dense; spikelets about 10 mm. long; glumes unequal, the 1st distinctly shorter, the 2nd about equal to floret; lemma 7-8 mm. long, tufted at base; awns of lemma spreading, 8-15 mm. long, the laterals only slightly shorter than the central one.

Distribution: Central and South America, north to the southwestern United States, to California, Colorado, and Missouri; also reported from the Old World.

Missouri. Rare and scattered, waste ground, reported from Jackson, Jasper, Maries, and Madison counties, probably adventive. Flowering in July-August.

9. **Aristida intermedia** Scribn. & Ball. Fig. 147.

Annual, forming tufts; culms slender, branching from the middle and lower nodes, to about 50 cm. tall; leaf blades 1-2 mm. wide, involute toward tip; panicles narrow, flexuous; spikelets about 10 mm. long, similar to species 8, but glumes somewhat more equal, the lemma not tufted at base; awns of lemma longer, flexuous, spreading, the central one to 2 cm. or longer, the laterals about three-fourths as long.

Distribution: Central United States from Michigan and Nebraska south to Mississippi and Texas.

Missouri. Open ground and fields, sandy soils, scattered, Jackson, Jasper, Iron, Washington, and St. Louis counties. Flowering in July-August.

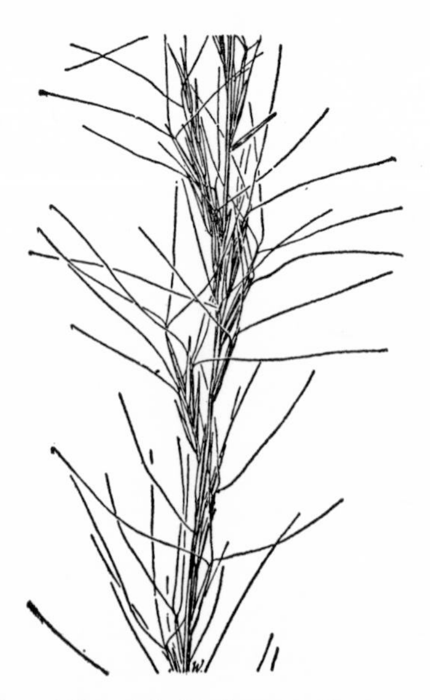

FIG. 147.—*Aristida intermedia,* × 1.

TRIBE VI. CHLORIDEAE

47. LEPTOCHLOA Beauv.

Annuals or perennials; inflorescence consisting of numerous, slender, spike-like branches or racemes, floriferous the entire length, arranged along the main axis; spikelets 2-several-flowered, sessile or nearly so, on 1 side of the rachis, separating above the persistent glumes; glumes mostly unequal; lemmas 3-nerved, usually awnless, or merely awn-tipped; palea about equal to lemma. This genus includes several species which are placed by some authors in the genus *Diplachne* Beauv.

KEY TO MISSOURI SPECIES

1. Panicles flexuous, the branches narrow, spreading; spikelets 2-4-flowered, minute, the lemmas at most 1.5 mm. long........1. *L. filiformis*
1. Panicles coarser, the branches stiffer, more ascending; spikelets 5-10-flowered, the lemmas larger, 2-5 mm. long........2
    2. Lemmas short-awned from a bi-dentate apex; common species........2. *L. fascicularis*
    2. Lemmas awnless; rare species from New Madrid County........3. *L. panicoides*

1. **Leptochloa filiformis** (Lam.) Beauv. SPRANGLETOP. Fig. 148.

Annual; culms usually branching from base, erect, about 50 cm. tall, sometimes more; sheaths sparsely pilose; leaf blades thin, soft, 5-10 mm. wide; panicles

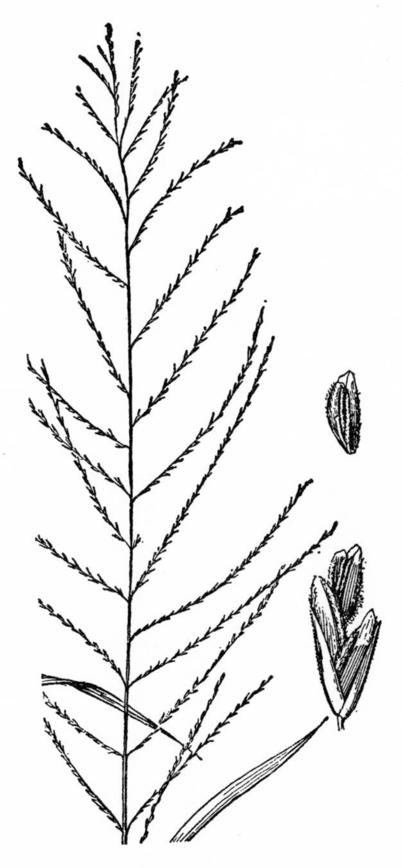

FIG. 148.—*Leptochloa filiformis*. Plant, × ½; spikelet and floret, × 10.

about one-half the length of entire plant, consisting of numerous, very slender, spike-like racemes; spikelets 2-4 flowered, reddish-purple, 1.5-2.5 mm. long; glumes lanceolate-subulate, 1-3 mm. long, mostly shorter than the upper floret; lemmas small, 0.5-1.5 mm. long, awnless. Plants distinguished from the typical variety (var. *filiformis*) by minute lemmas, less than 1 mm. in length, these generally exceeded by the relatively long, narrow-pointed glumes to 3 mm. long, are designated as var. *attenuata* (Nutt.) Steyermark & Kucera (*Oxydenia attenuata* Nutt., Gen. Pl. 1:76. 1818).

Distribution: Tropical America and northward through the southern and central United States.

Missouri. Fields, open ground, on moist sands or alluvium, scattered but most common south of the Missouri River, absent from the extreme northern counties. Flowering in July-August.

2. **Leptochloa fascicularis** (Lam.) Gray. SALT-MEADOW GRASS. Fig. 149.

Annual, forming tufts or clumps; culms branching from base, erect to somewhat reclining, to 1 m. tall; foliage glabrous, the leaf blades 1-3 mm. wide, the margins sometimes inrolled; panicles narrow, the branches appressed-ascending, partly included in the sheath; spikelets 6-10-flowered, 5-10 mm. long; glumes 1.5-3 mm. long; lemmas distinctly imbricated, sparsely pubescent, 3-4 mm. long, with a minute awn. (*Diplachne fascicularis* [Lam.] Beauv.) Plants distinuished from the typical variety (var. *fascicularis*) by coarser spikelets, less distinctly imbricated, the glumes and lemmas larger, approaching 4-5 mm. in length are separated as var. *acuminata* (Nash) Gl. In Missouri, the latter variety is also distinguished by the decumbent habit of the lower culms, forming spreading tufts (*Diplachne acuminata* Nash).

Distribution: Widely scattered throughout the United States, and in the lower latitudes to South America. The range of var. *acuminata* is less southerly.

Missouri. Wet depressions, mud flats, borders of ponds, and natural sinks, frequently on brackish or saline ground, widely scattered. Var. *acuminata* is less common than the typical variety and occurs primarily in the central and northern counties. Flowering in July-August.

3. **Leptochloa panicoides** (Pres.) Hitchc. Fig. 150.

Annual; culms branching, erect to somewhat decumbent, to 1 m. tall; foliage glabrous, the leaf blades as much as 10 mm. wide; panicles with numerous short, ascending branches, giving a compact appearance; spikelets 5-7-flowered, about 4 mm. long; glumes 1-2 mm. long; lemmas about 2.5 mm. long, with a short tip from notched apex. (*Diplachne Halei* Nash.)

Distribution: Central and lower Mississippi Valley; also South America.

Missouri. Rare, open sandy banks of Mississippi River, New Madrid County (Palmer 61658). Flowering in late summer.

Remarks: This species and the preceding one are placed by some authors in *Diplachne* Beauv. of the Festuceae, Tribe II, on the basis of similarity to the festucoid spikelet. The treatment of Hitchcock (1951) in using *Leptochloa* is followed here. The spikelets are mainly sessile or minutely stalked and are arranged in 1-sided spikes, a character which is usually employed to distinguish most members of the Chlorideae.

FIG. 149.—*Leptochloa fascicularis*. Panicle, × 1; two views of floret, × 10.

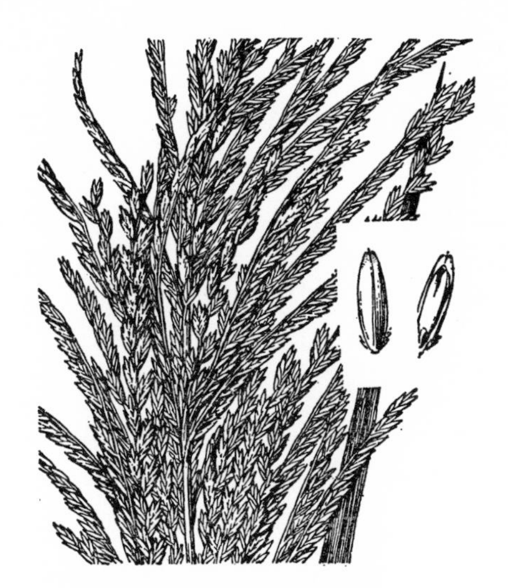

FIG. 150.—*Leptochloa panicoides*. Panicle, × 1; two views of floret, × 10.

48. ELEUSINE Gaertn.

Annuals; inflorescence consisting of several broad spikes more or less digitately arranged at the summit of the flowering axis; spikelets several-flowered, sessile, in 2 rows on 1 side of the rachis, separating above the persistent glumes; glumes unequal; lemmas compressed, awnless.

1. **Eleusine indica** (L.) Gaertn. YARDGRASS. Fig. 151.

Plants tufted; culms branching near base, erect or decumbent, to about 50 cm. tall; sheaths flattened, glabrous or nearly so; leaf blades about 5 mm. wide; spikes 4-6 mm. wide, 3 or more from summit of central stalk; spikelets 4-6-flowered, compressed, arranged on 1 side of the broad, smooth rachis; glumes unequal, the 1st about one-half as long as 2nd; lemmas conspicuously 3-nerved, 3-4 mm. long; grain dark, furrowed, becoming loose within the floret. This species is distinguished from crabgrass, *Digitaria,* also characterized by digitate inflorescence, by the several-flowered spikelets and broad, flat rachis.

Distribution: Widespread in the United States, occasionally a troublesome plant in lawns; adventive from tropical regions.

Missouri. Open ground, lawns, cultivated areas, generally distributed. Flowering in July-August.

49. CYNODON Richard.

Perennials; inflorescence consisting of several narrow spikes arranged digitately at summit of flowering stalk; spikelets 1-flowered, sessile, on 1 side of rachis, separating above the persistent glumes; glumes about equal; lemma flattened, awnless; palea about equal to lemma; rachilla extended behind palea as a noticeable stalk-like projection.

FIG. 151.—*Eleusine indica.* Plant, × ½; spikelet, floret, and seed (without pericarp), × 5.

1. **Cynodon Dactylon** (L.) Pers. BERMUDA GRASS. Fig. 152.

Plants forming thick mats, spreading by tough runners on the surface or below ground; culms leafy, 10-25 cm. or sometimes taller; leaf blades short, thin, 3-4 mm. wide; ligule a fringe of white hairs at summit of sheath; inflorescence 4-6 short, narrow spikes, about 5 cm. long, from summit of flowering stalk; spikelets about 2.5 mm. long, flattened, overlapping along the rachis; 1st glume curved, the 2nd straight, both shorter than the floret; lemma pubescent on keel. This species is distinguished from crabgrass, *Digitaria,* also characterized by terminal, digitate spikes, by its perennial habit and the presence of tough runners. The species of crabgrass in our region are all annuals.

Distribution: Widespread in the United States, particularly in the South; a warm season species known from both hemispheres, probably native to India; introduced as a forage and turf grass in the southern states, frequently spreading as a noxious weed in lawns and open ground.

Missouri. Lawns, gardens, fields, most common in the southern counties,

FIG. 152.—*Cynodon Dactylon.* Plant, × ½; spikelet and two views of floret, × 5.

particularly along the Mississippi River, occasional or absent in the northern counties. Bermuda Grass is a drought-resistant species, becoming dormant readily after frost. Flowering in summer.

50. SCHEDONNARDUS Steud.

Perennials; inflorescence consisting of a few narrow, spreading spikes scattered along the main axis; spikelets 1-flowered, sessile, arranged on 2 sides of the triangular rachis, separating above the persistent glumes; glumes somewhat unequal, narrow-lanceolate; lemma 3-nerved, also narrow, pointed; palea shorter than lemma.

1. **Schedonnardus paniculatus** (Nutt.) Trel. TUMBLEGRASS. Fig. 153.

Plants tufted, leafy toward base; culms erect, flowering stalks to 50 cm. tall; leaf blades narrow, 1 mm. wide, 5 cm. long; ligule conspicuous, 2-3 mm. long; inflorescence large, about one-half as long or more as entire plant, eventually breaking away; individual spikes of the inflorescence variable in length, as much as 10 cm. long; spikelets 4-5 mm. long, appressed along 2 sides of the 3-cornered rachis; glumes rigid, pointed, the 1st about 3 mm. long, the 2nd longer, and slightly exceeding floret; lemma firm, scabrous above, enveloping palea.

Distribution: Wide-ranging through the mid-continent, from central Canada to Louisiana and Arizona; also South America.

Missouri. Open ground and prairies, on dry soils, primarily in the central and western counties. Flowering in summer.

51. BECKMANNIA Host.

Annuals, or sometimes appearing as perennials; panicles stiff, spike-like, with short, crowded, lateral lobes, spikelets 1-2-flowered, strongly overlapping, separating below the glumes and falling entire; glumes equal, obovate, inflated; lemmas obscurely nerved, narrow, acuminate-tipped in contrast to broadened glumes; palea shorter than lemma.

1. **Beckmannia syzigachne** (Steud.) Fern. Fig. 154.

Plants sparsely tufted; culms to 1 m. tall; foliage glabrous or scabrous, the leaf blades 4-8 mm. wide; ligule conspicuous, 5-7 mm. long, acuminate; panicles narrow, elongate, with numerous short lobes or spikes, the latter about 1-1.5 cm. long; spikelets congested, overlapping, orbicular, about 3 mm. long; glumes prominently nerved, wrinkled, broadened upward and somewhat crescent-shaped, with abrupt tip; lemma narrow, the pointed, tapering apex slightly exceeding glumes.

Distribution: Northern and western United States; also Alaska and parts of the Old World.

Missouri. Rare and little known, reported from Jackson County (according to Bush). Flowering in June-July.

Remarks: The above collection report is based on a single specimen found near Courtney. No new collections are known. Considering its western and northern affinities, and also the fact that it was reported by Gates (1936) in only two counties in Kansas, its status in Missouri is doubtful.

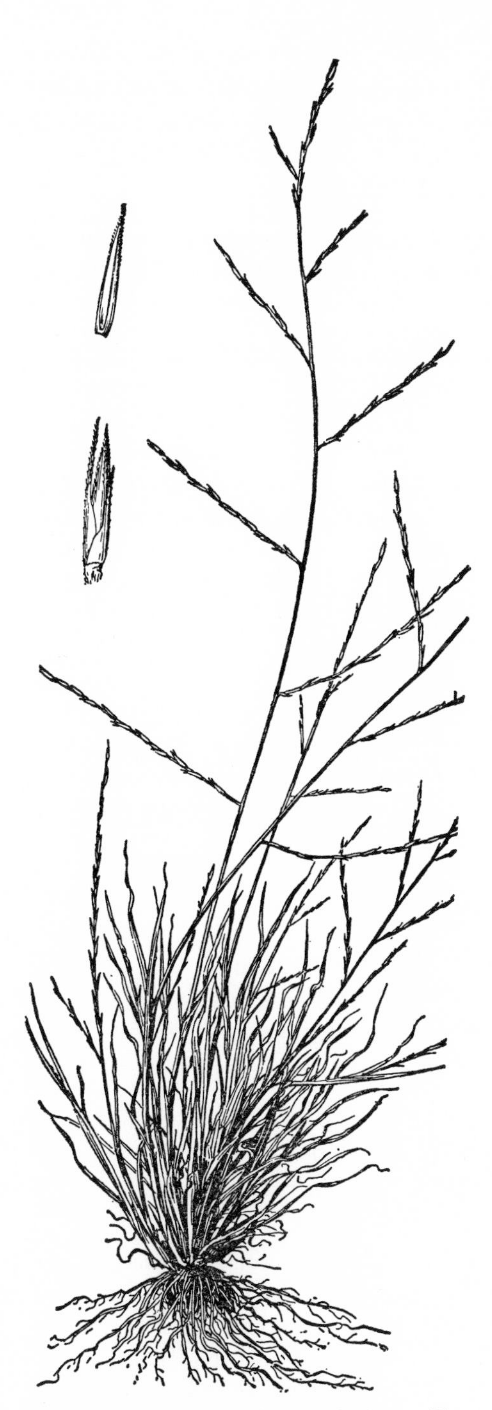

FIG. 153.—*Schedonnardus paniculatus*. Plant, × ½; spikelet and floret, × 5.

FIG. 154.—*Beckmannia syzigachne*. Plant, × ½; spikelet and floret, × 5.

52. SPARTINA Schreb.

Perennials; inflorescence consisting of ascending or somewhat spreading 1-sided spikes along the main axis; spikelets 1-flowered, sessile, crowded, conspicuously flattened, separating below the glumes and falling entire; glumes unequal, narrow-acuminate to awned; lemma hard, flattened, awnless; palea equal to lemma, or slightly longer.

1. **Spartina pectinata** Link. SLOUGHGRASS. Fig. 155.

Plants coarse, forming clumps, spreading by tough scaly rhizomes; culms erect, 1-2 m. tall; leaf blades sharp-edged, scabrous, about 1 cm. wide or more, becoming involute when dried; ligule consisting mostly of hairs, 1-2 mm. long; spikes as much as 10 cm. long, from short stalks; spikelets about 10 mm. long, excluding awn, closely appressed and imbricated in 2 rows on 1 side of the rachis; glumes, scabrous on keel, awned or merely long-pointed, unequal, the 2nd longer mostly overtopping the floret; palea slightly longer than lemma. Plants with narrower, more divergent spikes and longer peduncles have been designated as var. *Suttei* (Farw.) Fern. According to Moberly (1956) the division is weakly defined and does not constitute a distinct separation.

Distribution: Widespread in the United States, absent in the Southeast and Far West.

Missouri. Marshes, sloughs, prairie swales, generally distributed. Flowering in late summer.

Remarks: The coastal species, *S. cynosuroides* (L.) Roth, does not occur in Missouri. Various herbarium collections from the state with this designation are shown to be *S. pectinata.*

53. GYMNOPOGON Beauv.

Perennials; inflorescence broad, relatively large, consisting of divergent narrow-elongate spikes along the main axis; spikelets mostly 1-flowered, separating above the persistent glumes; glumes narrow, tapering, both exceeding the floret; lemma narrow, with straight awn; rachilla extended behind palea, usually short-awned.

1. **Gymnopogon ambiguus** (Michx.) B. S. P. Fig. 156.

Plants sparsely tufted, rhizomatous; culms stiff, leafy near base, erect, about 50 cm. tall; leaf blades glabrous, somewhat stiff, with rounded or cordate bases, 5-10 mm. wide, less than 10 cm. long; panicles large, as much as one-half the length of entire plant, consisting of slender, spreading spikes 10-15 cm. long; spikelets appressed along rachis, remote near base, becoming more numerous toward tip; glumes linear-lanceolate, 4-6 mm. long; lemma shorter than glumes, about 4 mm. long, pilose, the awn straight, 5-10 mm. long; rachilla terminating in shorter awn or sterile bract.

Distribution: Southeastern and Atlantic coastal plain, north to Ohio and Pennsylvania, west to Kansas and Texas.

Missouri. Dry wooded slopes and sandy open ground, scattered, south of line from Barton to St. Charles counties. Flowering in July-August.

FIG. 155.—*Spartina pectinata*. Plant, × ½; spikelet and floret, × 5.

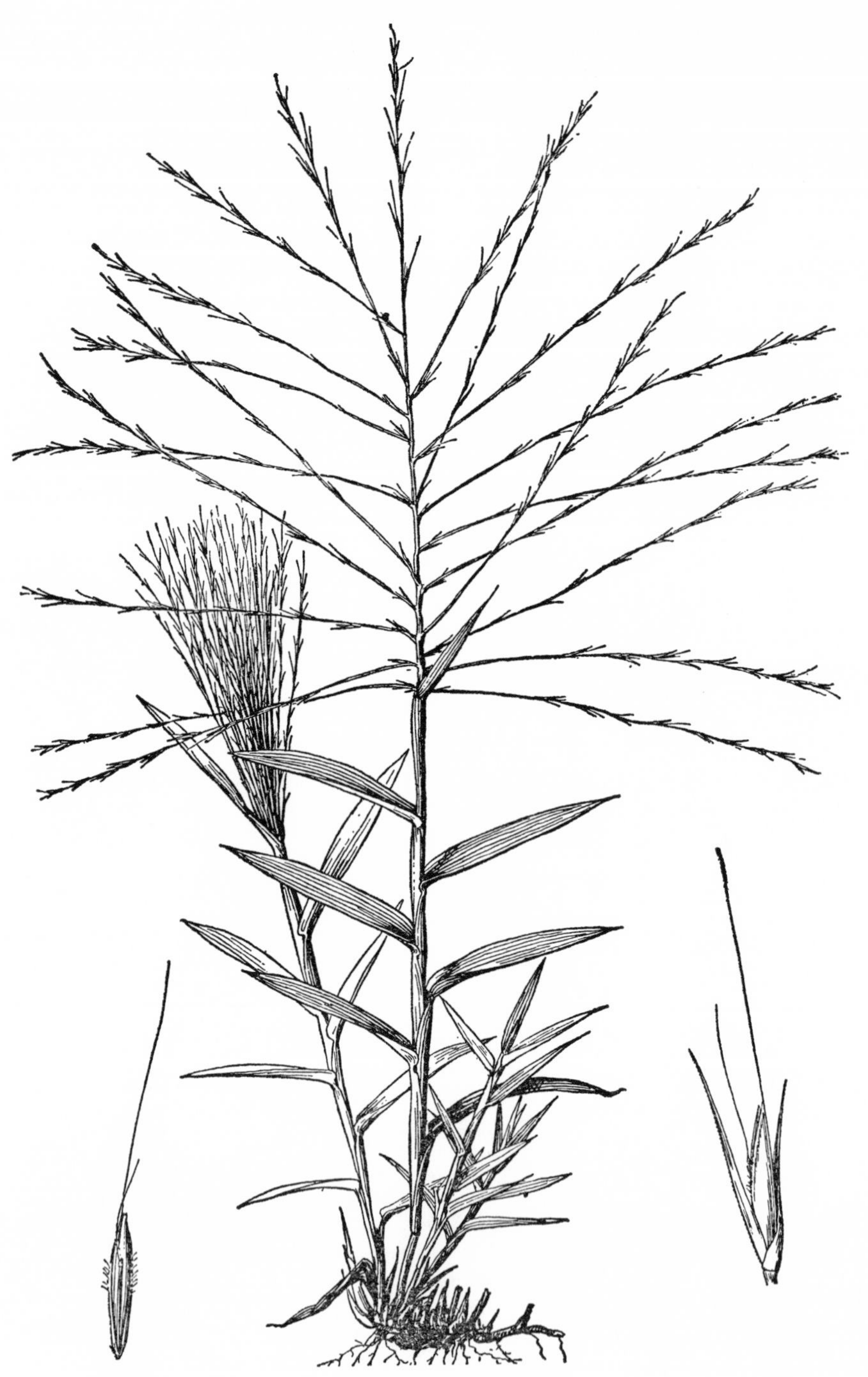

FIG. 156.—*Gymnopogon ambiguus*. Plant, × ½; spikelet and floret, × 5.

54. CHLORIS Swartz.

Annuals or perennials; inflorescence consisting of digitate clusters of narrow, spreading spikes at or near summit of flowering stalk; spikelets 2-several-flowered, separating above the persistent glumes; lower floret fertile, the upper ones sterile, reduced; glumes mostly unequal, acuminate, not exceeding the florets; fertile lemma awned from below apex, the sterile lemmas progressively reduced in size, awnless or short-awned.

1. **Chloris verticillata** Nutt. WINDMILL GRASS. Fig. 157.

Perennial, forming leafy clumps; culms occasionally rooting from lower nodes, erect to somewhat decumbent, 15-30 cm. tall; sheaths noticeably flattened; leaf blades about 3 mm. wide; spikes terminal, horizontally spreading 5-15 cm. long, the whole inflorescence readily breaking from plant at maturity; spikelets about 3 mm. long, excluding awn, arranged in 2 rows on 1 side of rachis; glumes elongate, with tapering apex, the 1st about 2 mm. long, the 2nd somewhat longer; fertile lemma conspicuously pubescent on nerves, about 2.5 mm. long, the awn straight, several times longer; sterile lemma broadened upward, truncate, short-awned.

Distribution: Southwestern United States, north to Colorado and Missouri; introduced elsewhere.

Missouri. Lawns, fields, waste areas, on dry soils, scattered, mostly in the central and western counties. Flowering in June-July.

2. **Chloris virgata** Sw. FEATHER FINGERGRASS. Fig. 158.

Annual, usually more robust than species 1; upper sheaths enlarged; leaf blades 3-6 mm. wide; spikes terminal, erect-ascending, with distinctive silky appearance; spikelets crowded, about 3-3.5 mm. long; 1st glume 1.5 mm. long, about one-half as long as the 2nd; fertile lemma ciliate near base and toward apex, about 3 mm. long, the awn as much as 10 mm. long; sterile lemma reduced, obovate, similarly awned.

Distribution: Scattered in the United States; adventive from tropical America.

Missouri. Rare, reported on waste ground from Jackson and St. Louis counties, probably not established.

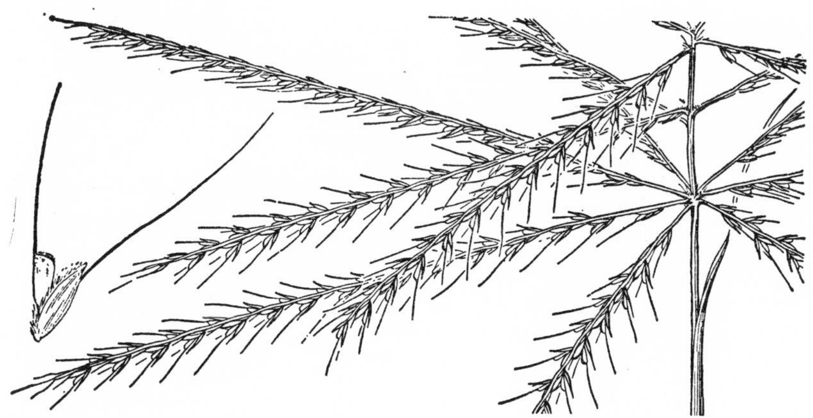

FIG. 157.—*Chloris verticillata.* Panicle, × 1; floret, × 5.

FIG. 158.—*Chloris virgata*. Plant, × ½; glumes and florets, × 5.

FIG. 159.—*Bouteloua curtipendula*. Plant, × ½; spikelet and floret, × 5.

55. BOUTELOUA Lag. GRAMA.

Perennials and a few annuals; inflorescence consisting of short, flag-like spikes along the main axis; spikelets 2-several-flowered, sessile, crowded on 1 side of the rachis, separating above the persistent glumes; lower floret fertile, the upper ones sterile, reduced; glumes unequal, narrow-acuminate; fertile lemma 3-nerved, short-awned or mucronate-tipped; sterile lemmas with 3 awns.

KEY TO MISSOURI SPECIES

1. Spikes numerous, usually 15 or more..1. *B. curtipendula*
1. Spikes not more than 3..2
   2. Uppermost spikelet of each spike exceeding and covering the end of the rachis ....2. *B. gracilis*
   2. Uppermost spikelet exceeded by the pointed end of the rachis............3. *B. hirsuta*

1. **Bouteloua curtipendula** (Hichx.) Torr. SIDEOATS GRAMA. Fig. 159.

Perennial, forming dense tufts, rhizomatous; culms erect to 80 cm. tall; leaf blades 3-4 mm. wide, becoming involute when dried; spikes numerous, 10-15 mm. long, on short peduncles twisted to 1 side of the erect flowering stalk; spikelets 4-7 per spike, about 7 mm. long; glumes dissimilar, the 1st subulate, 4 mm. long, the 2nd lanceolate and longer; fertile lemma with 3 short awns or mucronate tips; sterile lemma with central awn, conspicuous and longer than the 2 lateral awns.

Distribution: Widespread in the United States, absent in the Southeast, extending into Mexico and southward.

Missouri. Prairies, limestone glades, dry, rocky bluffs, generally distributed. Flowering in early summer.

2. **Bouteloua gracilis** (H. B. K.) Lag. BLUE GRAMA. Fig. 160.

Perennial, forming dense, leafy tufts; culms erect, to about 50 cm. tall; leaf blades 1-2 mm. wide, involute and curling; spikes 1-2 on each flowering stalk, 3-5 cm. long; spikelets about 5 mm. long, imbricated, on 1 side of the arching rachis; glumes narrow, acuminate, the 1st 2-3 mm. long, the 2nd 4-5 mm. long; fertile lemma villous, 3-awned; sterile lemma on short stipe, conspicuously villous, with 3 slender awns.

Distribution: Continental interior, from the Mississippi Valley westward. Blue grama is a valuable range species of the Short Grass Plains, and occurs with the buffalo grass over wide areas.

Missouri. Rare, dry bluff prairies bordering the Missouri River, Atchison and Holt counties, reported as an adventive in Jackson and St. Louis counties. Flowering in July-August.

3. **Bouteloua hirsuta** Lag. HAIRY GRAMA. Fig. 161.

Perennial, densely tufted, resembling species 2 in general habit; sheaths hairy; leaf blades narrow, involute; spikes 1-3, 3-4 cm. long, the rachis extending beyond the last spikelet about 5 mm.; spikelets about 5 mm. long, numerous and closely imbricated; glumes dissimilar, the 1st subulate, the 2nd lanceolate, somewhat longer, with black papillose hairs on middle nerve; fertile lemma awned, the sterile lemma 3-awned, on slender stipe. This species is readily separated from the preceding by the extended rachis and the papillose glume.

Distribution: Widespread from the Middle West through the Central Plains to California and Old Mexico, local elsewhere.

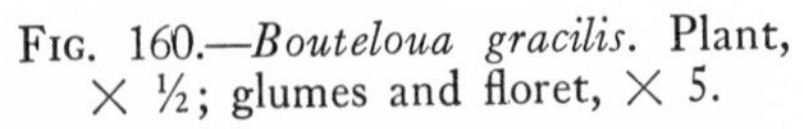

FIG. 160.—*Bouteloua gracilis*. Plant, × ½; glumes and floret, × 5.

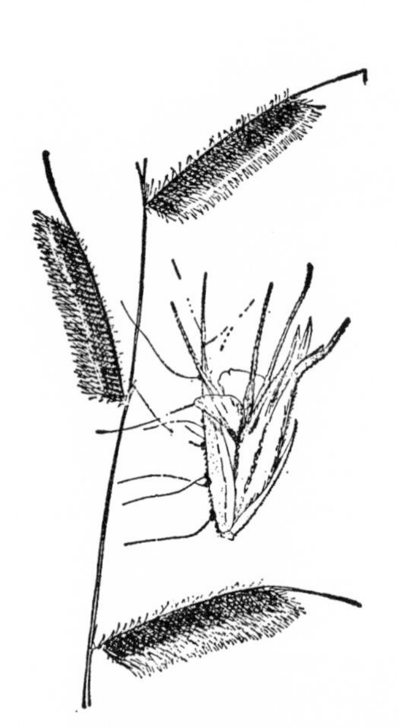

FIG. 161.—*Bouteloua hirsuta*. Panicle, × 1; spikelet, × 5.

Missouri. Rare, dry bluff prairies, Atchison and Holt counties, also sandy ground bordering Des Moines River in Clark County. Flowering in July-August.

56. BUCHLOE Englem. BUFFALO GRASS

Perennial, with a single species; plants dioecious; staminate spikelets 2-flowered, closely imbricated, from short 1-sided spikes above the basal foliage; pistillate spikelets 1-flowered, in rounded clusters or "heads" on short peduncles exceeded by the lower leaves; staminate florets separating above the persistent glumes; pistillate spikelet separating below the glumes, falling entire.

1. **Buchloe dactyloides** (Nutt.) Engelm. Fig. 162.

Plants sod-forming, spreading by stolons; culms short, 20-30 cm. tall; leaf blades narrow, curling, 1-2 mm. wide, usually not exceeding 10 cm. in length; staminate spikes about 1 cm. long, the spikelets 4-5 mm. in length with unequal

FIG. 162.—*Buchloe dactyloides.* Pistillate and staminate plants, × ½; pistillate spike and floret, × 5; staminate spikelet, × 5.

glumes and 3-nerved, awnless lemmas; pistillate "heads" consisting of 4-5 spikelets, the latter 5-6 mm. long, with thick, rounded, 3-lobed 2nd glume oriented to the outside, and exceeding the floret; 1st or inner glume obscure, thin, or obsolete; lemma indurate, 3-lobed, awnless, enveloped by the 2nd glume.

Distribution: Plains of the mid-continent, from lower Canada to Old Mexico. Buffalo grass is an important forage species occurring over wide areas as a natural associate of the blue grama.

Missouri. Rare, dry bluff prairies bordering the Missouri River, Atchison and Holt counties in the extreme northwest, reporting recently as an adventive in St. Louis County, but not established. Flowering in June-July.

TRIBE VII. PHALARIDEAE

57. ANTHOXANTHUM L.

Annuals or perennials, with fragrant scent; panicles terminal, spike-like; spikelets with 1 fertile floret and 2 sterile lemmas, separating above the persistent glumes; glumes unequal; lemma of the fertile floret awnless, falling with and enveloped by the larger, awned sterile lemmas.

1. **Anthoxanthum odoratum** L. SWEET VERNALGRASS. Fig. 163.

Perennial, forming clumps, culms erect, to about 50 cm. tall; sheaths glabrous; ligule conspicuous, membranaceous; leaf blades 3-5 mm. wide, glabrous or sparsely pilose, the edges ciliate toward base; panicles erect, yellowish-brown, dense, 3-6 cm. long; spikelets 7-8 mm. long; glumes unequal, acuminate, the 1st one about one-half as long as the 2nd, both exceeding the florets; fertile lemma smooth, dark, about 2 mm. long; sterile lemmas pilose, about twice as long, notched at apex, the awns twisted, one attached dorsally from near base, the other from near the summit.

Distribution: Eastern and central United States, also the Far West; adventive from Eurasia; formerly used in forage mixtures for its fragrance.

Missouri. Waste ground and pastures, infrequent, reported from Jackson, Boone, Iron, and St. Louis counties. Flowering in spring.

58. PHALARIS L. CANARY GRASS

Annuals or perennials; panicles dense, spike-like; spikelets 1-flowered, separating above the persistent glumes; 2 reduced or minute sterile bracts usually present, these appressed to and falling with the floret; glumes equal, flattened or winged on keel; lemma awnless, exceeded by glumes.

KEY TO MISSOURI SPECIES

1. Large coarse perennial; panicles short-lobed, interrupted....................1. *P. arundinacea*
1. Annuals; panicles dense, oblong-elliptic or ovoid, continuous..2
   2. Panicles ovoid, about 4 cm. long or less; glumes broadly winged......2. *P. canariensis*
   2. Panicles oblong-elliptic, as much as 8 cm. long, but usually shorter; glumes narrower, not broadly winged..3. *P. caroliniana*

FIG. 164.—*Phalaris arundinacea*. Plant, × 1; glumes and floret, × 4.

FIG. 163.—*Anthoxanthum odoratum*. Plant, × ½; spikelet, sterile lemmas, and fertile floret, × 5.

FIG. 165.—*Phalaris canariensis*. Plant, × ½; spikelet and floret, × 5.

1. **Phalaris arundinacea** L. REED CANARY GRASS. Fig. 164.

Perennial, forming sod or clumps, rhizomatous; culms erect, to 1.5 m. tall or more; foliage mostly glabrous, the leaf blades 1-2 cm. wide; ligule large, white, membranaceous, 3-5 mm. long; panicles light-colored, narrow, spike-like, with short, appressed lobes; spikelets about 5 mm. long, the glumes flattened, more or less winged, overtopping the floret; fertile lemma ovate, 3-4 mm. long, sparsely pilose near its base; sterile bracts narrow, about 1 mm. long, conspicuously villous, appressed to base of fertile lemma. Plants distinguished by white-striped leaves and grown as an ornamental are designated as var. *picta* L., commonly known as ribbon-grass.

Distribution: Northern United States and Canada, and higher elevations in the West; also Europe; native in some regions, but also planted extensively for gully control and to some extent as forage.

Missouri. Wet embankments, sloughs, waterways, scattered, primarily in the northern and central counties. Flowering in June-July.

2. **Phalaris canariensis** L. CANARY GRASS. Fig. 165.

Annual; culms erect, 50-70 cm. tall; leaf blades as much as 1 cm. wide; ligule conspicuous; panicle ovoid, compact, about 2-3 cm. long, 1.5-2 cm. thick; spikelets about 7 mm. long, the glumes flattened, broadly winged, with abrupt tip; fertile lemma ovate, 5 mm. long, appressed-pubescent, the sterile bracts linear, about one-half as long.

Distribution: Scattered in the United States; introduced from the Mediterranean region as a pasture and forage species; used also in birdseed mixtures. Unlike the reed canary grass in which the grains fall readily, this species can be harvested because there is less shattering of the spikelets.

Missouri. Fields, waste ground, scattered and not common, Jackson, Johnson, Jasper, Greene, Butler, Scott, and Dunklin counties. Flowering in June-July.

Remarks: Recently *P. brachystachys* Link, has been reported for Missouri,

FIG. 166.—*Phalaris caroliniana.* Plant, × 1; glumes and floret, × 5.

from Laclede County, based on a 1938 collection (G. Moore F932464) identified as *P. canariensis*. It is relatively rare in the United States, and is native to the Mediterranean Region. According to the *Manual of Grasses* (Hitchc. 1951), the separation of *P. brachystachys* is based on somewhat smaller spikelets and relatively shorter sterile bracts. Otherwise the species are similar.

3. **Phalaris caroliniana** Walt. Fig. 166.

Annual; culms erect to 1 m. tall but mostly shorter; leaf blades 4-8 mm. wide; ligule conspicuous; panicles 4-8 cm. long, compact, elliptic, tapering to both ends; spikelets 4-6 mm. long, the glumes compressed, acute, not noticeably winged as in species 2; fertile lemma ovate, 3-4 mm. long, somewhat pubescent, the sterile bracts, linear, 1-2 mm. long.

Distribution: Southern United States, from Virginia to California.

Missouri. Open ground, infrequent and scattered, primarily south of the Missouri River. Flowering in May-June.

TRIBE VIII. ORYZEAE

59. ORYZA L. RICE

Annuals and a few perennials; panicles terminal, large, with nodding or spreading branches; spikelets 1-flowered, laterally compressed, separating below the glume-like bracts (sterile lemmas); true glumes reduced to a broadened flange at summit of pedicel; fertile lemma and palea nearly equal.

1. **Oryza sativa** L. CULTIVATED RICE. Fig. 167.

Annual; culms coarse, erect, to 2 m. tall; leaf blades elongate, about 1 cm. wide or more; panicles large, flexuous, 15-30 cm. long, the branches somewhat drooping; spikelets 7-8 mm. long; fertile lemma flattened, oblong, appressed-pubescent, with short abrupt tip, or sometimes awned; sterile lemmas much shorter, 1-3 mm. long, awnless.

Distribution: Eastern Asia and other warm regions; cultivated in the southern United States, occasionally self-established.

Missouri. Grown as a crop in the southeastern lowlands and to some extent northward along the Mississippi River, where collected as an escape, Marion County (Steyermark 80729).

60. LEERSIA Sw.

Perennials; panicles consisting of short, spike-like racemes toward ends of spreading or ascending branches; spikelets 1-flowered, laterally compressed, falling entire; true glumes and sterile lemmas lacking (see *Oryza* for comparison); fertile lemma broad, keeled, usually ciliate; palea narrower, about as long as lemma.

KEY TO MISSOURI SPECIES

1. Spikelets broad-ovate, 4-5 mm. long, almost as wide....1. *L. lenticularis*
1. Spikelets narrower, less than 2 mm. wide....2

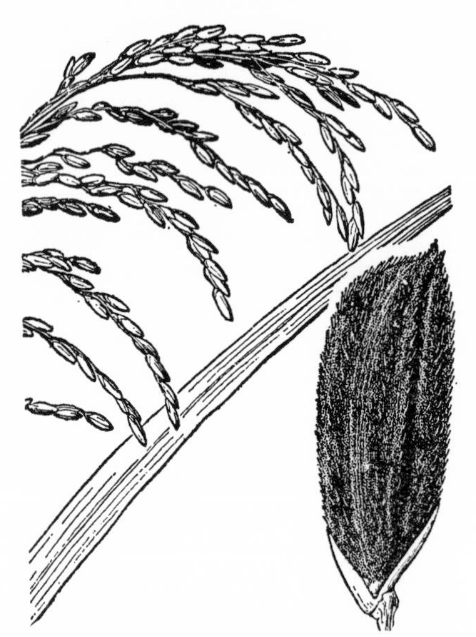

FIG. 167.—*Oryza sativa*. Plant, × ½; spikelet, × 5.

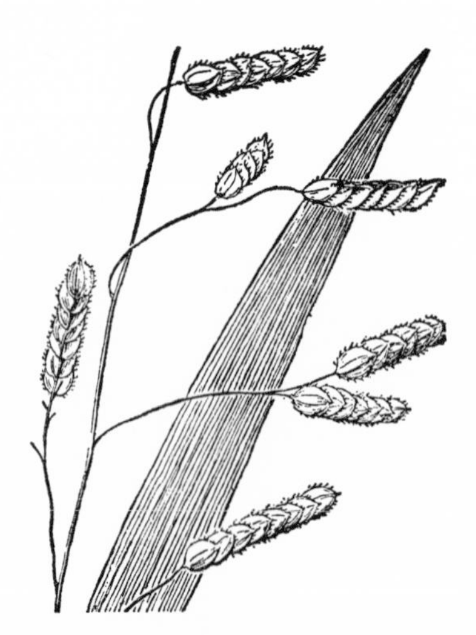

FIG. 168.—*Leersia lenticularis*, × 1.

FIG. 169.—*Leersia oryzoides*. Plant, × ½; spikelet, × 5.

2. Plants stiff, with coarse, rough leaf blades and sheaths; panicles with numerous branches, some of these whorled.......2. *L. oryzoides*
2. Plants slender, weak; panicles sparsely flowered, with few distant branches.......3. *L. virginica*

1. **Leersia lenticularis** Michx. CATCHFLY GRASS. Fig. 168.

Plants erect, 4-10 cm. tall; foliage mostly glabrous, the leaf blades 1-2 cm. wide; ligule about 1 mm. long, truncate; panicles open, flexuous, with crowded imbricated spikelets toward ends of the slender branches; spikelets (the fertile lemma) very flat, elliptic to oval, 4-5 mm. long, fringed with stiff cilia, awnless; stamens 2.

Distribution: Mid-Atlantic and Gulf regions, west to Minnesota to Texas.

Missouri. Bottomland forests, swampy meadows, riverbanks, marshes, scattered but most common in the eastern counties. Flowering in summer.

2. **Leersia oryzoides** (L.) Sw. RICE CUTGRASS. Fig. 169.

Plants erect to somewhat spreading or decumbent, to 1 m. or taller; foliage harsh, strongly scabrous to touch; leaf blades about 1 cm. wide; panicles spreading, drooping; spikelets (the fertile lemma) compressed, 4-5 mm. long, about 2 mm. wide or less, the keel fringed with cilia; stamens 3. Plants with panicles wholly or partially included in the sheaths have been separated as forma *inclusa* (Wiesh.) Dorfl. The division according to Fassett (1951) is weakly defined, and constitutes merely a late season phase of growth.

Distribution: Widespread in the United States and southern Canada; reported also from Europe.

Missouri. Pond borders, marshes, flatwoods, generally distributed. Flowering in summer and fall.

3. **Leersia virginica** Willd. WHITEGRASS. Fig. 170.

Plants slender, erect or decumbent near base, rooting at the lower nodes, to 1 m. or taller; leaf blades as much as 1 cm. wide or more, slightly scabrous; pani-

FIG. 170.—*Leersia virginica,* × 1.

cles diffuse, with few spreading branches; spikelets somewhat overlapping, 3-4 mm. long, about 1 mm. wide, with sparse cilia on keel; stamens 2.

Distribution: Eastern and central United States, west to South Dakota to Texas.

Missouri. Flatwoods, creek banks and spring branches, generally distributed. Flowering in summer.

TRIBE IX. ZIZANEAE

61. ZIZANIA L. WILD RICE

Annuals or perennials; panicles large, terminal, with spreading or ascending branches; spikelets unisexual, 1-flowered, falling entire; glumes reduced or lacking; staminate spikelets acuminate, pendulous, from the lower branches, the lemma awnless; pistillate spikelets linear, firm, stiffly ascending from the upper branches of same panicle, the lemma long-awned.

1. **Zizania aquatica** L. var. **interior** Fassett. Fig. 171

Annuals; culms coarse, erect to somewhat decumbent near base, frequently 2 m. or taller; leaf blades as much as 3 cm. wide; ligule conspicuous, 1 cm. or more in length; staminate spikelets pendulous, from the spreading lower branches, about 10 mm. long, awnless; stamens 6, the anthers large, 4-5 mm. long; pistillate (upper) portion of panicles with stiffly ascending branches; fertile lemma linear, firm, glabrous, about 15-20 mm. long, tapering abruptly to long, straight awn. The typical variety does not occur in Missouri but has been cited for Illinois; it is separated from var. *interior* by the scabrous lemmas and gradually tapering awns.

Distribution: North-central United States and southern Canada. Var. *aquatica* is more widespread, occurring farther east and south, to the Atlantic seaboard and Gulf region. Wild rice is an important food plant for waterfowl. In the northern states and Canada it is harvested for food by Indians, and also packaged and marketed.

Missouri. Sloughs, marshes, along streams, scattered, Clay, Jackson, Newton, Greene, Butler, Dunklin, New Madrid, St. Charles, and Clark counties. Flowering in summer.

62. ZIZANIOPSIS Doell & Aschers.

Perennials; panicles large, terminal, with whorled branches; spikelets unisexual, 1-flowered, falling entire; glumes lacking; staminate spikelets occurring below the pistillate on the same branches of the panicle; lemmas of staminate spikelets awnless, or merely awn-tipped, those of the pistillate spikelets short-awned.

1. **Zizaniopsis milacea** (Michx.) Doell & Aschers. SOUTHERN WILD RICE. Fig. 172.

Plants spreading by rhizomes; culms erect, to 3 m. or taller; leaf blades elongate, scabrous, about 2 cm. wide; ligules conspicuous; panicles large, as much

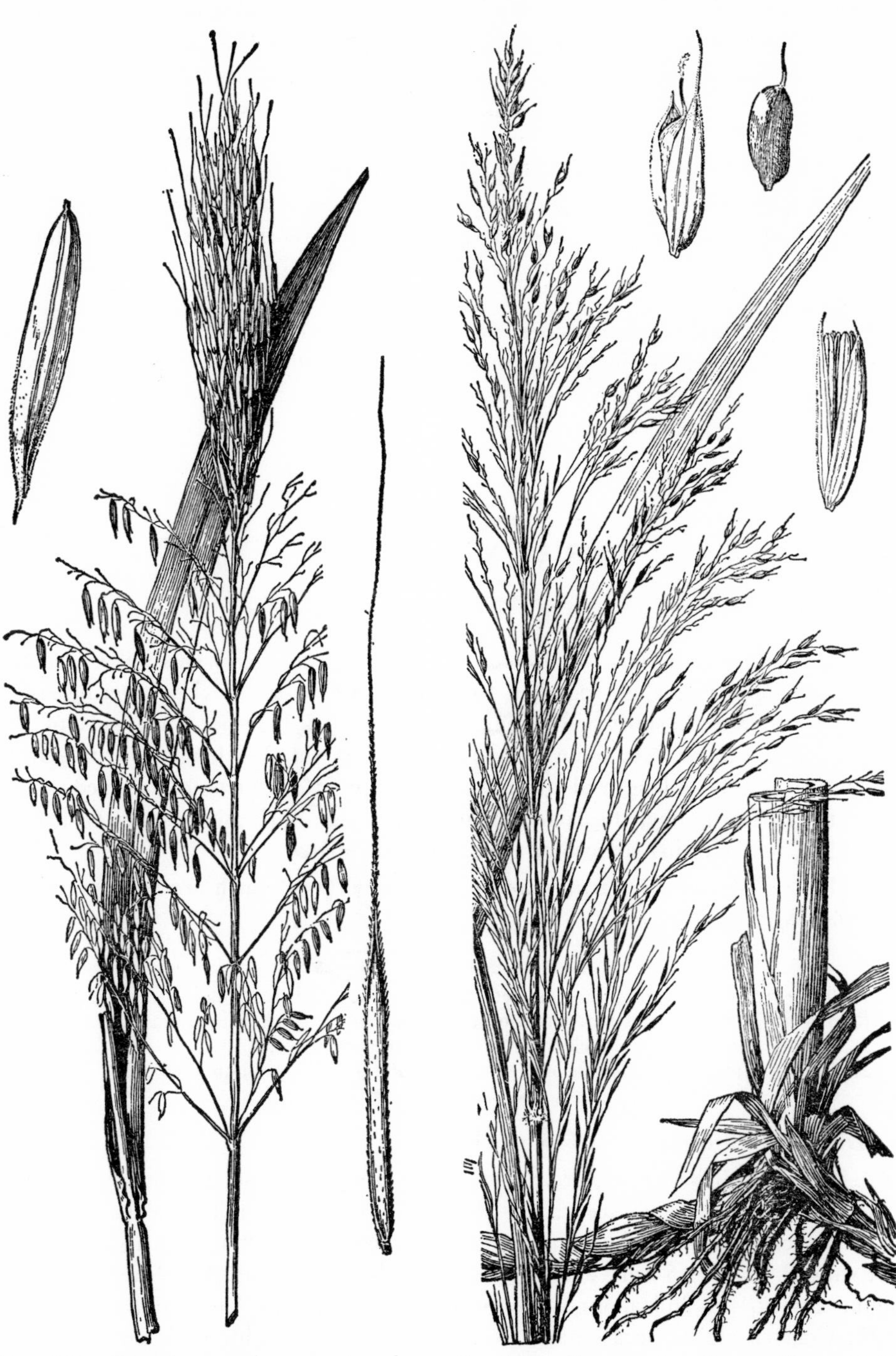

FIG. 171.—*Zizania aquatica* var. *interior*. Plant, × ½; pistillate spikelet, × 2; staminate spikelet, × 5.

FIG. 172.—*Zizaniopsis milacea*. Plant, × ½; staminate spikelet, pistillate spikelet, and ripe caryopsis, × 5.

as 50 cm. long, with whorled, nodding branches; staminate spikelets conspicuously nerved about 7-8 mm. long, the lemma and palea about equal; stamens 6, the anthers large, 4-5 mm. long; pistillate spikelets also conspicuously nerved, about the same length as the staminate spikelets; lemma with awn 1-2 mm. or slightly more; palea exceeding body of lemma; grain plump, about 3 mm. long, with stiff persistent style. This grass is distinguished from the preceding species of *Zizania* which it resembles in general habit by the presence of rhizomes, staminate and pistillate spikelets from the same branches, and the shorter, less elongate florets.

Distribution: Southern and mid-Atlantic states, west to Oklahoma and Texas.

Missouri. Sinkhole depressions, swampy ground, infrequent and restricted to the southeastern section including Shannon, Butler, Dunklin, Pemiscot, and New Madrid counties. Flowering in spring.

TRIBE X. PANICEAE

63. DIGITARIA Heist. CRABGRASS

Annuals or perennials; inflorescence consisting of several spike-like racemes, somewhat digitate or close together, from terminal portion of the flowering stalk; spikelets 1-flowered, short-pedicelled, solitary or 2-3 together on 1 side of the rachis, falling entire; 1st glume reduced or lacking, the 2nd longer, varying from one-half to equal the length of spikelet; sterile lemma conspicuously nerved, about equal to the fertile one, the latter smooth, nerveless, both awnless; fertile lemma with thin, flat margins somewhat enveloping the palea.

The crabgrasses are warm season species, several of which are adventive from the Old World.

KEY TO MISSOURI SPECIES

1. Rachis narrow, triangular in cross-section, about as thick as broad........1. *D. filiformis*
1. Rachis flat, with winged margins, not triangular or as thick as broad............................2
   2. Fertile lemma dark, blackish; foliage glabrous.................................2. *D. Ischaemum*
   2. Fertile lemma greenish-yellow or straw-colored; foliage pubescent..............................
   ....3. *D. sanguinalis*

1. **Digitaria filiformis** (L.) Koch. Fig. 173.

Annual; culms slender, erect, branching from the base, to about 50 cm. or taller; lower sheaths pubescent; leaf blades 1-4 mm. wide; inflorescence consisting of 1-5 delicate racemes of varying length, subdigitate or remote; rachis triangular, not winged, about 0.5 mm. wide; spikelets in 2's or 3's, ovate, 1.5-2 mm. long; 1st glume absent, the 2nd about three-fourths as long as the lemmas; fertile lemma dark. Coarser plants occasionally exceeding 1 m. in height, with densely pilose lower sheaths and spikelets larger than those of the typical variety, usually exceeding 2 mm., have been designated as var. *villosa* (Walt.) Fern.

Distribution: Eastern and central United States, west to Iowa, Kansas to Texas.

Missouri. Open ground, sandy prairies, thin woods, primarily in the central and southern counties. The coarser variety with conspicuously pilose sheaths and larger spikelets occurs scattered with typical plants, but is less common. Flowering in July-August.

2. **Digitaria Ischaemum** (Schreb.) Muhl. SMOOTH CRABGRASS. Fig. 174.

Annual; culms spreading, branching, rooting at the nodes, similar in general habit to species 3, but generally not as tall; foliage glabrous; ligule about 1.5 mm. long; inflorescence consisting of 1-several racemes, digitate or approximately so; rachis about 1 mm. wide, winged; spikelets usually in pairs, ovate, 2 mm. long; 1st glume generally absent, the 2nd equal to spikelet length; fertile lemma smooth, dark purplish or blackish. Tall plants, often 1 m. in height, with more numerous racemes are sometimes referred to var. *mississippiensis* (Gatt.) Fern. According to Henrard (1950) these represent only a robust condition.

Distribution: Widespread in the United States, most common in the eastern areas; introduced from Eurasia.

Missouri. Fallow ground, lawns, gardens, generally distributed. Flowering in midsummer, usually somewhat earlier than the following species.

3. **Digitaria sanguinalis** (L.) Scop. Fig. 175.

Annual; culms branching, spreading and rooting at the nodes, to 50 cm. or sometimes taller; foliage pilose-pubescent, the leaf blades soft, 5-10 mm. wide; ligule about 3 mm. long, membranaeous; racemes spike-like, with winged rachis about 1 mm. wide; spikelets usually in pairs, elliptic-pointed, 3 mm. long; 1st glume minute or obsolete, the 2nd about one-half the spikelet length; sterile lemma strongly nerved; fertile lemma glabrous, straw-colored. This species is easily distinguished from the preceding by the pubescent foliage and somewhat longer, more elongate spikelets.

FIG. 173.—*Digitaria filiformis.* Plant, × 1; spikelet and floret, × 10.

FIG. 174.—*Digitaria Ischaemum.* Plant, × 1; spikelet and floret, × 10.

FIG. 175.—*Digitaria sanguinalis*. Plant, × ½; two views of spikelet, and floret, × 10.

Distribution: Widespread in the United States, most common in the East and South; introduced from Europe.

Missouri. Fields, lawns, waste areas, generally distributed. Flowering in July-August.

64. LEPTOLOMA Chase.

Perennials; panicles diffuse, with stiff, spreading branches; spikelets 1-flowered, solitary on long pedicels, falling entire; 1st glume minute or absent, the 2nd about equal to spikelet length; sterile lemma present, equaling fertile lemma, both awnless, the latter thin, with flat margins, not inrolled. Pilger (1940) combines this genus with *Digitaria*; however, the inflorescence types are different, and in most manuals the division has been maintained.

1. **Leptoloma cognatum** (Schult.) Chase. FALL WITCHGRASS. Fig. 176.

Plants tufted; culms with leafy bases, stiffly erect, 30-70 cm. tall; lower sheaths mostly pilose; leaf blades pale green, 2-5 mm. wide, tapering to fine tip; panicles erect, diffuse, with divergent branching; spikelets elliptic-pointed, purplish, about 3 mm. long, on long, straight pedicels as much as 5-7 cm. long; fertile lemma smooth, shiny, about 2 mm. long; palea similar.

Distribution: Eastern and southern United States, west to Minnesota to Arizona.

Missouri. Fields, waste ground, sandstone glades, generally distributed. Flowering in June-July.

65. ERIOCHLOA H. B. K. CUPGRASS

Annuals or perennials; inflorescence consisting of short spike-like racemes along a common axis; spikelets 1-flowered, sessile or nearly so, mostly solitary, in 2 rows on 1 side of the rachis, falling entire; 1st glume obsolete, forming with the rachilla joint a thickened ring below the 2nd glume; 2nd glume and sterile lemma similar and equal to spikelet length; fertile lemma indurate, with inrolled margins, awnless or with very short awn.

1. **Eriochloa contracta** Hitchc. PRAIRIE CUPGRASS. Fig. 177.

Annual, forming tufts; culms branching, decumbent near base, to 1 m. tall; leaf blades soft, short-pubescent, 3-7 mm. wide; inflorescence strict, the racemes short, ascending, 1-2 cm. long; spikelets ovate-oblong, pointed, pubescent, about 4 mm. long; fertile lemma with short aristate tip less than 1 mm. in length.

Distribution: Southwestern United States, north and east to Colorado and Nebraska, widely scattered elsewhere.

Missouri. Low ground, creek areas, levees, scattered and not common, Jackson, Ray, Boone, Pike, St. Louis, and Pemiscot counties. Flowering in July-August.

2. **Eriochloa gracilis** (Fourn.) Hitchc. Fig. 178.

Annual, mostly coarser than species 1, with branching culms, somewhat decumbent near base; foliage glabrous; leaf blades as much as 1 cm. wide or more; racemes spreading, 2-5 cm. long; spikelets elliptic-pointed, slightly pubescent, 4-5 mm. long; fertile lemma smooth with minute tip. This species is

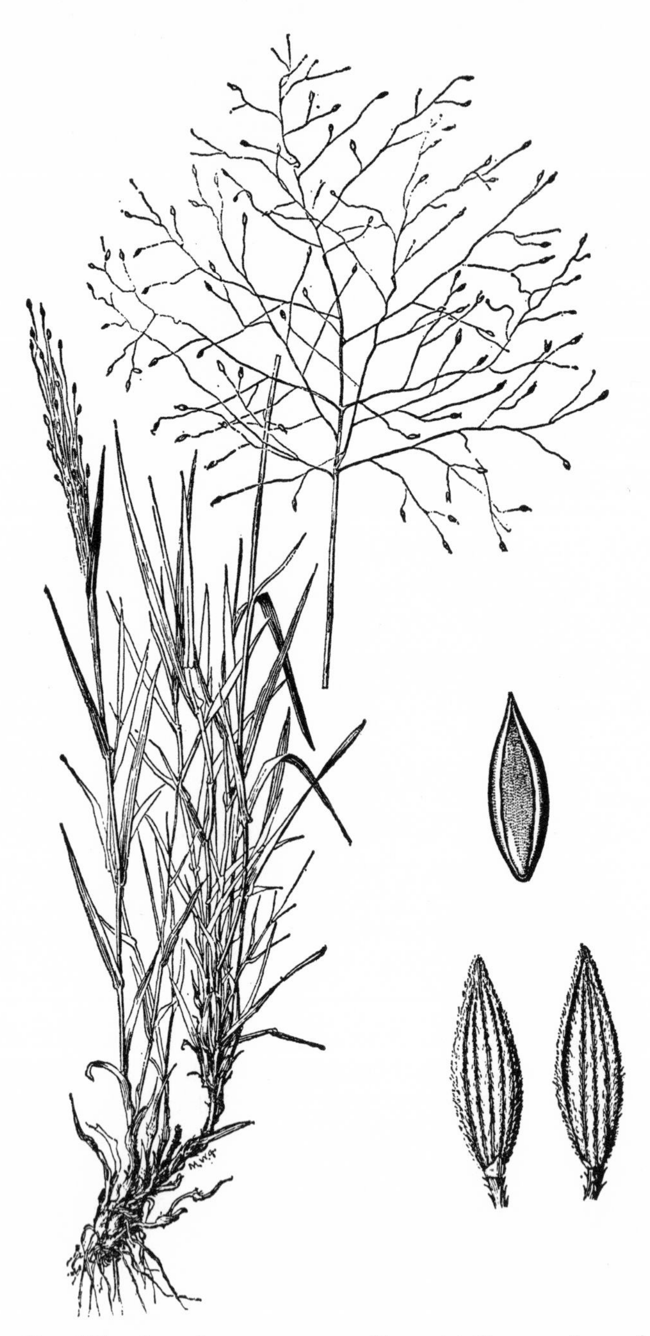

FIG. 176.—*Leptoloma cognatum.* Plant, × ½; two views of spikelet, and floret, × 10.

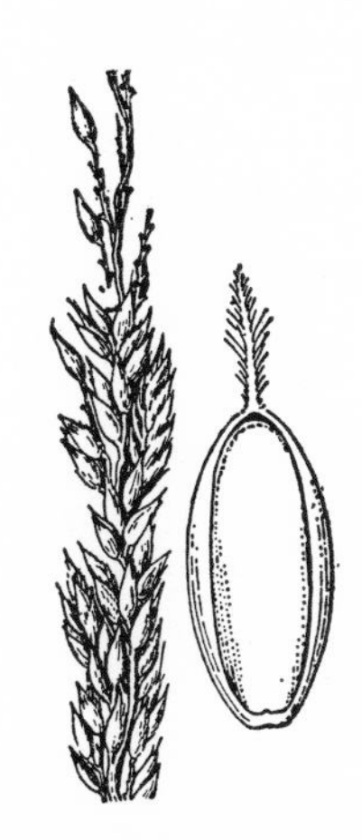

FIG. 177.—*Eriochloa contracta.* Panicle, × 1; floret, × 10.

FIG. 178.—*Eriochloa gracilis.* Plant, × ½; two views of spikelet, and floret, × 10.

distinguishable from the preceding by the coarser habit, glabrous foliage, and awnless lemma.

Distribution: Southwestern United States, northeastward to Oklahoma, introduced elsewhere, as in *Missouri,* collected in open ground, Mississippi County, (Steyermark 79553).

66. BRACHIARIA (Trin.) Griseb.

Annuals or perennials; inflorescence consisting of several spreading-ascending spike-like racemes along a common axis; spikelets 1-flowered, sessile, solitary, in 2 rows on 1 side of the rachis, falling entire; 1st glume present; 2nd glume and sterile lemma similar, equaling length of spikelet; fertile lemma indurate, awnless with inrolled margins enclosing palea. The presence of a 1st glume distinguishes this genus from *Eriochloa.*

1. **Brachiaria erucaeformis** (J. E. Smith) Griseb. Fig. 179.

Annual; culms branching, decumbent-spreading, to about 50 cm. tall; leaf blades 3-6 mm. wide; racemes ascending, 1-2 cm. long; spikelets elliptic, noticeably pubescent, about 2 mm. long.

Distribution: Widely scattered in the United States; adventive from the Old World.

Missouri. Local, collected from gravel bed of creek, Stone County (Steyermark 80556).

2. **Brachiaria platyphylla** (Griseb.) Nash. Fig. 180.

Annual; culms branching, decumbent near base, rooting at the lower nodes, about 50 cm. tall; leaf blades somewhat coarse-textured, 5-10 mm. wide; racemes few, 3-6 cm. long, distant along the axis; rachis flat, smooth, about 2 mm. wide; spikelets ovate-elliptic, glabrous, 4 mm. long; 1st glume thin, broadly ovate about 1.5 mm. long; fertile lemma rugose, 3.5 mm. long. (*B. extensa* Chase.)

Distribution: Southern United States, from Florida to Texas and Oklahoma, north to southeastern *Missouri,* where local, open sandy ground, Scott and Dunklin counties. Flowering in August.

67. PASPALUM L.

Annuals or perennials; inflorescence consisting of 1-several spike-like racemes along a common axis; spikelets 1-flowered, nearly sessile, elliptic-oblong to orbicular, plano-convex, solitary or in pairs, forming 2 or 4 rows on 1 side of the rachis; spikelets falling entire, or sometimes the entire raceme; 1st glume minute or absent, the 2nd glume and sterile lemma equal to length of spikelet; fertile lemma smooth, indurate, awnless, with inrolled margins enclosing palea.

The paspalums are warm season grasses, in Missouri perennials, some of which have limited forage value.

KEY TO MISSOURI SPECIES

1. Rachis distinctly winged or leaf-like, as wide or wider than the individual spikelets; spikelets solitary, arranged in 2 rows along the rachis....................2
1. Rachis not winged or leaf-like, not as wide as an individual spikelet except in *P. pubiflorum* in which the spikelets are paired and form 4 rows along the rachis............3
   2. Racemes few, 5 or less per flowering stalk, the rachis terminated by spikelet........ ....1. *P. dissectum*

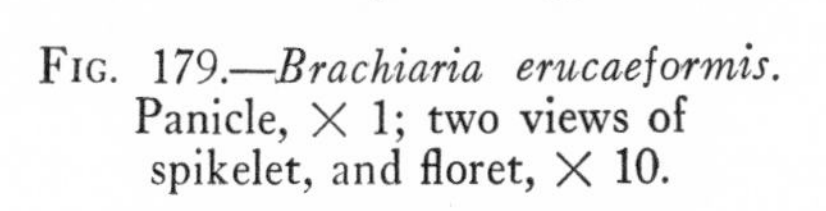

FIG. 179.—*Brachiaria erucaeformis.* Panicle, × 1; two views of spikelet, and floret, × 10.

FIG. 180.—*Brachiaria platyphylla.* Plant, × ½; two views of spikelet, and floret, × 10.

2. Racemes usually numerous, 15-20 or more, the rachis projecting beyond the terminal spikelet........2. *P. fluitans*
3. Spikelets conspicuously villous; 2nd glume and sterile lemma tapering to point; introduced forage species........3. *P. dilatatum*
3. Spikelets mostly glabrous, or only slightly pubescent, rounded or obtuse at apex; native species........4
4. Spikelets 4-rowed, elliptic-oblong, about 3 mm. long........4. *P. pubiflorum* var. *glabrum*
4. Spikelets 2-rowed, circular to oblong, 1.5-4 mm. long........5
5. Spikelets large, ovoid, 3.5-4 mm. long........5. *P. floridanum*
5. Spikelets smaller, 1.5-3 mm. long........6
6. Spikelets rounded to broadly elliptic, 2.5-3 mm. long, solitary........6. *P. laeve*
6. Spikelets 1.5-2.5 mm. long, in pairs........7
7. Spikelets roundish, averaging about 2 mm. long; common species throughout the state........7. *P. ciliatifolium*
7. Spikelets elliptic, about 1.5 mm. long; rare Coastal Plain species from the southeastern counties........8. *P. setaceum*

1. **Paspalum dissectum** (L.) L. Fig. 181.

Plants decumbent-spreading, the culms branching, rooting at the nodes; sheaths somewhat inflated; leaf blades glabrous, linear, about 5 mm. wide or less; racemes 1-5, short, 1-3 cm. long, the rachis green, leaf-like, exceeded by the terminal spikelet; spikelets solitary, broad-elliptic, about 2 mm. in length.

Distribution: Illinois and Missouri, south to Gulf region and along east coast.

Missouri. Muddy shores and flats, not common, Jasper, Howell, and Dunklin counties. Flowering in August-September.

2. **Paspalum fluitans** (Ell.) Kunth. Fig. 182.

Plants submerged or terrestrial; culms soft, creeping, rooting at the nodes; sheaths inflated, glabrous or occasionally papillose-hispid; leaf blades thin, lanceolate, 1-2 cm. wide; racemes numerous, 2-5 cm. long, falling entire, the rachis

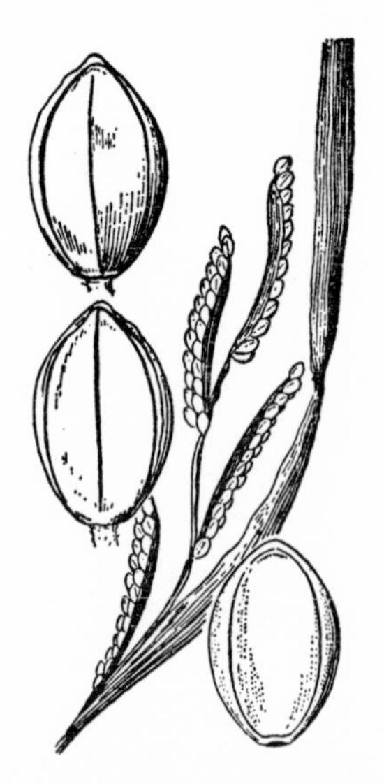

FIG. 181.—*Paspalum dissectum.* Panicle, × 1; two views of spikelet, and floret, × 10.

FIG. 182.—*Paspalum fluitans*. Panicle, × 1; two views of spikelet, and floret, × 10.

tapering to point, exceeding the terminal spikelet; spikelets solitary, narrow-elliptic, about 1.5 mm. long or slightly less.

Distribution: Middle Mississippi Valley, south to Texas, to Florida, and along the east coast.

Missouri. Muddy shores, ditches, swampy areas, scattered, central and southern counties. Flowering in August-September.

3. **Paspalum dilatatum** Poir. DALLIS GRASS. Fig. 183.

Plants forming tufts or loose sod; culms robust, erect or somewhat decumbent near base, to 1 m. or taller; sheaths glabrous to slightly pubescent; leaf blades glabrous, about 1 cm. wide; racemes several, 4-6 cm. long; spikelets ovate, acutely-pointed, 3-3.5 mm. long, conspicuously ciliate along the margins.

Distribution: Southern United States and along east coast to New Jersey; introduced from South America about 1875, as a forage species.

Missouri. This rare species has been collected on waste ground, St. Louis County (Muhlenbach 1355). Flowering in late summer.

4. **Paspalum pubiflorum** Rupr. var. **glabrum** Vasey. Fig. 184.

Plants stout, the culms rooting at the lower nodes, to about 1 m. tall; sheaths keeled, glabrous; leaf blades 8-12 mm. wide; racemes several, usually 5 or more, the lower ones as much as 10 cm. long; rachis broad, about 2 mm. wide; spikelets glabrous, obovate, about 3 mm. long, in pairs, forming 4 rows along the rachis. Plants of typical *pubiflorum* are characterized by smaller habit and pubescent spikelets. These are more southerly and do not reach Missouri.

Distribution: Southeastern United States and mid-Atlantic area, west to Texas and Nebraska, as far north as Pennsylvania.

Missouri. Fields, bottomlands, roadsides, on damp ground, primarily in the central and southern counties, north to Boone County. Flowering in August-September.

5. **Paspalum floridanum** Michx. Fig. 185.

Plants solitary or in small clumps, with short rhizomes; culms robust, to 1.5 m. or sometimes taller; sheaths glabrous or sometimes pubescent; leaf blades 6-10 mm. wide, elongate below becoming shorter upward; racemes stiff, coarse, usually 5 or less, 5-10 cm. long; spikelets glabrous, broadly ovate, 3.5-4 mm. long, mostly

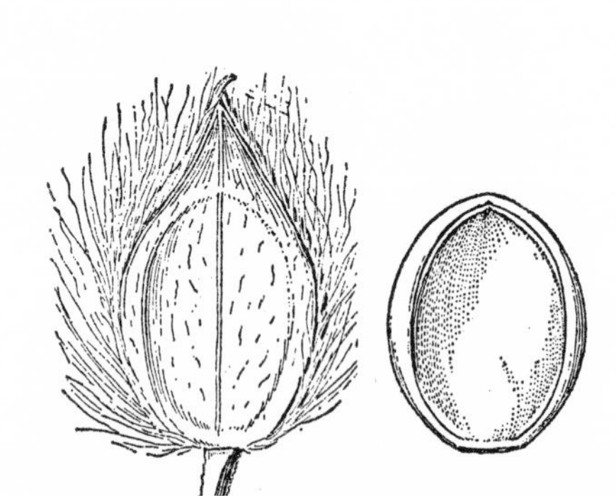

FIG. 183.—*Paspalum dilatatum.* Plant, × ½; two views of spikelet, and floret, × 10.

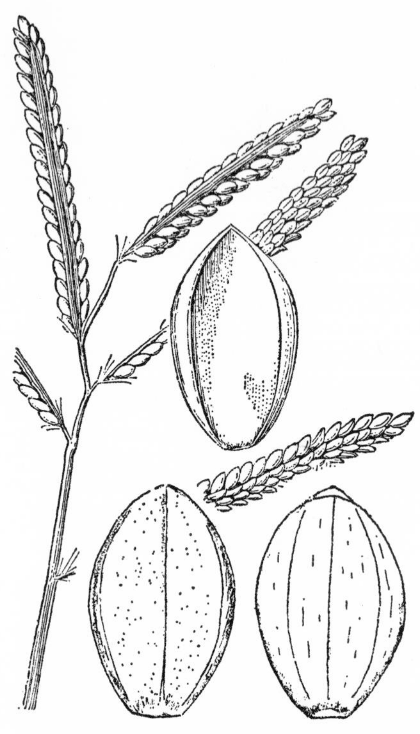

FIG. 184.—*Paspalum pubiflorum* var. *glabrum.* Panicle, × 1; two views of spikelet, and floret, × 10.

solitary, but a second pedicel usually present, its spikelet reduced or obsolete. Plants distinguished by the minor difference of mostly glabrous sheaths are sometimes separated as var. *glabratum* Engel.

Distribution: Southern and eastern United States, west to Texas and Nebraska, as far north as Pennsylvania.

Missouri. Low ground, fields, roadsides, on damp, sandy soils, south of a line from Vernon County to Mississippi County, but not common in the Ozarks. Flowering in August-September.

6. **Paspalum laeve** Michx. Fig. 186.

Plants leafy, erect, 50-100 cm. tall; foliage glabrous to pilose, with keeled or somewhat flattened sheaths, the leaf blades 4-10 mm. wide; racemes several, usually less than 5, as much as 10 cm. long; spikelets glabrous, obovate, elliptic-ovate or roundish, 2.5-3 mm. long. The species has been divided into several varieties. Plants with glabrous foliage and more or less ovate spikelets represent the typical variety (var. *laeve*). Those with pilose foliage but which are otherwise similar to the typical variety are var. *pilosum* Scribn. (*P. longipilum* Nash). Other plants, glabrous but with rounded or circular spikelets, are designated as var. *circulare* (Nash) Stone. These variations or character tendencies are recognizable in some Missouri specimens; however, indistinct gradations occur which actually are more common than the extremes.

Distribution: Southern and eastern United States, to Texas, Missouri, and southern New England.

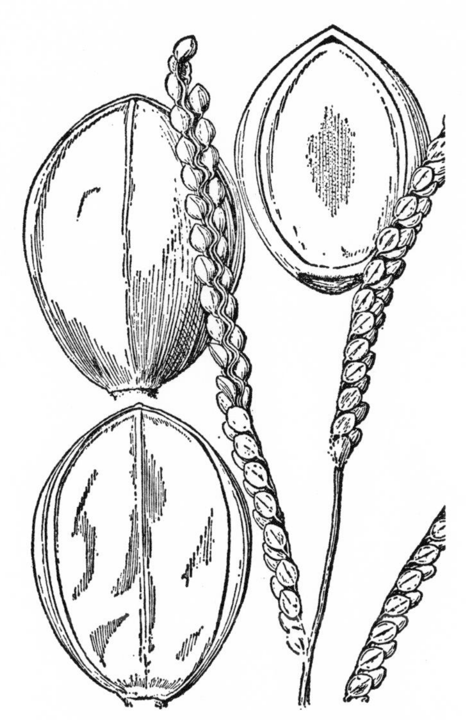

FIG. 185.—*Paspalum floridanum.* Panicle, × 1; two views of spikelet, and floret, × 10.

Missouri. Upland prairies, woods, spring branches, on moist soils, in the central and southern sections, south of a line from Jackson, Randolph, and Lincoln counties. Flowering in July-August.

7. Paspalum ciliatifolium Michx. Fig. 187.

Plants somewhat tufted; culms slender, leafy, spreading to erect, 40-100 cm. tall; sheaths glabrous to variably pubescent; leaf blades also variable, glabrous, minutely pubescent, pilose or sometimes sparsely-long-ciliate, as much as 15 mm. wide or more; racemes 1-4, slightly curving, from long, slender peduncles; spikelets glabrous to slightly pubescent, rounded or nearly so, averaging about 2 mm. long, in pairs and mostly crowded along the rachis. Several varieties have been recognized, mainly on the basis of pubescence types, these not always distinct or easily separated. On the basis of these criteria, typical plants (var. *ciliatifolium*) are primarily glabrous with occasionally sparse cilia. Specimens with pilose surfaces are referred to var. *Muhlenbergii* (Nash) Fern. (*P. pubescens* Nash), while still others with puberulent surfaces, and sometimes with longer, scattered hairs are designated as var. *stramineum* (Nash) Fern. (*P. stramineum* Nash). Including *P. Bushii* Nash).

Distribution: Eastern and central United States, west to Minnesota, Nebraska, Colorado, and the Southwest.

Missouri. Dry woods, prairies, glades, generally distributed, the pubescent varieties occurring most commonly. Flowering in July-August.

FIG. 186.—*Paspalum laeve.* Plant, × ½; two views of spikelet, and floret, × 10.

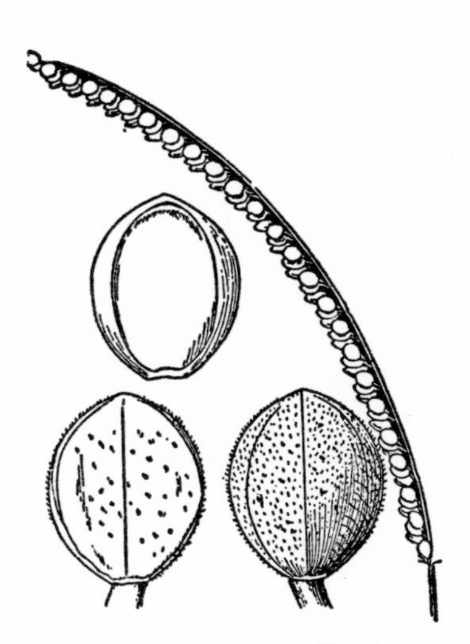

FIG. 187.—*Paspalum ciliatifolium.* Raceme, × 1; two views of spikelet, and floret, × 10.

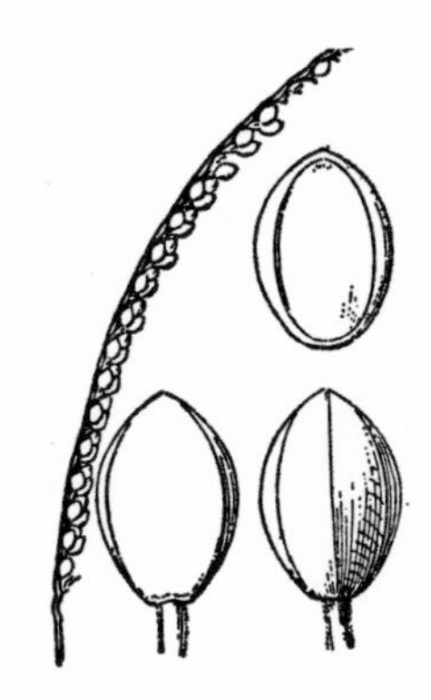

FIG. 188.—*Paspalum setaceum.* Raceme, × 1; two views of spikelet, and floret, × 10.

8. **Paspalum setaceum** Michx. Fig. 188.

Plants tufted; culms slender, 35-50 cm. long; sheaths pilose; leaf blades narrow, also pilose, 2-5 mm. wide; racemes usually solitary, about 5 cm. long, from delicate peduncles; spikelets similar to those of species 7 but smaller, about 1.5 mm. long or less, in pairs and crowded along the rachis.

Distribution: Coastal Plain region, rare elsewhere, reported as far inland as *Missouri,* collected on dry sandy slopes, Crowley's Ridge, Stoddard County (Steyermark 76726). Flowering in July-August.

68. PANICUM L.

Annuals or perennials; panicles terminal, contracted or spreading, frequently axillary also, or in a few species, racemose; spikelets 1-flowered, mostly pedicellate, lanceolate to broadly ovate, separating below the glumes and falling entire; 1st glume reduced, usually ovate; 2nd glume longer, similar to sterile lemma, these conspicuously nerved and equaling spikelet length; fertile lemma indurate, nerveless, acute to obtuse at apex, with inrolled margins enclosing palea; palea of similar texture.

The genus has a world-wide distribution and is most abundantly represented in warmer latitudes. It is the largest of the grass genera with an estimated 500 species. In Missouri the panicums comprise the largest group, here accorded to 38 species, in addition to a number of infraspecific entities.

KEY TO MISSOURI SPECIES

1. Spikelets produced in expanded terminal panicles occurring in spring, and also in contracted clusters from basal and lower sheaths later in the season; perennials with rosettes of basal leaves.........2
1. Spikelets produced in open panicles, or rarely racemes, flowering only once; annuals or perennials, without basal rosettes.........33
    2. Culm leaves long and narrow, 5 mm. wide or less, 20 times or more as long, close ascending to form erect tufts.........3

2. Culm leaves varying in width from less than to more than 5 mm., but usually not 15-20 times as long....5
3. Spikelets about 2-2.5 mm. long, obtuse or blunt-tipped....1. *P. linearifolium*
3. Spikelets exceeding 2.5 mm. in length, usually 3-4 mm. or more, obtuse or distinctly pointed....4
4. Spikelets pointed or beaked....2. *P. depauperatum*
4. Spikelets blunt or rounded at apex....3. *P. perlongum*
5. Ligule a conspicuous tuft of hairs, 2 mm. or longer; spikelets 1.5-2.5 mm. long (see also species 19, *P. Ravenelii* with spikelets exceeding 3 mm. in length....6
5. Ligule shorter or obsolete (except in *P. Ravenelii*)....10
6. Sheaths and leaf blades glabrous or nearly so; spikelets about 1.5 mm. long....4. *P. lanuginosum* var. *Lindheimeri*
6. Sheaths and leaf blades sparsely pubescent to conspicuously soft pilose or blades essentially glabrous above with few scattered cilia toward base and along margins; spikelets 1.5-2.5 mm. long....7
7. Leaf blades glabrous, short pubescent, or sparsely long pilose on upper surface, mostly short appressed-pubescent below....8
7. Leaf blades long pilose on both surfaces, the hairs 2-5 mm. long; sheaths also pilose, with horizontally spreading hairs....9
8. Upper surface of leaf blades glabrous, sparsely ciliate or short pubescent; sheaths nearly glabrous to somewhat pubescent....5. *P. lanuginosum* var. *fasciculatum*
8. Upper surface of leaf blades mostly long pilose, the whitish hairs to 4-5 mm. long; sheaths also generally pilose....6. *P. lanuginosum* var. *implicatum*
9. Spikelets 2 mm. long or less....7. *P. praecocius*
9. Spikelets longer than 2 mm., to 2.5 mm. long....8. *P. villossissimum*
10. Some of the leaf blades at least 2 cm. wide, not over 5 times as long; spikelets about 3 mm. or longer....11
10. None of the leaf blades as much as 2 cm. wide; spikelets 1.5-4 mm. long....13
11. Sheaths papillose-hispid; coarse leafy plants of low ground and creek banks....9. *P. clandestinum*
11. Sheaths glabrous or pubescent, not hispid; plants of upland woods and slopes....12
12. Nodes conspicuously bearded....10. *P. Boscii*
12. Nodes glabrous....11. *P. latifolium*
13. Spikelets numerous, spherical or nearly so, averaging about 1.5 mm. long; leaf blades cordate at base....14
13. Spikelets oblong-elliptic, mostly exceeding 2 mm. in length, if shorter, about 1.5 mm., then leaf blades tapering to base, not cordate....15
14. Panicles longer than broad; leaf blades 1-2 cm. wide, sometimes wider....12. *P. polyanthes*
14. Panicles ovoid, or roundish; leaf blades narrower, usually about 1 cm. wide....13. *P. sphaerocarpon*
15. Widest leaf blades mostly exceeding 1.5 cm....16
15. Widest leaf blades 1.5 cm. or less....20
16. Spikelets 3 mm. or longer....17
16. Spikelets less than 3 mm. long....18
17. Sheaths glabrous; leaf blades thin; ligule obsolete or absent....10. *P. Boscii*
17. Sheaths hirsute; leaf blades somewhat thick-textured; ligules a prominent tuft of hairs....19. *P. Ravenelii*
18. Sheaths conspicuously soft, velvety-pubescent....15. *P. scoparium*
18. Sheaths glabrous, or harsh, hispid-pubescent....19
19. Sheaths hispid; spikelets from slightly less than 3 mm. long to mostly longer; culms freely branching....9. *P. clandestinum*
19. Sheaths glabrous; culms more or less simple, only sparingly branched....14. *P. commutatum*
20. Sheaths conspicuously soft, velvety-pubescent; spikelets about 2.5 mm. long; species of low, damp ground....15. *P. scoparium*
20. Sheaths glabrous to variably pubescent, if somewhat velvety as in species 18, *P. malacophyllum,* then spikelets turgid, to 3 mm. long, and typically occurring on dry soils....21
21. Leaf blades stiff, cordate at base, often with purplish color....14. *P. commutatum*
21. Leaf blades tapering to base, not cordate....22

22. Spikelets obtuse, turgid, usually large, at least 2.5 mm. long, but mostly longer; principal leaf blades averaging at least 1 cm. wide........23
22. Spikelets not turgid or plump, mostly less than 2.5 mm. long........26
23. Ligule conspicuous, stems and sheaths hirsute; spikelets 3.5-4 mm. long........19. *P. Ravenelii*
23. Ligule obsolete or lacking........24
24. Foliage and culms soft pubescent; nodes with tufted hairs........18. *P. malacophyllum*
24. Foliage and culms glabrous to hispid, not soft; nodes not tufted........25
25. Leaf blades generally glabrous on upper surfaces; spikelets glabrous or nearly so........16. *P. oligosanthes*
25. Leaf blades distinctly hispid; spikelets pubescent........17. *P. Leibergii*
26. Spikelets 1.5-2 mm. long; glabrous; autumnal foliage bushy, top-heavy, reclining or spreading, with numerous, short, acuminate leaves........27
26. Spikelets 2-3 mm. long, glabrous or pubescent; autumnal foliage not bushy, or top-heavy........28
27. Spikelets about 1.5 mm. long; nodes bearded; plants sprawling, occurring in damp ground and swales........21. *P. microcarpon*
27. Spikelets averaging about 2 mm. in length; nodes glabrous or bearded; plants bushy, but not sprawling, occurring in dry rocky ground........20. *P. dichotomum*
28. Spikelets 2.5-3 mm. long; leaf blades ascending, elongate, to 15 cm. long, conspicuously tapering toward base........29
28. Spikelets less than 2 mm. long; leaf blades shorter, not narrowing toward base........30
29. Base of leaf blades noticeably narrowed to about width of sheath summit........24. *P. Bicknellii*
29. Base of leaf blades narrowing but rounded........25. *P. calliphyllum*
30. Basal foliage soft, lax, forming spreading clumps; culm leaves about same width as lower or basal leaves........26. *P. laxiflorum*
30. Basal foliage stiffer, not lax; culm leaves mostly narrower than basal leaves......31
31. Spikelets glabrous or nearly so; common species........20. *P. dichotomum*
31. Spikelets pubescent; rare species........32
32. Leaf blades soft pubescent on upper surface; plants of dry ground........22. *P. annulum*
32. Leaf blades glabrous or nearly so; plants of damp ground........23. *P. nitidum*
33. Panicles narrow, the short spike-like racemes appressed-ascending; southern and subtropical grasses becoming rare adventives as far north as Missouri........34
33. Panicles with typically spreading branches sometimes contracted, but not spike-like........36
34. Spikelets obovoid, blunt, with 1st glume nearly equal to 2nd glume........27. *P. obtusum*
34. Spikelets pointed, 1st glume at most one half as long as 2nd glume........35
35. Spikelets about 2 mm. long; perennial species........28. *P. geminatum*
35. Spikelets 3 mm. or longer; coarse annual species........29. *P. texanum*
36. Sheaths and culms mostly glabrous; native perennials of wet ground or prairies, except the coarse annual *P. dichotomiflorum* occurring in waste ground and fields........37
36. Sheaths and culms hairy, mostly conspicuously so; all annuals usually in dry waste ground, prairies, or sandy areas........41
37. Coarse, smooth annual, somewhat decumbent-spreading at base; leaf blades frequently 1.5 cm. wide........30. *P. dichotomiflorum*
37. Perennials mostly erect; leaf blades much narrower........38
38. Palea of sterile floret conspicuous, equal to the latter, exceeding the fruit and spreading the spikelet........31. *P. hians*
38. Palea of sterile floret typically obsolete or lacking........39
39. Plants lacking rhizomes; spikelets 2-2.5 mm. long........32. *P. agrostoides*
39. Plants rhizomatous; spikelets larger, usually exceeding 3 mm. in length........40
40. Individual spikelets sessile or nearly so, crowded along the panicle branches........33. *P. anceps*
40. Individual spikelets pedicellate, not crowded........34. *P. virgatum*

41. Spikelets plump, about 5 mm. long; panicles compact, heavy, somewhat nodding; cultivated species, occasionally escaping.........35. *P. milaceum*
41. Spikelets not plump, smaller, 2-3.5 mm. long; panicles diffuse, erect.........42
   42. Spikelets elongate, lanceolate-acuminate, 3-3.5 mm. long; panicles narrow, at least twice as long as wide, with slender flexuous branches.........36. *P. flexile*
   42. Spikelets ovate-acute or acuminate, 2-2.5 mm. long (as much as 3 mm. or more in *P. capillare* var. *occidentale* with somewhat stiff, spreading panicle branches and conspicuous axillary pulvini); panicles broadly ovate.........43
43. Panicles from one-third to one-half or more as long as entire plant, somewhat inserted at base, or becoming exserted; leaf blades to 1 cm. or wider; culms erect to geniculate, sometimes rooting at lower nodes.........37. *P. capillare*
43. Panicles mostly one-third or less as long as entire plant, well-exserted; leaf blades 3-8 mm. wide; culms mostly erect.........38. *P. philadelphicum*

1. **Panicum linearifolium** Scribn. Fig. 189.

Perennial, forming tufts; culms slender, erect, 15-40 cm. tall; foliage mostly pubescent, or sometimes glabrous with only sparse cilia, the leaf blades elongate, ascending, 2-4 mm. wide, 20 times as long or more, terminal panicles long-exserted, the axillary panicles or clusters concealed or somewhat obscured among the basal or lower leaves; spikelets ovate, blunt, averaging about 2-3 mm. long. The species is commonly divided on the basis of pubescence into two varieties. Plants with pubescent foliage are included in the typical variety (var. *linearifolium*). Those with glabrous tendency are separated as var. *Werneri* (Scribn.) Fern. (*P. Werneri* Scribn.). A few Missouri plants are distinctly glabrous and easily separated. Most, however, exhibit some degree of pubescence.

Distribution: Eastern and central United States, west to Kansas and Texas.

Missouri. Thin woods, glades, open ground, on dry, cherty or sandy soils, generally distributed. Plants with glabrous foliage are less common and occur primarily in the southern counties. Flowering in May-June, and later in summer from axillary panicles.

2. **Panicum depauperatum** Muhl. Fig. 190.

Perennial, forming tufts; leafy culms erect, 15-50 cm. tall; sheaths and leaf blades glabrous to somewhat pubescent, the latter mostly narrow, ascending, 5 mm. wide or less; terminal panicles exserted, sparsely flowered, the secondary panicles or clusters from the lower sheaths; spikelets acute-pointed, mostly glabrous, about 3.5 mm. or longer in some specimens; second glume and sterile lemma forming a point, exceeding the fertile lemma.

Distribution: Eastern and central United States, west to Minnesota, Kansas, and Texas.

Missouri. Open woods, glades, rocky slopes, on dry soils, most common in the southern and east-central counties of the Ozarks region. Flowering in May-June, and later in summer from axillary panicles.

3. **Panicum perlongum** Nash. Fig. 191.

Perennial, forming tufts, resembling species 2 in general habit; sheaths and elongate-ascending leaf blades mostly pilose; terminal and axillary panicles few-flowered, the former long-exserted; spikelets broadly ellipsoid, averaging about 3 mm. long; 2nd glume and sterile lemma blunt, closely conforming to the fertile lemma, thus differing from the distinctly pointed spikelets of the preceding species.

Distribution: Central United States, from lower Canada to Texas.

Missouri. Open woods and upland prairies, on dry soils, generally distributed. Flowering in May-June, and later in summer from axillary panicles.

4. **Panicum lanuginosum** Ell. var. **Lindheimeri** (Nash) Fern. Fig. 192.

Perennial, forming tufts; culms slender, erect, simple, becoming branched and somewhat sprawling in the autumnal phase; sheaths and nodes mostly glabrous; ligule a conspicuous brush of hairs; leaf blades glabrous, 3-8 mm. wide, in autumnal fascicles from the middle and upper nodes; terminal panicles with spreading,

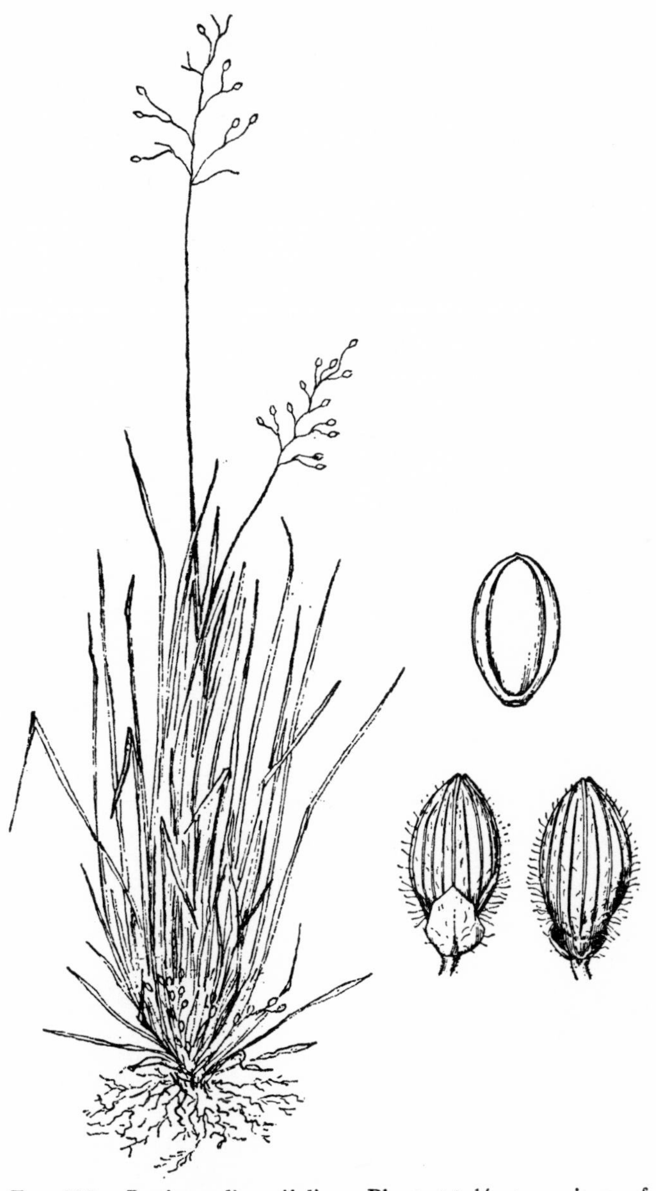

FIG. 189.—*Panicum linearifolium.* Plant, × ½; two views of spikelet, and floret, × 10.

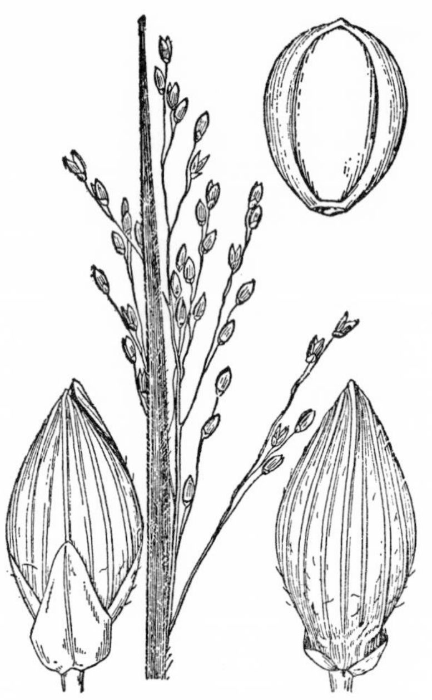

FIG. 190.—*Panicum depauperatum.* Panicle, × 1; two views of spikelet, and floret, × 10.

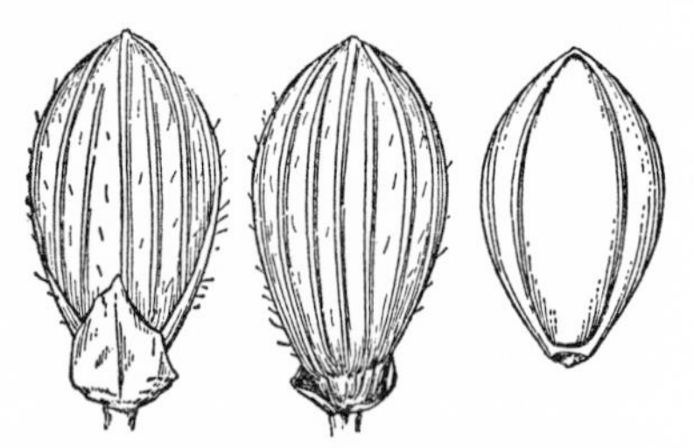

FIG. 191.—*Panicum perlongum.* Two views of spikelet, and floret, × 10.

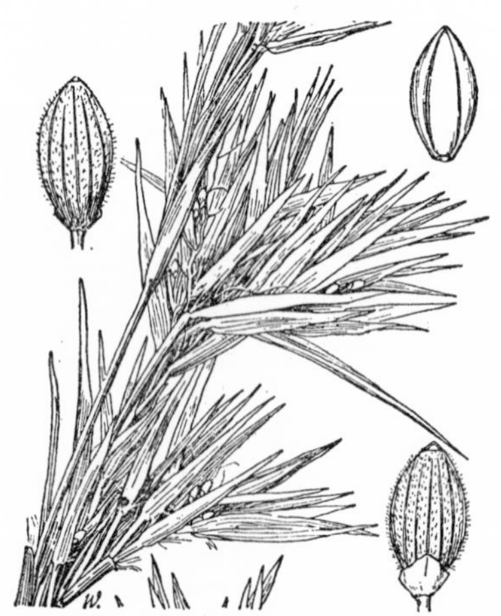

FIG. 192.—*Panicum lanuginosum* var. *Lindheimeri.* Plant, × 1; two views of spikelet, and floret, × 10.

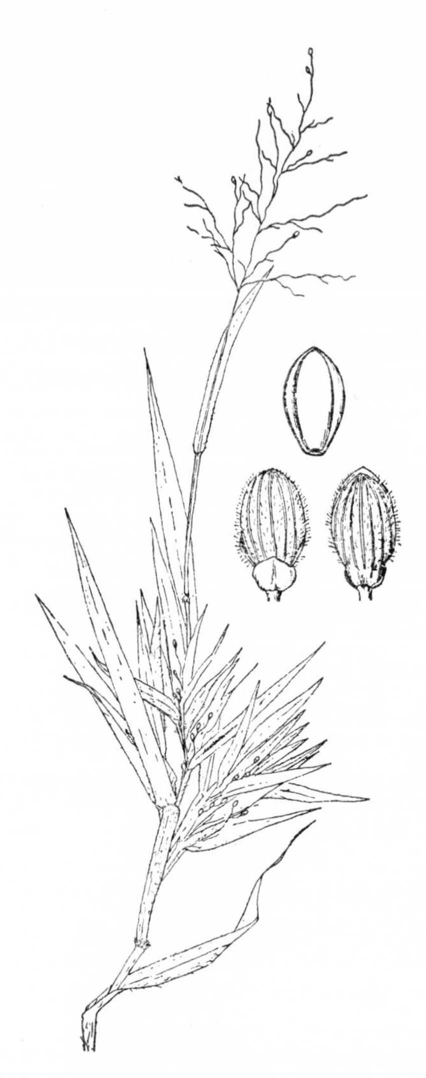

FIG. 193.—*Panicum lanuginosum* var. *fasciculatum.* Plant, × ½; two views of spikelet, and floret, × 10.

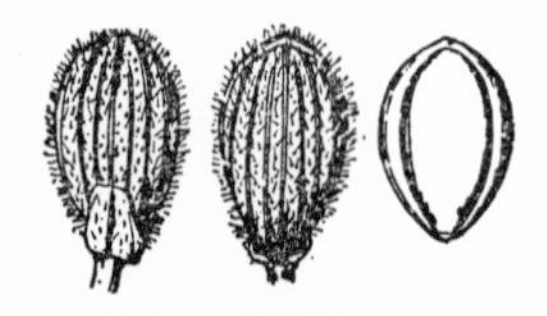

FIG. 194.—*Panicum lanuginosum* var. *implicatum.* Two views of spikelet, and floret, × 10.

glabrous branching, the axillary panicles reduced or included in the sheaths; spikelets small, ovoid, generally glabrous, about 1.5 mm. long. (*P. Lindheimeri* Nash.) A collection from Newton County (Palmer 63506) designated as *P. longiligulatum* Nash is included here, having spikelets only slightly smaller than the average, otherwise the plants are similar.

Distribution: Primarily eastern and central United States, west to Kansas, Oklahoma, and Texas.

Missouri. Low ground, shaded habitats, generally distributed. Flowering in May-June, and later in summer from axillary panicles.

Remarks: Var. *Lindheimeri* is part of a complex group of allied forms, including the following two varieties, 5 and 6. Interpretation of this involved group varies from one treatment to another. The intermingling of characters, particularly those based on pubescence, and the difficulty of satisfactorily placing intergrading specimens indicates the need for further evaluation. The typical variety, i.e. var. *lanuginosum,* is Coastal Plain in distribution, and does not reach Missouri. Pohl (1947) stated that the inland forms, encompassing a broad assemblage of previous combinations, are distinct from Coastal Plain types and accordingly ascribes to the former the single designation, *P. implicatum* Scribn. The retention of varietal status under *lanuginsum* is adopted here, following in modified form the treatment of Gleason (1952). For Missouri plants three intergrading varieties are recognized in this spectrum of variation, in which var. *Lindheimeri* represents the glabrous extreme. The following two varieties are characterized mainly by increasing tendency for pubescence.

5. **Panicum lanuginosum** Ell. var. **fasciculatum** (Torr.) Fern. Fig. 193.

Perennial, forming tufts; culms erect, simple, becoming branched, somewhat top-heavy and reclining in the autumnal stage, 25-50 cm. or taller; sheaths variably pubescent, from sparsely so or nearly glabrous to papillose-hirsute; ligule conspicuously tufted; leaf blades 4-8 mm. wide, glabrous above with few cilia around margins and near base, or appressed pubescent, the lower surface mostly with some short pubescence less than 2 mm. long; terminal panicles glabrous or pubescent, long-exserted, the axillary panicles reduced; spikelets ovoid, to 2 mm. long. (*P. tennesseense* Ashe; *P. huachucae* Ashe).

Distribution: Widespread in the United States, but most common in the eastern and central regions.

Missouri. Open woods, prairies, open ground, generally distributed. This is our most common variety in the *lanuginosum* group. Flowering in May-June and later in summer from axillary panicles.

Remarks: Var. *septentrionale* Fern. in some recent manuals is listed for Missouri. The pubescence characters which Fernald used to define it are difficult to evaluate because of the intermediacy between vars. *Lindheimeri* and *fasciculatum.* It is close to Ashe's original description of *P. tenneesseense,* tending toward the glabrous extreme. Most of the "*septentrionale*" specimens from Missouri are consolidated with var. *fasciculatum.* The small remainder is classified with var. *Lindheimeri.* No northern or eastern specimens of var. *septentrionale* were observed. To these, Fernald's designation is possibly better suited than to our plants from farther west.

6. **Panicum lanuginosum** Ell. var. **implicatum** (Scribn.) Fern. Fig. 194.

Perennial, tufted, similar to the preceding, but with spreading pilose hairs, exceeding 2 mm. on sheaths and upper surfaces of the leaf blades, appressed-pubescent below; spikelets, short-pilose, broadly ellipsoid or ovoid. (*P. implicatum* [Scribn.].)

Distribution: Eastern and north-central United States, south to Missouri and Kentucky.

Missouri. Woods, glades, sandy open ground, scattered, and not as common as the preceding variety. Flowering in May-June, and later in summer from axillary panicles.

7. **Panicum praecocius** Hitch. & Chase. Fig. 195.

Perennial, forming tufts; culms simple, erect, soon becoming branched and spreading, to about 50 cm. tall; sheaths pilose; ligule tufted; leaf blades about 5 mm. wide, with long, spreading, pilose hairs on both upper and lower surfaces; terminal panicles oval, the axis pubescent; axillary panicles reduced and included among the middle sheaths; spikelets pubescent, ovoid, 1.5-2 mm. long. This species is distinguished from the preceding by the presence of pilose hairs on the lower leaf surfaces, and early branching.

Distribution: North-central United States, south to Oklahoma and Texas.

FIG. 195.—*Panicum praecocius.* Two views of spikelet, and floret, × 10.

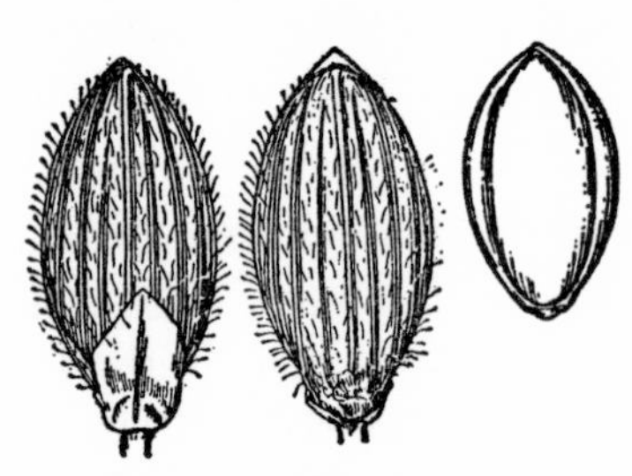

FIG. 197.—*Panicum clandestinum.* Two views of spikelet, and floret, × 10.

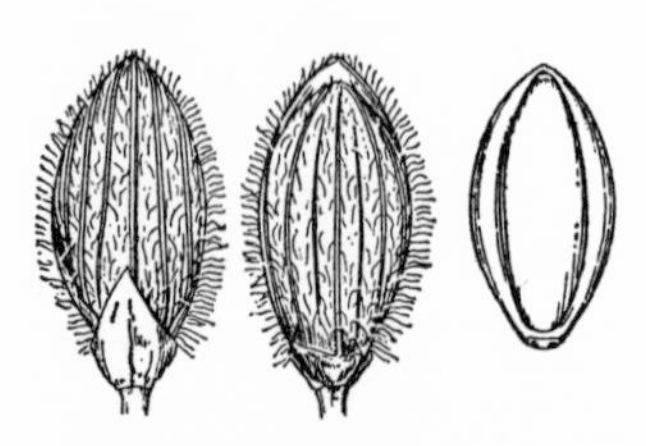

FIG. 196.—*Panicum villosissimum.* Two views of spikelet, and floret, × 10.

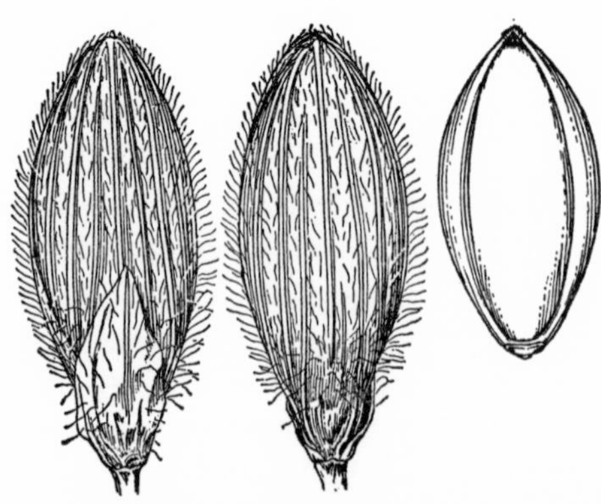

FIG. 198.—*Panicum Boscii.* Two views of spikelet, and floret, × 10.

Missouri. Upland woods, slopes, open ground, on dry, rocky or sandy soils, generally distributed. Flowering in May-June and from axillary panicles shortly thereafter.

8. **Panicum villosissimum** Nash. Fig. 196.

Perennial, forming tufts; culms erect or spreading, becoming branched, about 50 cm. tall; sheaths with pilose spreading hairs or sometimes sparsely so, to rarely glabrous; ligule a conspicuous brush about 3 mm. long; leaf blades usually stiffly ascending, mostly long-pilose on both surfaces, sometimes less marked below, 5-10 mm. wide; terminal panicles oval, with spreading branches, the axillary ones reduced, from the middle sheaths; spikelets pubescent, broad-elliptic, 2-2.5 mm. long. Plants with conspicuous, horizontally-spreading, long-pilose hairs on the sheaths and leaf blades represent the typical variety (var. *villosissimum*). Those with less marked pilosity, particularly on the lower leaf surfaces, are sometimes recognized as var. *pseudopubescens* (Nash) Gl. (*P. pseudopubescens* Nash). The latter distinction as applied to Missouri plants is minor, ours corresponding primarily to the typical variety.

Distribution: Eastern and central United States, west to Kansas, Oklahoma, and Texas.

Missouri. Upland woods, slopes, waste areas, on dry, rocky soils, confined to the Ozarks region except for several eastern counties north of the Missouri River. Flowering in May-June, the axillary phase developing soon after.

Remarks: A few plants from southwestern Missouri have been called *P. subvillosum* Ashe. According to Ashe's original description (1898), these have small spikelets less than 2 mm. long, and therefore are easily separated from the preceding species. However, pubescence characters are more difficult to differentiate and the number of specimens involved is limited. The regional distribution according to Hitchcock (1951) is primarily the north-central United States and eastward. Our plants at the extreme southern range are possibly different from those observed farther north.

9. **Panicum clandestinum** L. Fig. 197.

Perennial, forming clumps or colonies; culms coarse, branching above, erect or reclining, to 1 m. or taller; upper sheaths mostly bristly-hispid; leaf blades glabrous, stiff-ciliate on margins especially near the cordate base, as much as 2.5 cm. wide or more; terminal panicles broad, exserted, the axillary ones narrow, partly included; spikelets sparsely pilose, blunt, about 3 mm. long.

Distribution: Eastern and central United States, west to Kansas and Oklahoma.

Missouri. Low open ground, creek banks, on sandy or alluvial soils, generally distributed. Flowering in May-June and later in summer from axillary panicles.

10. **Panicum Boscii** Poir. Fig. 198.

Perennial, sparsely tufted, or solitary; culms slender, erect, or somewhat bent at the lower nodes, 30-70 cm. tall; sheaths glabrous or sparsely pubescent; nodes conspicuously bearded; leaf blades glabrous to soft-downy, cordate, as much as 2.5 cm. wide; terminal panicles few-flowered, with spreading branches, the axillary ones narrow or reduced, partly included; spikelets oblong, 3.5-4.5 mm. long; 1st glume narrow, the 2nd shorter than the sterile lemma. Plants with glabrous leaves represent the typical variety (var. *Boscii*). Those with velvety condition have been separated as var. *molle* (Vasey) Hitchc. & Chase.

Distribution: Eastern and central United States, west to Oklahoma and Texas.

Missouri. Upland woods, primarily in the eastern and southern counties, not common north of the Missouri River. Plants with velvety condition are infrequent and scattered, but also occur primarily in the south. Flowering in May-June and later in summer from the axillary panicles.

11. **Panicum latifolium** L. Fig. 199.

Perennial, forming tufts; culms erect, somewhat coarser than species 10; foliage, primarily glabrous, or sparsely ciliate; nodes glabrous; leaf blades cordate, 2.5-3 cm. wide; terminal panicles few-flowered with ascending branches, the axillary ones reduced, partly included; spikelets about 3.5 mm. or longer; fertile lemma exceeding the 2nd glume and sterile lemma. This species is distinguished from *P. Boscii* on the basis of smaller spikelets and the glabrous nodes. Some Missouri specimens have been observed, however, which otherwise appear to be *P. latifolium* but have large spikelets exceeding those dimensions usually attributed to this species.

Distribution: Eastern and central United States, west to Kansas.

Missouri. Upland woods and slopes, generally distributed. Flowering in May-June and also later from axillary panicles.

12. **Panicum polyanthes** Schult. Fig. 200.

Perennial, forming sparse tufts; culms erect, to about 1 m. tall; sheaths overlapping, mostly glabrous; leaf blades glabrous or sparsely ciliate at cordate base, as much as 2.5 cm. wide; panicles elliptic, longer than broad; spikelets numerous, more or less ovoid, about 1.5 mm. long.

Distribution: Eastern and southern United States, west to Oklahoma and Texas.

FIG. 199.—*Panicum latifolium.* Plant, × 1; two views of spikelet, and floret, × 10.

Missouri. Swampy ground, creek banks, spring branches, primarily in the east-central and southern counties. Flowering in May-June and later in summer from axillary panicles.

13. **Panicum sphaerocarpon** Ell. Fig. 201.

Perennial, in small tufts; culms sparingly branched, erect, or somewhat spreading in the autumnal phase, 50-60 cm. tall or more; sheaths glabrous, or sparsely pilose, rarely with glandular dots; leaf blades glabrous, papillose-ciliate toward base, firm, cordate, 6-15 mm. wide; terminal panicles long-exserted, oval, about as broad as long; spikelets numerous, roundish, about 1.5 mm. long, or slightly more in some of our specimens. A variant with loose sheaths which are glandular-dotted has been designated as var. *inflatum* (Scribn. & Smith) Hitchc. & Chase.

Distribution: Eastern and central United States, west to Kansas, Oklahoma, and Texas.

Missouri. Upland, woods, open ground, on dry, sandy or cherty soils, primarily in the southern and east-central counties, not common north of the Missouri River. Flowering in May-June and later in the summer from axillary panicles.

14. **Panicum commutatum** Schult. Fig. 202.

Perennial, forming sparse tufts; culms simple, becoming sparingly branched in the autumnal phase, mostly erect, 20-70 cm. tall; sheaths glabrous or only sparsely pubescent; nodes smooth; leaf blades glabrous or with sparse cilia near the cordate base, 1-2 cm. wide; terminal panicles exserted, with spreading branches, the axillary ones narrow, reduced, partly included in middle and upper sheaths; spikelets slightly pubescent, elliptic-oblong, 2.2-2.8 mm. long. Plants

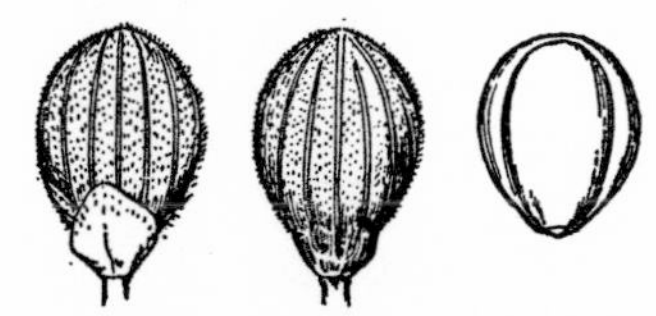

FIG. 200.—*Panicum polyanthes.* Two views of spikelet, and floret, × 10.

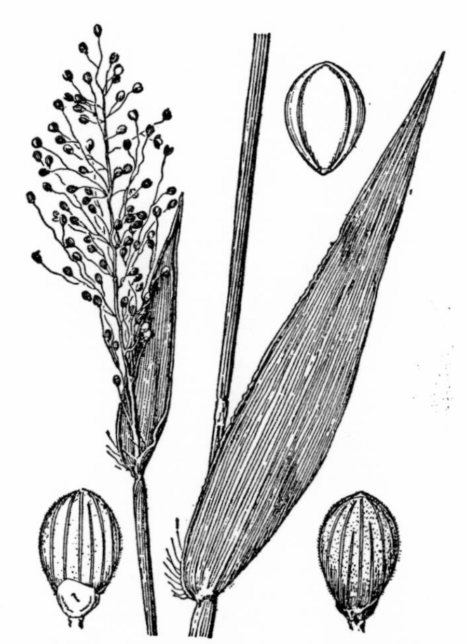

FIG. 201.—*Panicum sphaerocarpon.* Plant, × 1; two views of spikelet, and floret, × 10.

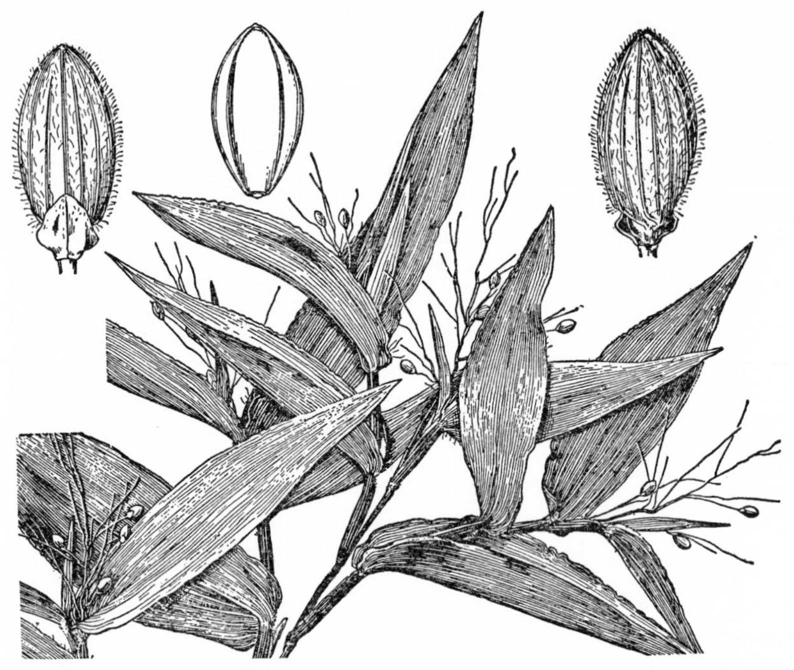

FIG. 202.—*Panicum commutatum.* Plant, × 1; two views of spikelet, and floret, × 10.

FIG. 203.—*Panicum scoparium.* Plant, × 1; two views of spikelet, and floret, × 10.

with broad leaf blades as much as 2 cm. wide, and spikelets approaching 2.8 mm. in length represent the typical variety (var. *commutatum*). Those plants with narrower leaf blades, usually stiff and with purplish color, in most cases not exceeding 1 cm. in width, and smaller spikelets 2.5 mm. long or less are designated as var. *Ashei* (Pearson) Fern. The latter is usually distinctive although some intermediate specimens are difficult to place (*P. Ashei* Pearson).

Distribution: Eastern and southern United States, west to Missouri, Oklahoma, and Texas.

Missouri. Dry oak-pine woods, rocky slopes, also low ground and spring branches, in southern and southeastern counties. In general var. *Ashei* is found on the drier sites. Flowering in May-June, and later in summer from axillary panicles.

15. **Panicum scoparium** Lam. Fig. 203.

Perennial, forming sparse tufts, or solitary; culms simple, branching from upper nodes in the autumnal phase, erect, to about 1 m. tall; sheaths and internodes soft-villous, the latter glabrous immediately below the bearded nodes; leaf blades downy-pubescent, rounded at base, as much as 1.5 cm. wide; panicles pubescent, viscid, few-flowered, the axillary ones reduced, included in the fascicled upper sheaths; spikelets obovoid, about 2.5 mm. long. The villous character of this species is distinctive and easily recognized.

Distribution: Southern and eastern United States, from the Coastal Plain, inland to Oklahoma, Kentucky to southern New England.

Missouri. Low ground, prairie swales, on moist soils, central and southern counties, but primarily south of the Missouri River. Flowering in May-June, and later in summer from axillary panicles.

16. **Panicum oligosanthes** Schult. Fig. 204.

Perennial, forming tufts; culms simple, erect, becoming branched, to about 70 cm. tall; sheaths glabrous to variably pubescent; leaf blades glabrous, pilose, or appressed-pubescent, with occasional cilia along margins near the cordate base, about 1 cm. wide or less, somewhat stiffly ascending, aggregated in the autumnal phase; terminal panicles broadly ovate, stiffly branched, the axillary ones narrow, sparsely flowered, from fascicled upper sheaths; spikelets glabrous or sparsely pubescent, broadly elliptic or plump, 3-4 mm. long, sometimes slightly less. Several varieties in this complex are sometimes distinguished, although the separations for some Missouri specimens are not always distinct. Plants distinguished by large spikelets 3.5-4 mm. long, and mostly soft, appressed-pubescent leaf blades represent the typical variety (var. *oligosanthes*). Plants also with large spikelets, but generally glabrous leaf blades are designated as var. *Scribnerianum* (Nash) Fern. (*P. Scribnerianum* Nash), and those with conspicuously smaller spikelets averaging 3 mm. or slightly less are referred to var. *Helleri* (Nash) Fern.

Distribution: Eastern and southern United States as a group complex, with var. *Scribnerianum* being the most widespread.

Missouri. Prairies, open woods, waste ground, on dry to moist soils, commonly distributed as var. *Scribnerianum*. Var. *Helleri* is infrequent, occurring primarily in the western counties, while distinctly typical *oligosanthes* has not been observed. Flowering in May-June and later in summer from axillary panicles.

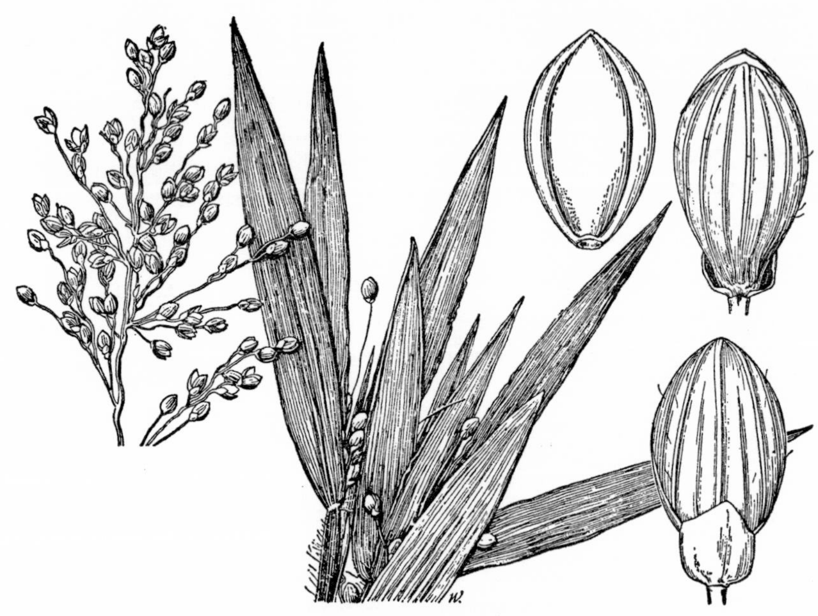

FIG. 204.—*Panicum oligosanthes* var. *Scribnerianum.* Plant, × 1; two views of spikelet, and floret, × 10.

17. **Panicum Leibergii** (Vasey) Scribn. Fig. 205.

Perennial, sparsely tufted or solitary; culms erect to somewhat geniculate at lower nodes, to about 50 cm. tall or more; sheaths variably pubescent, not as long as the internode; leaf blades from nearly glabrous to short-pubescent, usually ciliate on the margins and near the rounded or cordate base, thin-textured, 7-15 mm. wide; terminal panicles with short, ascending branches, few-flowered; axillary panicle reduced; spikelets distinctly hairy, elliptic, 3.5-4 mm. long. This species is distinguishable from the preceding by the thinner, softer appearance of the leaves, more or less pubescent on both surfaces, and the hairy spikelets.

Distribution: North-central and eastern United States from North Dakota to New York, south to Kansas and Missouri, also Texas.

Missouri. Open woods, on dry cherty soils, scattered and infrequent, Jackson, Morgan, Phelps, Shannon, and St. Louis counties. Flowering in May-June and later in summer from axillary panicles.

18. **Panicum malacophyllum** Nash. Fig. 206.

Perennial, tufted; culms conspicuously villous, with bearded nodes, erect to about 50 cm. tall; sheaths villous with retrorse-spreading hairs; leaf blades soft-pubescent, thin, somewhat lax, cordate, 7-15 mm. wide, those of the autumnal phase considerably reduced in size; terminal panicles villous, few-flowered; axillary panicles, narrow, more or less included in middle and upper sheaths; spikelets pubescent, ellipsoid, somewhat pointed, 2.5-3 mm. long.

Distribution: South-central United States north to Kansas, Missouri, and Kentucky.

Missouri. Open woods and dry slopes, primarily in the southwestern part, also Johnson and Pemiscot counties. Flowering in May-June and later in summer from axillary panicles.

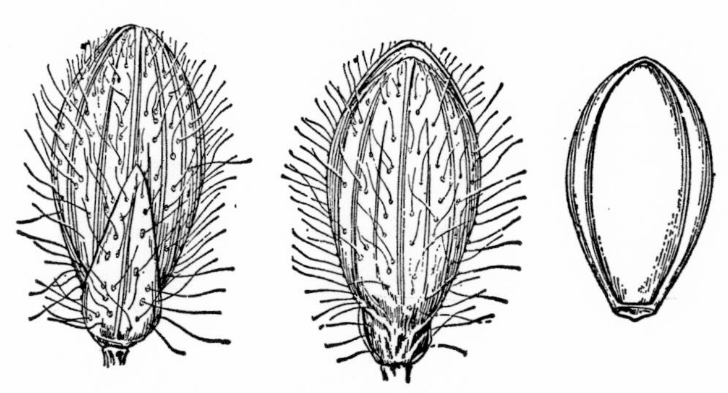

FIG. 205.—*Panicum Leibergii.* Two views of spikelet, and floret, × 10.

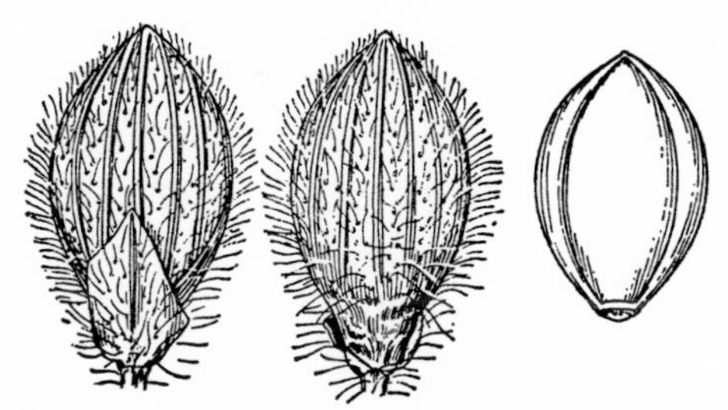

FIG. 206.—*Panicum malacophyllum.* Two views of spikelet, and floret, × 10.

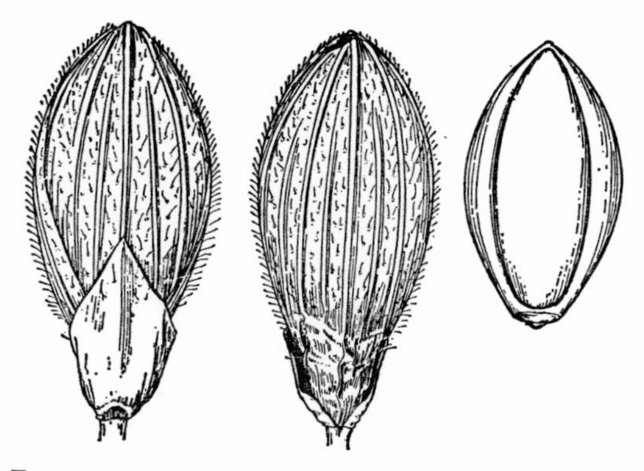

FIG. 207.—*Panicum Ravenelii.* Two views of spikelet, and floret, × 10.

19. **Panicum Ravenelii** Scribn. & Merr. Fig. 207.

Perennial, sparsely tufted; culms erect, branched and somewhat spreading in the autumnal phase, about 50 cm. tall or more; sheaths stiff-hirsute; nodes bearded; ligule a conspicuous tuft of hairs 3-4 mm. long; leaf blades glabrous on upper surface, soft-downy below, ciliate on the margins, cordate, as much as 2 cm. wide; terminal panicles with short, spreading branches, few-flowered, the axillary panicles small, included in upper sheaths; spikelets short-pubescent, broadly ellipsoid, about 4 mm. long.

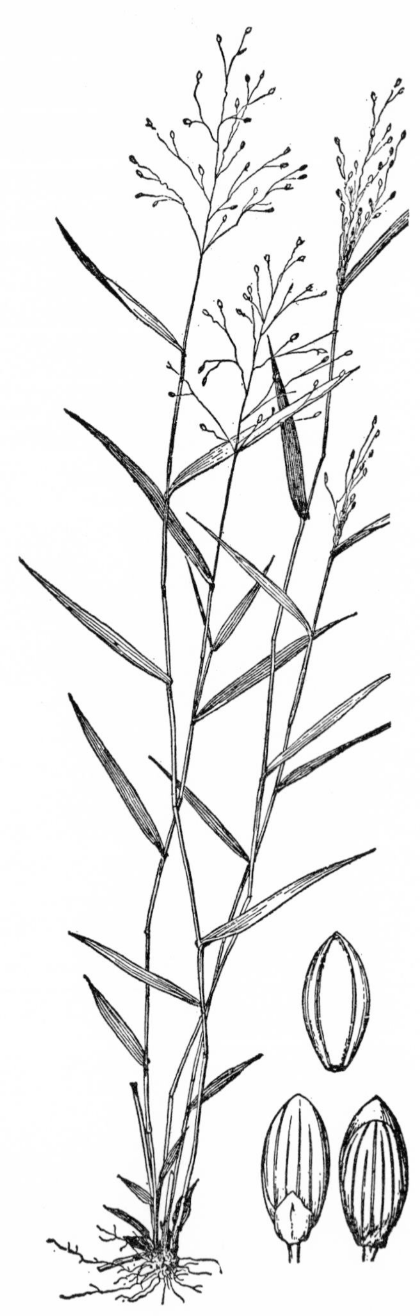

FIG. 208.—*Panicum dichotomum.* Plant, × ½; two views of spikelet, and floret, × 10.

Distribution: Southern and mid-Atlantic region, west to Missouri, Oklahoma, and Texas.

Missouri. Wooded slopes, on dry, cherty or sandy soils, throughout the Ozarks counties east to Crowley's Ridge. Flowering in early June, and later in summer from axillary panicles.

20. **Panicum dichotomum** L. Fig. 208.

Perennials; culms slender, erect, the autumnal phase conspicuously branched above, becoming top-heavy and somewhat reclining, to about 50 cm. tall or more; sheaths mostly glabrous, shorter than the internodes; nodes smooth, or the lower ones sometimes bearded; leaf blades of the culm spreading, glabrous, acuminate-tapering, 3-7 mm. wide; terminal panicles ovoid, long-exserted; axillary panicles few-flowered, from the crowded upper sheaths; spikelets glabrous to puberulent, elliptic-oblong, about 2 mm. long; fertile lemma slightly exceeding the sterile one. Two varieties are frequently recognized. Plants with glabrous nodes represent the typical variety (var. *dichotomum*). Those distinguished by bearded nodes are separated as var. *barbulatum* (Michx.) Wood (*P. barbulatum* Michx.).

Distribution: Eastern and south-central United States, west to Missouri, Oklahoma, and Texas.

Missouri. Thin woods and slopes, on cherty or sandy ground, southern and east-central counties, primarily in the Ozark region, not common north of the Missouri River. Flowering in May-June and later in summer from axillary panicles.

21. **Panicum microcarpon** Muhl. Fig. 209.

Perennial, forming tufts or mats; culms slender, erect at first, becoming bushy-sprawling in the autumnal phase; sheaths glabrous or sparsely ciliate; nodes conspicuously bearded; leaf blades of the culm numerous, glabrous or ciliate near base, short-lanceolate, 5-10 mm. wide or more; terminal panicles with spreading branches, many-flowered; axillary panicles reduced, narrow, sparsely-flowered; spikelets usually glabrous, elliptic-oblong, about 1.5 mm. long. (*P. nitidum* Lam. var. *ramulosum* Torr, new Britton & Brown, Gleason, 1952.)

FIG. 209.—*Panicum microcarpon.* Plant, × 1; two views of spikelet, and floret, × 10.

Distribution: Eastern and central United States, west to Missouri, Oklahoma, and Texas.

Missouri. Low moist ground, creek banks, south of the Missouri River, primarily in the eastern Ozark region. Flowering in May-June and later in summer from axillary panicles.

22. **Panicum annulum** Ashe. Fig. 210.

Perennial, forming tufts; culms erect, to about 50 cm. tall; sheaths pubescent on the lower parts, glabrous above; nodes bearded, culm leaf blades velvety, as much as 1 cm. wide or more; terminal panicles many-flowered, the axillary ones with few short branches and sparsely-flowered; spikelets pubescent, elliptic, averaging about 2 mm. long. This species is distinguished from *P. dichotomum* by the pubescent spikelets and downy foliage.

Distribution: Coastal Plain region, inland to several localities including Missouri.

Missouri. Rare and little known, based on a single collection in 1893, "woods," Carter County, leg. H. Eggert.

23. **Panicum nitidum** Lam. Fig. 211.

Perennial, tufted, with bearded nodes, similar in habit to *P. microcarpon,* but distinguished by the pubescent, somewhat longer spikelets which average about 2 mm. in length. Gleason (1952) includes *microcarpon* under this species as var. *ramulosum* Torr. See species 21.

Distribution: Coastal Plain, New Jersey to Texas and Missouri.

Missouri. Rare and little known, collected from Carter County (Eggert 288). No other collections have been made.

24. **Panicum Bicknellii** Nash. Fig. 212.

Perennial, tufted; culms erect, to about 50 cm. tall; sheaths sparsely ciliate at summit, otherwise glabrous; leaf blades mostly glabrous, with few cilia at the conspicuously narrowed base, elongate, ascending, 2-8 mm. wide; terminal panicles narrow, with short branches; axillary panicles reduced, few-flowered; spikelets glabrous, elliptic, about 2.5 mm. long.

Distribution: Eastern and central United States, west to Missouri and Arkansas.

Missouri. Upland woods, dry, rocky slopes, infrequent, occurring mainly in the southern counties, not present north of the Missouri River. Flowering in May-June and later in summer from axillary panicles.

25. **Panicum calliphyllum** Ashe. Fig. 213.

Perennial, forming tufts, generally similar to species 24, but leaf blades less elongate, as much as 1 cm. wide or more, with distinctly rounded bases; spikelets averaging about 3 mm. in length. (*P. Bicknellii* var. *calliphyllum* [Ashe] Gl., new Britton & Brown, Gleason, 1952.)

Distribution: Eastern United States, west to Missouri, where rare and little known, reported from Ripley and Callaway counties.

26. **Panicum laxiflorum** Lam. Fig. 214.

Perennial, forming dense basal, spreading tufts or mats; culms simple, conspicuously branched from the lower nodes in the autumnal phase; sheaths

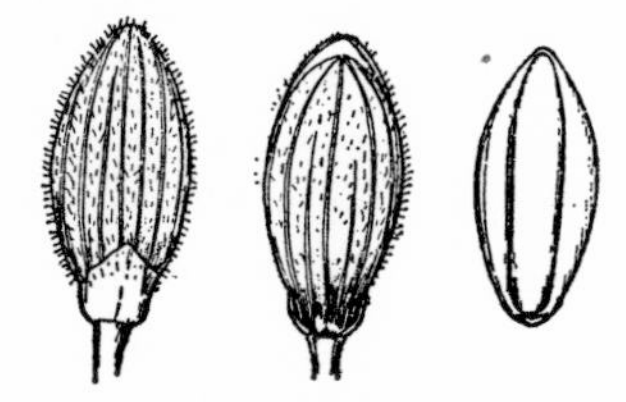

FIG. 210.—*Panicum annulum*. Two views of spikelet, and floret, × 10.

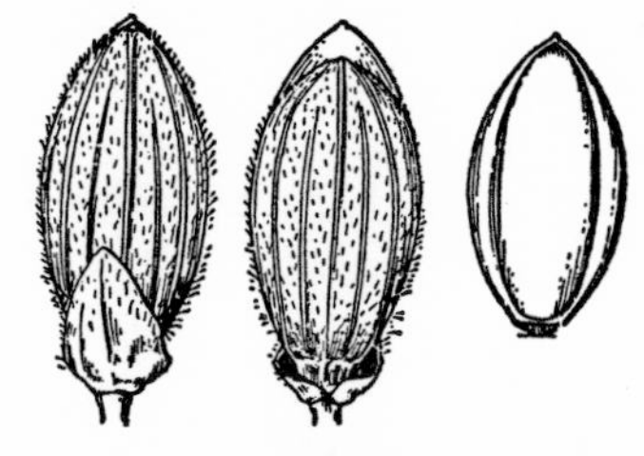

FIG. 213.—*Panicum calliphyllum*. Two views of spikelet, and floret, × 10.

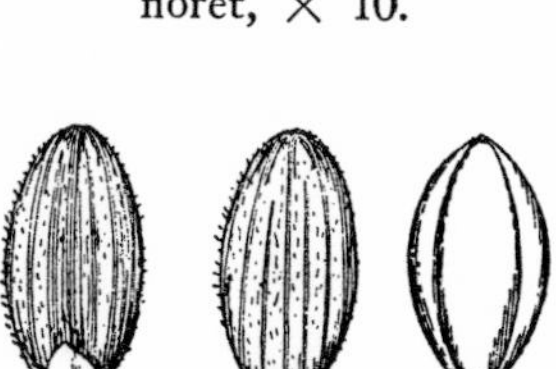

FIG. 211.—*Panicum nitidum*. Two views of spikelet, and floret, × 10.

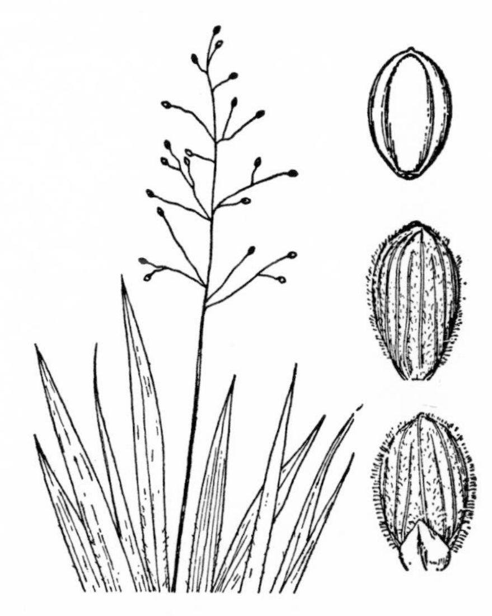

FIG. 214.—*Panicum laxiflorum*. Panicle, × ½; two views of spikelet, and floret, × 10.

FIG. 212.—*Panicum Bicknellii*. Plant, × 1; two views of spikelet, and floret, × 10.

FIG. 215.—*Panicum obtusum*. Panicle, × ½; spikelet and floret, × 10.

pilose; nodes sparsely bearded; leaf blades glabrous, mostly ciliate along the margins, soft, lax, as much as 1 cm. wide, gradually narrowing toward base; terminal panicles long-exserted, the axillary ones much reduced, few-flowered; spikelets pubescent, obovate, 1.5-2 mm. long or slightly more; fertile lemma exceeding second glume and sterile lemma. (Including *P. xalapense* [H. B. K.] Hitchc.)

Distribution: Mid-Atlantic and Coastal Plain region, west to Missouri, Arkansas, and Texas.

Missouri. Dry woods, sandy prairies, central and southern counties, mainly in the Ozarks region. Flowering in May-June and later in summer from axillary panicles.

27. **Panicum obtusum** H. B. K. VINE MESQUITE. Fig. 215.

Perennial, slender tufted, developing long creeping runners or stolons with swollen, bearded nodes; culms slender, erect, to about 1 m. tall; sheaths mostly glabrous; leaf blades elongate, 3-5 mm. wide; panicles narrow, with short, ascending branches or racemes; spikelets glabrous, obovoid, blunt, about 3.5 mm. long; 1st glume about equaling length of spikelet.

Distribution: Southwestern United States and Mexico, north to Colorado and east to *Missouri* where rare and probably adventive, a single collection from Jackson County (Bush 1832). No other collections are known.

28. **Panicum geminatum** Forsk. Fig. 216.

Perennial, forming tufts, stoloniferous; culms erect or decumbent near base, 50-100 cm. tall; foliage glabrous, the leaf blades 3-5 mm. wide, tapering to involute tip; panicles narrow, with short, appressed, spike-like racemes; spikelets broadly elliptic, about 2 mm. long; 1st glume blunt or truncate.

Distribution: Southern coastal region of United States and lower latitudes, rare northward as in *Missouri* where collected as an adventive, St. Louis County (Muhlenbach 1246).

29. **Panicum texanum** Buckl. CONCHO GRASS. Fig. 217.

Annual; culms coarse, erect to somewhat decumbent and rooting from lower nodes, frequently 1 m. or taller; foliage soft-pubescent, the leaf blades cordate, as much as 1.5 cm. wide; panicles narrow, with short, appressed-ascending racemes; spikelets conspicuously nerved, pilose, oblong, about 5 mm. long, with pointed apex.

Distribution: Southwestern United States and Mexico; introduced elsewhere including *Missouri,* where local, collected from St. Louis County (Muhlenbach 517).

30. **Panicum dichotomiflorum** Michx. Fig. 218.

Annual; culms branching, erect or geniculate, to 1 m. or taller; foliage glabrous, the leaf blades elongate, 4-15 mm. wide; panicles more or less open with spreading or ascending branches, exserted or sometimes partially included; spikelets glabrous, elliptic, about 2.5-3 mm. long, with acuminate apex. Plants distinguished by bent lower nodes, the culms prostrate or decumbent near base, and panicles somewhat included have been separated as var. *geniculatum* (Wood) Fern. The separation is not altogether distinct although some plants in Missouri

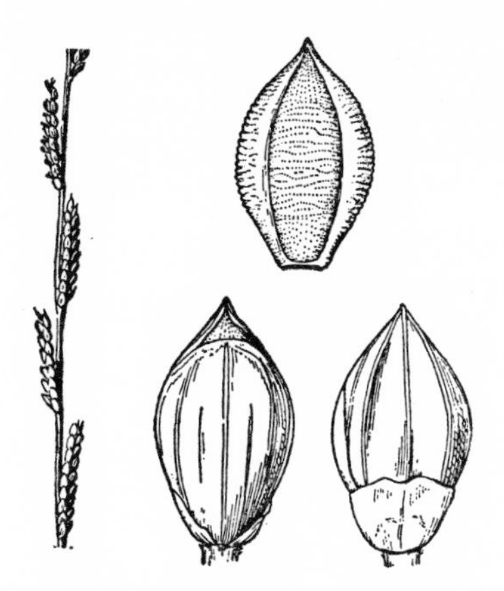

FIG. 216.—*Panicum geminatum.* Panicle, × ½; two views of spikelet, and floret, × 10.

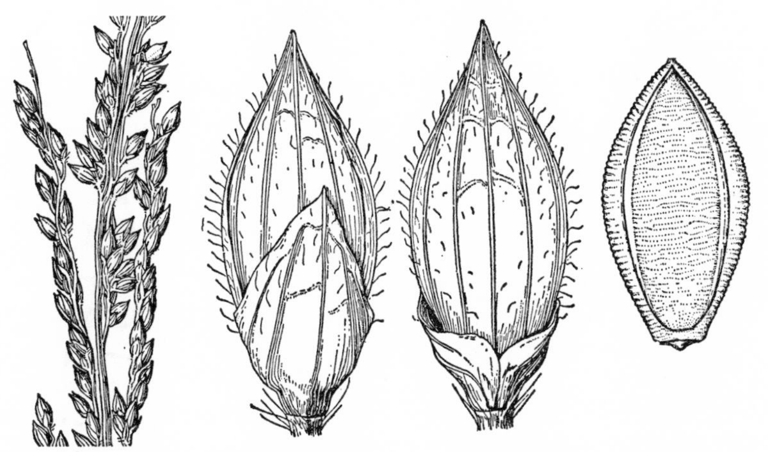

FIG. 217.—*Panicum texanum.* Panicle, × 1; two views of spikelet, and floret, × 10.

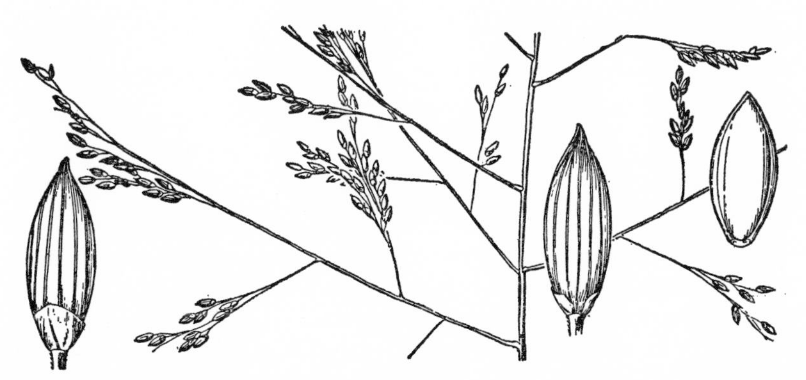

FIG. 218.—*Panicum dichotomiflorum.* Panicle, × 1; two views of spikelet, and floret, × 10.

may be recognized as such. In others the tendencies are present but less marked. According to Fernald (1936) this condition is more common eastward where the division possibly is better defined.

Distribution: Primarily in the eastern and central United States, west to Nebraska to Texas.

Missouri. Fields, waste areas, low or damp ground, generally distributed. Flowering in August-September.

31. **Panicum hians** Ell. Fig. 219.

Perennial, forming small tufts; culms slender, erect or decumbent near base, to about 50 cm. tall; sheaths glabrous, keeled; leaf blades glabrous, elongate, 1-5 mm. wide; panicles diffuse, the branches delicate, spreading or nodding; spikelets glabrous, sessile or nearly so, about 2 mm. long, clustered toward ends of the panicle branches; sterile palea present, enlarged, slightly exceeding the sterile lemma, distending the spikelet.

Distribution: Coastal Plain region as far north as Virginia, west to Texas, inland to *Missouri* where restricted to spring branches, alder swamps, Ripley, Butler, Stoddard, New Madrid, and Dunklin counties. Flowering in July-August.

32. **Panicum agrostoides** Spreng. Fig. 220.

Perennial, forming dense tufts; culms coarse, erect, to 1 m. tall or more; sheaths glabrous, flattened, crowded near base; leaf blades glabrous, elongate, usually not exceeding 1 cm. in width; panicles with ascending or divaricate branching, the crowded numerous spikelets sessile and arranged mostly on one side of the branchlets; spikelets glabrous, ovoid to lanceolate-pointed, about 2-2.5 mm. long; 2nd glume and sterile lemma exceeding fertile lemma. Plants with ovoid spikelets about 2 mm. long represent the typical variety (var. *agrostoides*). Those with larger, lanceolate-pointed spikelets, measuring about 2.5 mm. in length, the fertile lemma short-stalked, are designated as var. *elongatum* Scribn. (*P. stipitatum* Nash). Scarcely distinguishable plants with congested panicles have been acknowledged by some authors as var. *condensum* (Nash) Fern, and those with sparsely-flowered panicles as var. *ramosius* (Mohr.) Fern.

Distribution: Eastern and central United States, west to Kansas, to Texas.

Missouri. Swamps, prairie swales, alluvium, primarily in the central and southern counties, not common north of the Missouri River. Var. *elongatum* is confined to the southeastern Ozarks and the "bootheel" region. Flowering in July-August.

33. **Panicum anceps** Michx. Fig. 221.

Perennial, with thick, scaly rhizomes; culms coarse, erect, to about 1 m. tall; sheaths glabrous, or pubescent on lower part of plant, compressed; leaf blades glabrous or nearly so, elongate, 5-10 mm. wide; panicles open, the branches stiff, distant, spreading or ascending; spikelets glabrous, lanceolate, somewhat falcate, sessile, 3-4 mm. long, arranged toward 1 side of the branchlets.

Distribution: Mid-Atlantic and Gulf regions, inland to Ohio, Missouri, and Oklahoma.

Missouri. Swales, spring branches, moist, sandy ground, primarily south of a line from Barton to St. Louis counties. Flowering in July-August.

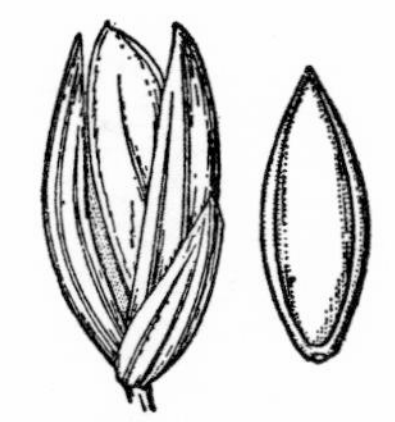

FIG. 219.—*Panicum hians.* Spikelet, and floret, × 10.

FIG. 220.—*Panicum agrostoides.* Panicle, × 1; two views of spikelet, and floret, × 10.

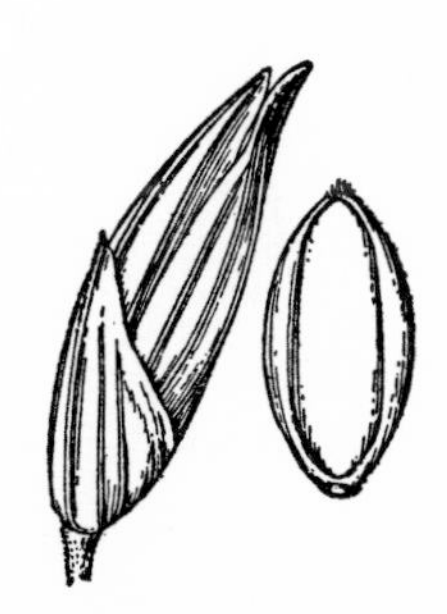

FIG. 221.—*Panicum anceps.* Spikelet, and floret, × 10.

34. **Panicum virgatum** L. SWITCHGRASS. Fig. 222.

Perennial, forming extensive clumps or stands, rhizomatous; culms erect, to 1 m. or taller; sheaths glabrous; ligule consisting of hairs about 2 mm. long; leaf blades glabrous, sparsely pilose near base, elongate, 5-10 mm. wide; panicles smooth with somewhat stiff, spreading or ascending branches; spikelets glabrous, pointed, 4-5.5 mm. long; 1st glume acuminate, about one-half or more as long as the 2nd, the latter long-pointed, exceeding the sterile lemma.

Distribution: Widespread in the United States, throughout the East and South, west to North Dakota, Wyoming, and Nevada.

Missouri. Prairie swales, glades, sand flats of the Missouri River, generally distributed. Flowering in midsummer.

35. **Panicum milaceum** L. BROOM-CORN MILLET. Fig. 223.

Annual; culms coarse, erect or somewhat decumbent, to about 1 m. tall; sheaths hirsute; leaf blades glabrous to soft pubescent, elongate, as much as 2 cm. wide; panicles dense, mostly nodding, with ascending branches partly included at base; spikelets large, glabrous, 4-5 mm. long, with pointed apex; fertile lemma shiny yellowish-brown.

FIG. 222.—*Panicum virgatum*. Plant, × ½; two views of spikelet, and floret, × 10.

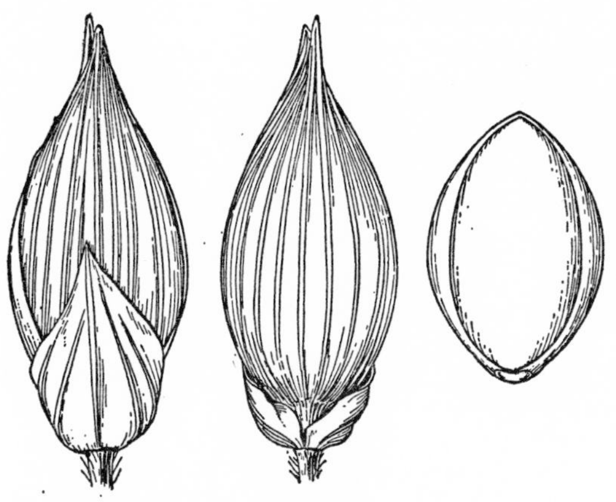

FIG. 223.—*Panicum miliaceum.* Two views of spikelet, and floret, × 10.

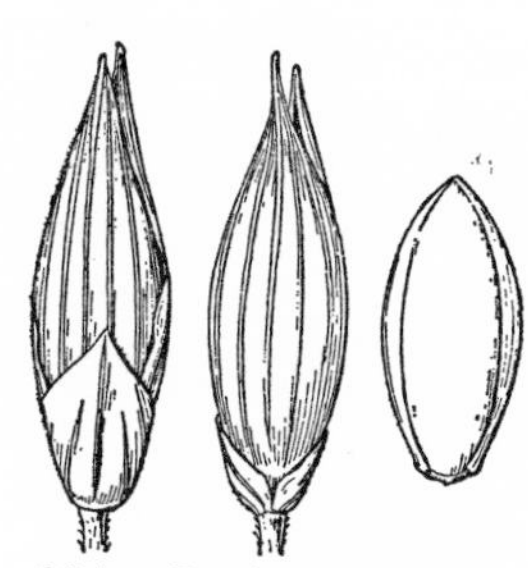

FIG. 224.—*Panicum flexile.* Two views of spikelet, and floret, × 10.

Distribution: Northern United States, occasionally volunteering on waste ground; forage and grain species introduced from the Old World.

Missouri. Scattered and not common, reported from Jackson, Chariton and Morgan counties. This species is utilized to some extent as a food plant in refuge areas for waterfowl. Flowering in July-August.

36. **Panicum flexile** (Gatt.) Scribn. Fig. 224.

Annual; culms slender, branched, erect, to about 50 cm. tall; sheaths and lower nodes pubescent; leaf blades glabrous to appressed-pubescent, sparsely ciliate on margins, elongate, 3-7 mm. wide; panicles diffuse, few-flowered, with slender flexuous branches; spikelets glabrous, narrow, lanceolate-acuminate, 3-3.5 mm. long.

Distribution: Eastern United States to the Middle West; introduced elsewhere.

Missouri. Upland woods, glades, waste areas, mostly on dry ground, generally distributed. Flowering in July-August.

37. **Panicum capillare** L. WITCH-GRASS. Fig. 225.

Annual, forming tufts; culms branching from near base, erect to decumbent-spreading sometimes rooting at the lower nodes, usually about 50 cm. tall; sheaths hispid-pubescent; leaf blades somewhat lax, soft-pubescent, as much as 1 cm. wide or more; terminal panicles diffuse, broadly spreading, exserted to somewhat included, sometimes as much as two-thirds the length of entire plant; smaller axillary panicles also present, these partly included, from the lower sheaths; spikelets 2-3.5 mm. long, ovoid-acuminate, from slender panicles. The species is sometimes divided into several varieties, which are not always easily distinguished. Plants characterized by relatively large, broad, terminal panicles, the basal branches of which are somewhat inserted in the upper sheaths, and spikelets measuring about 2-2.5 mm. long represent the typical variety (var. *capillare*). Those plants with similar spikelets but smaller, narrower, distinctly exserted panicles, usually about one-third to at most one-half the length of the entire plant are separated as var. *campestre* Gatt. (*P. Gattingeri* Nash). A third group,

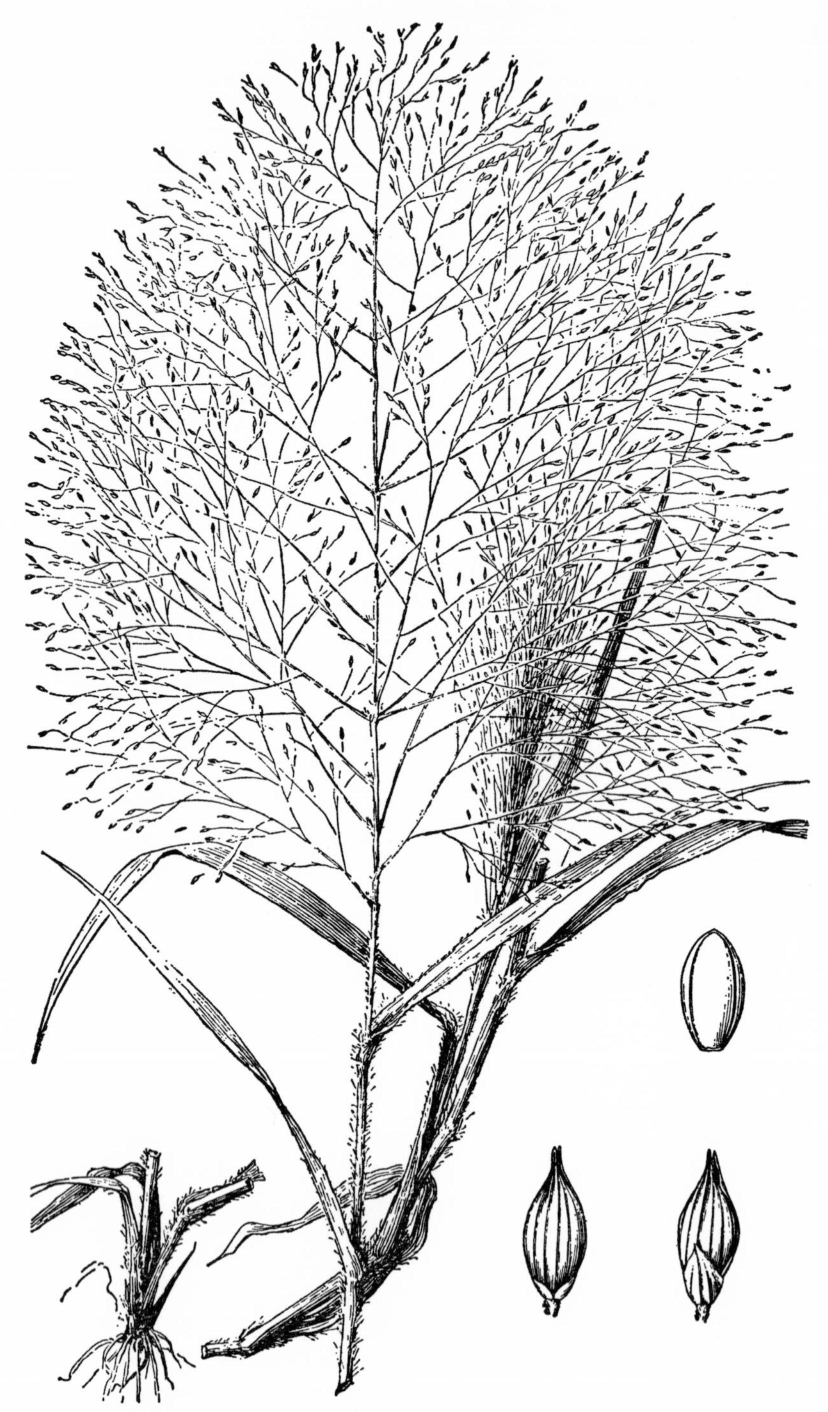

FIG. 225.—*Panicum capillare*. Plant, × ½; two views of spikelet, and floret, × 10.

var. *occidentale* Rydb. is distinguished by exserted panicles, these with conspicuous pulvini in the axils of the branches, and larger spikelets to 3.5 mm. long.

Distribution: Eastern and central United States, with var. *occidentale* extending westward and more widespread.

Missouri. Cultivated ground, old fields, sand bars, generally distributed, with the exception of var. *occidentale* which occurs infrequently and widely scattered. Flowering in July-August.

38. **Panicum philadelphicum** Bernh. Fig. 226.

Annual; culms slender, mostly erect, to about 50 cm. tall; sheaths pubescent, sometimes strongly papillose; leaf blades glabrous to sparsely pubescent, 3-8 mm. wide; panicles diffuse, with delicate branches, exserted, sparsely flowered; spikelets glabrous or nearly so, elliptic, averaging about 2 mm. long; sometimes in pairs at ends of branchlets. (Including *P. Tuckermani* Fern.)

Distribution: Eastern and Central United States, west to Missouri and Texas.

Missouri. Open woods, glades, waste ground, on dry soils, generally distributed, but most abundant in counties south of the Missouri River. Flowering in July-August.

69. ECHINOCHLOA Beauv.

Annuals; panicles terminal, consisting of dense, ascending branches or racemes along a central axis; spikelets 1-flowered, ovate to broadly elliptic, plump, mostly bristly-hispid, separating below the glumes, falling entire; 1st glume acute, about

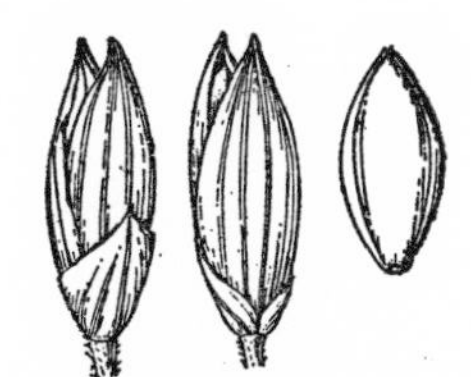

FIG. 226.—*Panicum philadelphicum.* Two views of spikelet, and floret, × 10.

FIG. 227.—*Echinochloa colonum,* × 1.

one-half as long as the 2nd, the latter and sterile lemma equal, pointed or minutely-awned, or only sterile lemma sometimes with long awn; fertile lemma smooth, with inrolled margins enclosing the palea excepting the apex.

KEY TO MISSOURI SPECIES

1. Panicles slender with few distant ascending racemes or branches, usually not bristly; rare species of tropical origin....1. *E. colonum*
1. Panicles with thick spreading or ascending racemes, these usually numerous, bristly-hispid or if not bristly as in *E. crus-galli* var. *frumentacea* then panicles dense, congested....2
   2. The numerous bristly hairs of spikelets (on the 2nd glume and sterile lemma) with enlarged pustular base; fertile lemma lacking ring of minute hairs below summit (use hand lens for examination)....3. *E. muricata*
   2. Bristly hairs of spikelets lacking pustular base; fertile lemma with distinct ring of hairs below summit....2. *E. crus-galli*

1. **Echinochloa colonum** (L.) Link. JUNGLE RICE. Fig. 227.

Plants erect to decumbent-spreading, about 50 cm. tall; sheaths glabrous, keeled; ligule absent; leaf blades glabrous, lax, 3-7 mm. wide; racemes few, remote, 1-2 cm. long; spikelets slightly pubescent, broadly elliptic, about 2.5 mm. long; 2nd glume and sterile lemma awnless.

Distribution: Widespread across the southern United States, as far north as Missouri; introduced from the Old World tropics.

Missouri. Rare and little known, reported from Jackson, St. Louis, Mississippi, and Pemiscot counties. Flowering in summer.

2. **Echinochloa crus-galli** (L.) Beauv. BARNYARD GRASS, MILLET. Fig. 228.

Plants coarse, branching from lower nodes, somewhat decumbent near base, to 1.5 m. tall; sheaths glabrous, flattened; ligule absent; leaf blades glabrous, long-

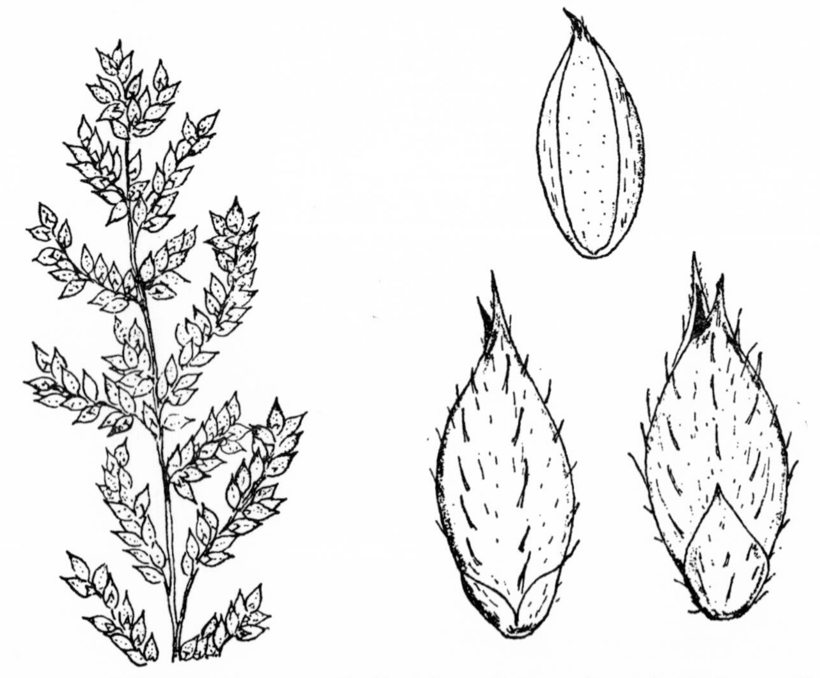

FIG. 228.—*Echinochloa crus-galli.* Panicle, × 1; two views of spikelet, × 10.

tapering, 5-10 mm. wide or more; panicles erect to nodding, the thick, spike-like racemes 2-4 cm. long; spikelets crowded, bristly-hispid, broadly-elliptic, 3-3.5 mm. long, mostly awnless or merely awn-tipped; the setae or bristles of the 2nd glume and sterile lemma lacking pustules at base; fertile lemma smooth, shiny, the tip encircled below the summit by a ring of minute hairs. A conspicuously long-awned form with awns 3-4 cm. long has been separated as forma *longiseta* (Trin.) Farw. Japanese millet, also known as billion-dollar grass, is var. *frumentacea* (Roxb.) Wight. It differs from typical *crus-galli* by its heavier, thicker racemes, and plump, glabrous spikelets which are awnless.

Distribution: Widespread in the United States; introduced from Europe. Var. *frumentacea,* cultivated in the cooler regions and occasionally naturalizing, is native to India.

Missouri. Waste areas, low fields, alluvial ground, on damp soils, generally distributed. The long-awned form has been reported from several localities. Flowering in middle and late summer.

3. **Echinochloa muricata** (Beauv.) Fern. Fig. 229.

Plants resembling species 2 in general habit and panicle development, these perhaps not altogether satisfactorily differentiated as species; spikelets crowded, ovoid 2.5-4.5 mm. long, typically long-awned, or some plants awnless or nearly so; 2nd glume and sterile lemma usually with pustular setae or bristles; fertile lemma lacking the ring of minute hairs below tip, this being one of the characters used in separating from the preceding species. Several varieties have been recognized. Plants with awned spikelets 3.5-4.5 mm. long represent the typical variety (var. *muricata*). Those with awnless spikelets, 2.5-3.5 mm. long, are segregated as var. *microstachya* (Wieg.) Fern. Other plants also awnless, with spikelets of similar dimensions, but in which the pustular bases of the setae are lacking are separated as var. *Wiegandii* Fassett (*E. occidentalis* [Wieg.] Rydb.). The latter variety can be distinguished from species 2, both of which lack the pustular condition, by the absence of minute hairs below tip of the fertile lemma. Still other varieties or even species have been designated, according to the views of different authors. (*E. pungens* [Poir.] Rydb.; *E. crus-galli,* in part.)

Distribution: Considered by some authors as a native American species, primarily of the eastern and central United States and adjacent Canada.

Missouri. Lake margins, alluvial flats, spring branches, open ground, generally distributed. Vars. *microstachya* and *Wiegandii* are less frequent than the typical variety, and occur primarily in the northern and central counties. Flowering in middle and late summer.

Remarks: The name *E. pungens* (Poir.) Rydb. has become well known in distinguishing the American species from its European counterpart, *E. crus-galli.* According to Fairbrothers (1956), however, the use of *pungens* in *Echinochloa* is incorrect and should be replaced by *muricata,* the older epithet used in a legitimate combination.

70. SETARIA Beauv.

Annuals or perennials; panicles terminal, dense, bristly, spike-like; spikelets 1-flowered, broadly elliptic, plump, mostly sessile, subtended by 1-several elongate bristles; at maturity spikelets usually separating below the glumes, falling entire,

FIG. 229.—*Echinochloa muricata.* Plant, × ½; two views of spikelet, and floret, × 10.

the bristles remaining on the floral axis; 1st glume ovate, about one-half or less as long as the 2nd, the latter and sterile lemma about equal or the glume shorter, both awnless; fertile lemma smooth or rugose, indurate, rounded on back; palea as long as lemma.

KEY TO MISSOURI SPECIES

1. Bristles subtending spikelets retrorsely barbed (pointing backward); spikelet clusters in whorls on the lower axis........1. *S. verticillata*
1. Bristles subtending spikelets either smooth or with barbs pointing forward; spikelet clusters not whorled, but more or less producing a continuous spike........2
   2. Each spikelet subtended by 5 or more bristles; fertile lemma distinctly cross-wrinkled........3
   2. Each spikelet subtended by less than 5 bristles, sometimes only 1; fertile lemma smooth to rugose, but not cross-wrinkled........4
3. Perennial, with short knotty rhizomes; sterile lemma with reduced palea........2. *S. geniculata*
3. Annual, fibrous-rooted; sterile lemma with well-developed palea........3. *S. glauca*
   4. Panicles large, to about 3 cm. thick, often interrupted along the lower axis; fertile lemma separating above the glumes and falling separately; cultivated species, sometimes self-established........4. *S. italica*
   4. Panicles narrower, at most 2-2.5 cm. thick; fertile lemma falling with glumes; weedy adventives........5
5. Spikelets about 3 mm. long; panicles nodding or flexuous........5. *S. Faberii*
5. Spikelets about 2 mm. or slightly longer; panicles mostly erect........6. *S. viridis*

1. **Setaria verticillata** (L.) Beauv. Fig. 230.

Annual, forming slender tufts; culms branching near base, decumbent, to 1 m. tall; sheaths glabrous, or the lower ones somewhat pubescent, flattened; ligule consisting of short hairs about 1 mm. long; leaf blades usually glabrous or ciliate

FIG. 230.—*Setaria verticillata*, × 1.

FIG. 231.—*Setaria geniculata*, × 1.

on margins, thin, lax, 5-10 mm. wide or more; panicles erect, somewhat interrupted, the lower spikelet clusters in whorls; spikelets crowded, about 2 mm. long, each subtended by a single bristle, 2-5 mm. long, the barbs of bristle retrorse or pointing backward; fertile lemma obscurely rugose. A form with barbs of the bristles pointing forward has been separated as var. *ambigua* (Guss.) Parl. (*S. viridis* var. *ambigua* [Guss.] Coss. & Dur.).

Distribution: Widely scattered in the United States, also tropical America; introduced from Europe.

Missouri. Waste ground, fields, generally distributed. The var. *ambigua* has been reported from St. Louis County. Flowering in summer.

2. **Setaria geniculata** (Lam.) Beauv. PRAIRIE FOXTAIL. Fig. 231.

Perennial, with short rhizomes; culms slender, erect or geniculate, to 70-80 cm. tall, sheaths keeled; leaf blades usually glabrous, elongate, 5-8 mm. wide; panicles usually short, 2-5 cm. long but sometimes longer, from long, slender, pubescent peduncles; spikelets 2-3 mm. long, each exceeded by several tawny bristles with forward-pointing barbs; fertile lemma finely cross-wrinkled.

Distribution: Southern United States, and eastern areas to southern New England; also tropical regions.

Missouri. Moist prairies, widely scattered but apparently absent in the northwestern counties; our only native species. Flowering in June-July.

3. **Setaria glauca** (L.) Beauv. YELLOW FOXTAIL. Fig. 232.

Annual, forming tufts; culms branching, decumbent near base, to 1 m. tall; sheaths glabrous or sparsely hairy, the lower ones distinctly keeled; ligule consisting of a fringe of short hairs; leaf blades glabrous, ciliate near base, scabrous on the margins, 5-10 mm. wide, tapering to fine, sometimes twisted point; panicles dense, erect, 5-10 cm. long, from long peduncles; spikelets about 3 mm. long, each exceeded by the 5-10 yellowish bristles with forward-pointing barbs; fertile lemma coarsely cross-wrinkled to apex. (*S. lutescens* [Weigel] Hubb.)

Distribution: Widely distributed in the United States; adventive from Europe.

Missouri. Open ground, cultivated fields, generally distributed. Flowering in late June-July.

4. **Setaria italica** (L.) Beauv. ITALIAN MILLET. Fig. 233.

Annual; culms coarse, erect, to 1 m. tall or more; sheaths somewhat pubescent or glabrous; ligule consisting of hairs, about 1 mm. long; leaf blades glabrous, usually pubescent near base, coarse, 1-2 cm. wide, panicles large, lobulate, somewhat interrupted near base, as much as 3-4 cm. thick, 25-30 cm. long; spikelets 2-3 mm. long, usually exceeded by the 1-3 purplish bristles; fertile lemma smooth or finely rugose, variously colored, red to yellow, or black, at maturity falling free of the glumes and sterile lemma. Numerous minor variants have been recognized. According to Hubbard (1915), fruit color, colors of the setae, and form and size of the panicles are most reliable differentiating characters.

Distribution: Widespread in the United States and extensively cultivated in the Great Plains; introduced from the Old World about the middle of the nineteenth century as a forage species, also used in birdseed mixtures.

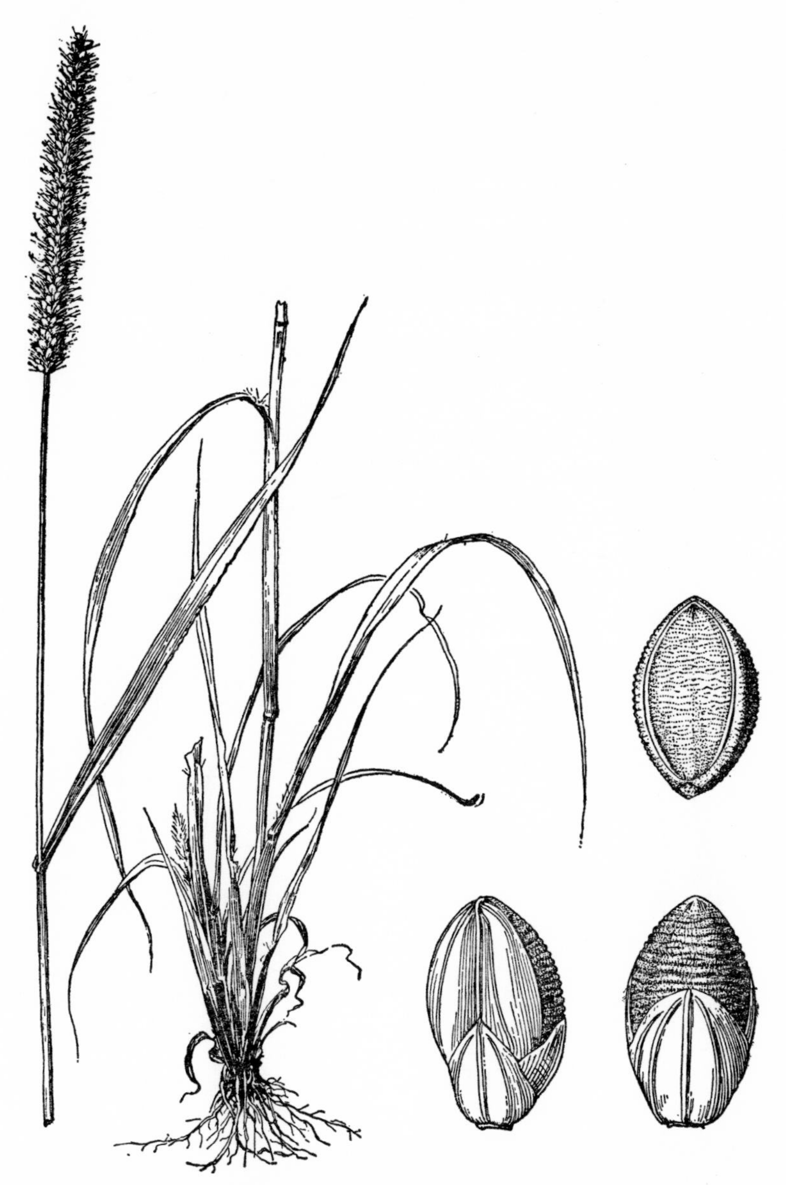

FIG. 232.—*Setaria glauca.* Plant, × ½; two views of spikelet, and floret, × 10.

Missouri. Occasionally volunteering in open ground and waste areas. Flowering in July-August.

5. **Setaria Faberii** Hermm. NODDING FOXTAIL. Fig. 234.

Annual; culms tall, sometimes reaching 1.5 cm. or more; leaf blades short-pubescent on the upper surface rarely glabrous, about 1-1.5 cm. wide; ligule consisting of short hairs; panicles nodding, usually 10 cm. or longer; spikelets 2.5-3 mm. long, exceeded by the tawny bristles; fertile lemma rugose, somewhat less so toward apex.

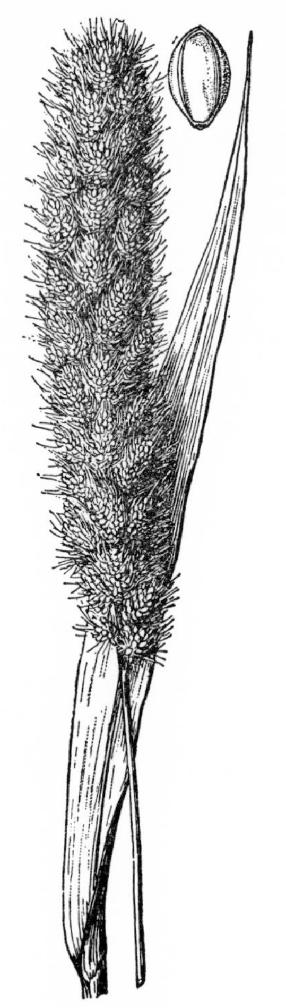

FIG. 233.—*Setaria italica*, × 1; floret, × 5.

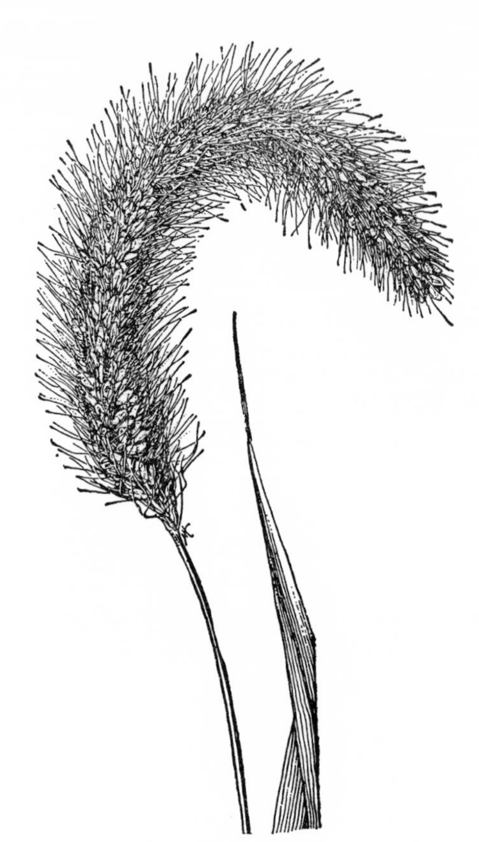

FIG. 234.—*Setaria Faberii*, × 1; floret, × 5.

FIG. 235.—*Setaria viridis*, × 1.

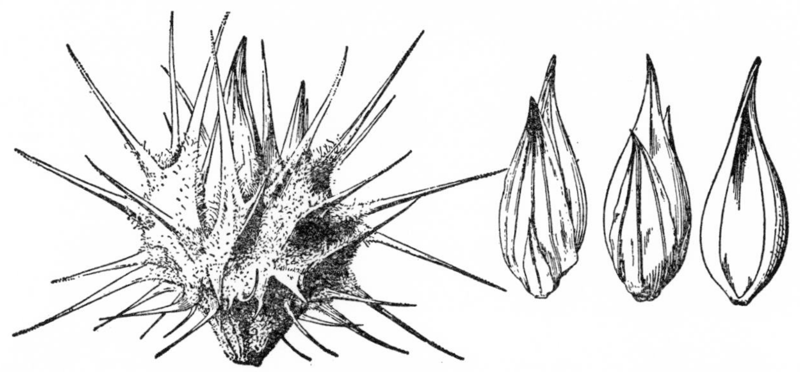

FIG. 236.—*Cenchrus pauciflorus.* Bur, two views of spikelet, and floret, × 5.

Distribution: Becoming widespread in the United States as a weed species; adventive from China, first known in this country in the vicinity of New York City about 1925.

Missouri. Open ground, fields, waste areas, probably in every county. Flowering in summer.

6. **Setaria virdis** (L.) Beauv. GREEN FOXTAIL. Fig. 235.

Annual; culms slender, branching, erect or decumbent-spreading, about 50 cm. tall; sheaths glabrous, ciliate near summit, or scattered pubescent toward base of plant; ligule consisting of hairs, 1-1.5 mm. long; leaf blades mostly glabrous, about 5-10 mm. wide, with sharp-pointed apex; panicles mostly erect, averaging about 5 cm. in length; spikelets about 2 mm. long, the 1-3 bristles greenish or sometimes distinctly purplish, the latter without taxonomic significance; fertile lemma obscurely rugose, (including var. *Weinmanni* [R. & S.] Brand). *S. viridis* somewhat resembles the preceding species but is generally distinguishable by its smaller habit, glabrous condition of the upper leaf surfaces, and the shorter, more erect panicles. According to Fairbrothers (1959), however, the erect versus nodding character of the panicle is not always reliable in distinguishing this species from the former.

Distribution: Widespread in the United States as a weed species, particularly in the cooler regions; introduced from Europe.

Missouri. Fields, waste areas, generally distributed. Flowering in midsummer.

71. CENCHRUS L. SANDBUR

Annuals or perennials; inflorescence consisting of clusters or loose racemes of spiny more or less oval burs, these falling readily at maturity; spikelets 1-flowered, ovate to acuminate, 1-3 enclosed in each bur; glumes unequal; palea of the sterile floret exceeding the lemma; fertile lemma pointed, the margins not inrolled; palea and lemma equal.

1. **Cenchrus pauciflorus** Benth. Fig. 236.

Annual; culms branching, spreading from the base, about 50 cm. long; sheaths mostly glabrous, keeled, somewhat inflated; leaf blades smooth to scabrous, 3-6 mm. wide; racemes consisting of several burs loosely spaced; burs subglobose, about 5 mm. in diameter, excluding the numerous sharp spines; spikelets 1-2 within each bur, the tips protruding. (*C. longispinus* [Hack.] Fern.)

Distribution: Wide-ranging in the United States and adjacent parts of Canada, also Mexico and southward.

Missouri. Open ground, alluvial banks, on dry, sandy soils, generally distributed. Flowering in midsummer.

TRIBE XI. ANDROPOGONEAE

72. MISCANTHUS Anderss.

Perennials; inflorescence a terminal, plume-like panicle consisting of numerous silky racemes with a continuous rachis; spikelets 1-flowered, in pairs, similar and pedicellate, both awned; at maturity spikelets falling entire, the unequal pedicels remaining on the rachis.

1. **Miscanthus sinensis** Anderss. EULALIA. Fig. 237.

Plants forming large clumps; culms erect, usually 2 m. or taller; leaf blades coarse, green or variegated, elongate, about 1 cm. wide, with sharp-scabrous margins; panicles whitish, fan-shaped, composed of numerous flexuous racemes, 10-20 cm. long, aggregated at the summit of flowering stalk; spikelets about 4-5 mm. long, long-tufted at base, the silky white hairs exceeding the length of spikelet. (*M. floridulus* [Labill.] Warb.) Plants with variegated leaf blades include var. *zebrinus* Beal, commonly called zebra grass, with white or pale bands, and var. *variegatus* Beal distinguished by length-wise white markings. The common name "Eulalia" should not be confused with the genus *Eulalia* Kunth., another member of the Andropogoneae distinguished by articulated racemes which break up at maturity.

Distribution: Cultivated in the United States as an ornamental and infrequently spreading; native of eastern Asia.

Missouri. Lawns, gardens, occasionally persisting in untended ground. Flowering in July-August.

73. ERIANTHUS Michx.

Perennials; inflorescence a conspicuous terminal panicle, broad, woolly, or narrow compact, the raceme-like branches with jointed rachis and eventually fragmenting; spikelets 1-flowered, in pairs, both perfect, awned, the lower one sessile, the upper one pedicellate; at maturity spikelets falling entire, the upper one separating from its pedicel, the sessile one falling intact with rachis joint and pedicel.

1. **Erianthus alopecuroides** (L.) Ell. SILVER PLUMEGRASS. Fig. 238.

Plants from thick rhizomes; culms robust, erect, 1-3 m. tall; nodes villous, leaf blades glabrous or sparsely pilose near base, 1-2 cm. wide with conspicuous midrib; panicles dense, woolly, silvery-brown, about 25 cm. long; upper part of flowering stalk appressed-pubescent; spikelets about 5 mm. long, excluding awn, densely tufted at base, the silky hairs exceeding the spikelet; rachis joint and

FIG. 237.—*Miscanthus sinensis*. Plant, much reduced; raceme, × ½; spikelet, × 5.

FIG. 238.—*Erianthus alopecuroides*, × ½.

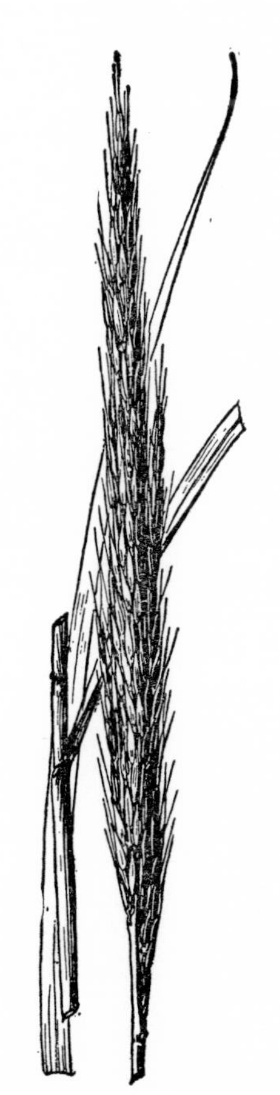

FIG. 239.—*Erianthus strictus*, × ½.

pedicel also long-villous; awn of fertile lemma loosely twisted, about 10 mm. or slightly longer.

Distribution: Southeastern United States and mid-Atlantic region west to Oklahoma and Texas.

Missouri. Open woods, sandy prairies, on moist ground, scattered in the southern and southeastern counties. Flowering in late summer.

2. **Erianthus strictus** Baldw. NARROW PLUMEGRASS. Fig. 239.

Plants less robust than the preceding species; culms erect, 1-2 m. tall; nodes with stiff short hairs; sheaths and leaf blades mostly glabrous, the latter about 1 cm. wide; panicles smooth, brownish, elongate, with stiffly ascending branches; spikelets somewhat scabrous, about 7-8 mm. long, with only a few short hairs at base, or none; rachis joint and pedicel merely scabrous; lemma with straight awn about 2 cm. long.

Distribution: Southeastern Coastal Plain region, north to Tennessee, and *Missouri,* where rare and little known, collected on swampy ground, Dunklin County (Bush 6383).

Erianthus ravennae (L.) Beauv., Ravenna grass, Fig. 240, is a tall, clump-forming ornamental introduced from southern Europe. The dense clumps of arching basal leaves and large, white-woolly panicles frequently reaching a height of 4-5 m. are conspicuous and easy to recognize.

74. ARTHRAXON Beauv.

Our species all annual; inflorescence consisting of digitate spike-like racemes, terminal, and also from the sheaths; spikelets 1-flowered, in pairs or singular, both conditions on the same rachis; spikelets falling entire, with the rachis joint; lemma awned or awnless.

1. **Arthraxon hispidus** (Thunb.) Makino var. **cryptatherus** (Hack.) HONDA. Fig. 241.

Plants branching from the base, low, decumbent-spreading; sheaths conspicu-

FIG. 240.—*Erianthus ravennae.* Racemes, × 1.

FIG. 241.—*Arthraxon hispidus* var. *cryptatherus,* × 1.

ously hispid; leaf blades ovate, with cordate base, thin-textured; racemes purplish, on slender peduncles; spikelets about 5 mm. long, with straight awn.

Distribution: Primarily in the southern United States, where widely scattered; introduced from the Orient.

Missouri. Local, collected in open ground, St. Louis County (Steyermark 8633).

75. ANDROPOGON L.

Perennials; inflorescence consisting of jointed spike-like racemes, fragmenting at maturity, digitate, paniculate, sometimes included in fascicled sheaths; spikelets 1-flowered, in pairs, the lower one sessile, perfect, the upper one pedicellate, either staminate, reduced or lacking; at maturity spikelets falling intact, together with rachis joint; lemma of the sessile spikelet usually awned.

This genus is widely distributed, occurring in the Americas, Africa, Asia, and Australia. It is represented by more than 200 species among which are many with considerable range and forage value.

KEY TO MISSOURI SPECIES

1. Racemes exserted, flexuous, 1 on each stalk; common upland prairie and glade species........1. *A. scoparius*
1. Racemes 2-several on each stalk........2
   2. Racemes digitately arranged at summit of flowering stalk, not feathery pubescent; paired spikelets similar in size........2. *A. Gerardi*
   2. Racemes digitate or paniculate, sometimes included in fascicled sheaths, feathery pubescent; spikelets dissimilar, the pedicellate one reduced or absent........3
3. Racemes partly or mostly included in the crowded spathe-like sheaths........4
3. Racemes exserted on elongate stalks........5
   4. Peduncles densely villous at junction with sheaths........3. *A. Elliottii*
   4. Peduncles glabrous or only sparsely villous at junction with sheaths; common old field species........4. *A. virginicus*
5. Racemes paniculate, numerous, forming dense inflorescence........5. *A. saccharoides*
5. Racemes digitate, usually 2, forming a V-shaped inflorescence........6. *A. ternarius*

1. **Andropogon scoparius** L. LITTLE BLUESTEM. Fig. 242.

Plants forming dense, leafy tufts; flower stalks to 1 m. tall; foliage glabrous to densely villous, sometimes distinctly bluish in some plants; sheaths compressed, keeled, toward base of clump; ligule thin, about 1.5 mm. long; leaf blades elongate averaging 5 mm. wide, curling when dried; racemes delicate, flexuous, 3-5 cm. long; sessile spikelet 4-8 mm. long, excluding bent awn; pedicellate spikelet and rachis section pubescent, the latter flattened and broadened upward, truncate; awn of lemma 10-15 mm. long, twisted in lower part. The recognition of varieties and forms has been attempted by several authors. These separations are based primarily on spikelet size and degree of pubescence. Missouri specimens exhibit a considerable range of variation; however, no distinctive groupings based on correlative characters seem evident. The bearded condition of the rachis, in conjunction with other characters, discussed by Fernald & Grisc. (1935) does not provide a consistent or satisfactory basis for dividing our plants.

Distribution: Widespread in the United States and adjacent parts of eastern Canada.

Missouri. Upland prairies, glades, thin woods, open ground, on dry soils; generally distributed and our most common species. A villous form with bluish-green

FIG. 242.—*Andropogon scoparius*. Plant, × ½; pair of spikelets, × 5.

FIG. 243.—*Andropogon Gerardi*. Plant, × ½; pair of spikelets, × 5.

foliage occurs in the limestone glades of the White River area. Flowering in late summer and early fall.

2. **Andropogon Gerardi** Vitman. BIG BLUESTEM, TURKEY-FOOT. Fig. 243.

Plants forming large clumps, from short rhizomes; flower stalks sometimes exceeding 2 m.; sheaths mostly glabrous or lower ones sometimes pilose toward base of clump; ligule collar-shaped, 1-2 mm. long; leaf blades glabrous or sparsely ciliate, elongate and spreading, as much as 1 cm. wide; racemes 2-5 cm., digitate, ascending, 5-10 cm. long, on long flower stalk, also some racemes partly included in sheaths; sessile spikelet about 8 mm. long, excluding bent awn, the pedicellate one about the same length, but awnless; pedicels and rachis joints with stiff hairs; awn 10-15 mm. long, twisted in lower part. (*A. furcatus* Muhl.)

Distribution: Widespread in the United States and southern Canada, as far west as Utah, south to Arizona and Old Mexico.

Missouri. Prairies, glades, open woods, generally distributed. Flowering in late summer and early fall. This species usually matures later than little bluestem, although flowering is initiated earlier. It is the superior species for range forage.

3. **Andropogon virginicus** L. BROOMSEDGE. Fig. 244.

Plants tufted; culms relatively simple or branching from middle and upper nodes, erect, to 1 m. tall; sheaths glabrous to pilose, sharply compressed at base of clumps, the upper ones distant or somewhat aggregated; ligule ciliate on the margin, less than 1 mm. long; leaf blades glabrous to pilose, 3-5 mm. wide; racemes flexuous, feathery, from the sheaths; peduncles smooth or only slightly pubescent at summit; sessile spikelets 3-4 mm. long, excluding straight awn; pedicellate spikelet reduced or absent; pedicel and rachis joint long-villous; awn delicate, about 10-15 mm. long. Throughout its total range the species exhibits considerable variation in branching of the inflorescence and aggregation of upper sheaths. Along these lines, plants with elongate, loosely branched inflorescences represent the typical variety (var. *virginicus*), these grading toward increasing congestion of sheaths and compactness of inflorescence, particularly in the eastern and southern parts of its range. In general, Missouri plants are circumscribed as a single though somewhat variable group and are treated as the typical variety. (Including var. *tetrastachys* [Ell.] Hack.)

Distribution: Eastern and southern United States, west to Kansas and Texas; also Mexico and West Indies.

Missouri. Old fields, waste ground, sand bars, common in the central and southern counties, scattered northward. Flowering in late summer and fall. In winter phase the foliage has a tawny to reddish-brown color which is conspicuous.

4. **Andropogon Elliottii** Chapm. Fig. 245.

Plants tufted, similar in general habit to species 3; upper sheaths more expanded, crowded, consisting of spathe-like fascicles enveloping or partly enclosing the feathery racemes, sometimes the latter exserted; ligule ciliate on the margin, less than 1 mm. long; peduncles densely villous toward summit; sessile spikelets 4-5 mm. long, excluding the straight awn; pedicellate spikelets reduced or lacking; pedicels and rachis joints long-villous; awn delicate, 10-15 mm. long. Those

FIG. 244.—*Andropogon virginicus.* Plant, × ½; spikelet with rachis joint and pedicel, × 5.

plants with elongate inflorescences and exserted racemes are sometimes separated as var. *projectus* Fern. & Grisc.

Distribution: Southeastern and mid-Atlantic region, to New Jersey, Indiana, and Texas.

Missouri. Old fields, thin woods, on dry soils, southern and eastern Ozarks area; also Boone County. Flowering in late summer and early fall. In winter aspect the foliage is tawny to reddish-brown.

5. **Andropogon ternarius** Michx. SILVERBEARD. Fig. 246.

Perennial, forming tufts; culms leafy, branching from upper nodes, to 1 m. tall; foliage glabrous to sparsely villous, the leaf blades narrow, curling, about 3 mm. wide; racemes silvery-white 3-5 mm. long, mostly in V-shaped pairs on long exserted peduncles, several pairs ascending along the main flower stalk; sessile spikelets 5-7 mm. long, excluding the bent awn; pedicellate spikelet obsolete; pedicel and rachis joint densely villous, both shorter than the sessile spikelet; awn of lemma delicate, sometimes twisted, 10-20 mm. long.

Distribution: Southern and mid-Atlantic region, west to Kansas and Texas.

Missouri. Prairies, glades, thin woods, on dry or sandy soils, scattered, south of line from Barton to Ste. Genevieve counties. Flowering in late summer.

6. **Andropogon saccharoides** Swartz. SILVERY BEARDGRASS. Fig. 247.

Perennial, forming dense tufts; culms leafy, branching from middle and lower nodes, somewhat decumbent near base, to about 1 m. tall; sheaths glabrous, somewhat purplish; ligule conspicuous, about 3 mm. long; leaf blades mostly glabrous, 3-8 mm. wide; panicles silvery pubescent, dense, 5-9 cm. long, from extended peduncles, also from shorter stalks of lower culm; sessile spikelets 4-5 mm. long, excluding bent awn; pedicellate spikelet reduced; pedicel and rachis joint long-villous; awn of lemma twisted below, 10-15 mm. long.

Distribution: Southern plains of the United States northeast to Missouri; also tropical America.

Missouri. Upland prairies, limestone bluffs, waste ground, on dry soils, scattered through the central and southern counties; adventive at its northern limits in Boone County. Flowering in midsummer.

76. SORGHUM Moench.

Annuals or perennials; inflorescence an open to compact, branching, terminal panicle; spikelets in pairs (in 3's at the end of the raceme); each 1-flowered, the lower one sessile, perfect, awned, the upper pedicellate, staminate or sterile, awnless; at maturity spikelet pair falling intact with rachis joint.

The true sorghums are warm season grasses primarily from the Old World, largely concentrated in eastern Africa and Asia Minor, several of which have been introduced in this country as hay and forage crops. Some representatives cause prussic acid poisoning under certain conditions.

1. **Sorghum halepense** (L.) Pers. JOHNSON GRASS. Fig. 248.

Perennial, forming large clumps, spreading by thick rhizomes; culms coarse, erect, 1-2 m. tall; sheaths mostly glabrous, compressed; ligule conspicuous, membraneous, about 5 mm. long; leaf blades glabrous or somewhat pubescent near

FIG. 245.—*Andropogon Elliottii*, × 1.

FIG. 246.—*Andropogon ternarius*, × 1.

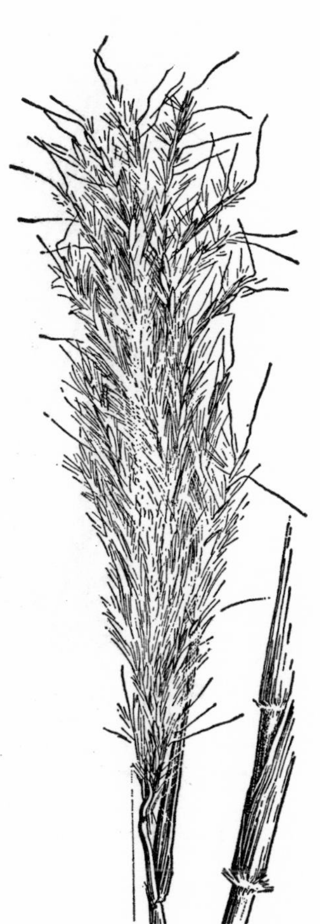

FIG. 247.—*Andropogon saccharoides*, × 1.

FIG. 248.—*Sorghum halepense*. Plant, × ½; two views of spikelet pair, × 5.

base, elongate, 1-2 cm. wide or more; panicles pyramidal, erect, as much as 40 cm. long; fertile or sessile spikelets ovate, about 5 mm. long, with bent awn, twisted in lower part, 10-15 mm. in length; upper spikelet lanceolate, lacking awn.

Distribution: Eastern and southern United States, introduced in South Carolina about 1830.

Missouri. Open ground, fields, waste areas, generally distributed, volunteering as an aggressive weed. Flowering in summer.

2. **Sorghum vulgare** Pers. SUDAN GRASS, CULTIVATED SORGHUMS. Fig. 249.

Annuals; culms leafy, erect, 1-3 m. tall; leaf blades mostly glabrous, of variable width; panicles open, spreading to dense, compact; sessile spikelets plump, about 6 mm. long, with bent awn, the pedicellate ones not as large, awnless. Sudan grass, var. *sudanense* Hitchc. has leaf blades 8-15 mm. wide, a short ligule about 1 mm. long, and open spreading panicles. (*S. sudanense* [Piper] Stapf.) Sudan grass is easily distinguished from Johnson grass by the absence of rhizomes. Numerous other varieties or races also occur, including such well known crop plants as cane, kafir, milo, and broomcorn. Detailed discussions and treatments of the sorghums, too lengthy to be included here, are provided by Snowden (1936) and Garber (1950).

Distribution: Cultivated over wide areas in the United States, sometimes occurring as waifs in open ground, but probably never persistent. Sudan grass was introduced in this country from Africa in the early part of this century.

77. SORGHASTRUM Nash.

Perennials; inflorescence a terminal panicle, consisting of numerous jointed racemes fragmenting at maturity; spikelets arranged in pairs, the lower one ses-

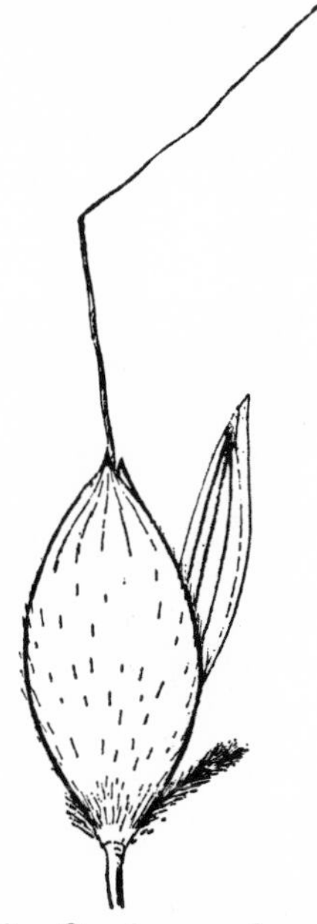

FIG. 249.—*Sorghum vulgare.* Spikelet pair, × 5.

FIG. 250.—*Sorghastrum nutans*. Plant, × ½; spikelet with pedicel and rachis joint, × 5.

FIG. 251.—*Manisurus cylindrica.* Plant, × ½; two views of rachis joint with fertile and sterile spikelets attached, × 5.

sile, 1-flowered, perfect, awned, the upper reduced to hairy pedicel; perfect spikelet, pedicel and rachis all falling together, intact.

1. **Sorghastrum nutans** (L.) Nash. INDIAN GRASS. Fig. 250.

Plants forming clumps, with short rhizomes; culms mostly coarse, erect, to 2.5 m. tall; sheaths glabrous to sparsely pilose; ligule conspicuous, rigid, 3-5 mm. long, leaf blades mostly glabrous, elongate, 5-10 mm. wide, somewhat narrowing toward base; panicles light brownish and somewhat shiny, becoming darker, elliptic, 15-30 cm. long, with numerous, ascending delicate branches each with 1-several spikelets; sessile spikelets hirsute, 7-8 mm. long, with bent, twisted awn, about 10 mm. or somewhat longer; sterile pedicels and rachis joints clothed with stiff, brownish hairs.

Distribution: Widespread in the United States, from the eastern seaboard to North Dakota, south to Arizona and Old Mexico.

Missouri. Upland prairies, glades, open woods, generally distributed. Flowering in late summer, at which time the large yellow anthers are conspicuous.

78. MANISURUS L.

Perennials; inflorescence a cylindric or compressed spike-like raceme with hard, thickened rachis joints, separating at maturity; spikelets in pairs, 1-flowered, both awnless, the lower one sessile, perfect, appressed to hollow of rachis, the upper one on short, thick pedicel, much reduced, sterile; spikelet pair falling with rachis joint; 1st or outer glume thick, hard, opposite the rachis, the 2nd or inner glume recessed.

1. **Manisurus cylindrica** (Michx.) Kuntze. JOINTGRASS. Fig. 251.

Plants tufted, with short rhizomes; culms erect, to 1 m. tall; sheaths smooth, rounded on back; leaf blades elongate, about 3 mm. wide; racemes pencil-like, somewhat arching on long peduncles from the nodes; sessile spikelet about 5 mm. long, closely appressed to hollow of rachis joint; 1st glume ovate, conspicuously pitted on back; sterile spikelet reduced to a short tip, the pedicel plump.

Distribution: Southeastern United States and Coastal Plain, inland to *Missouri,* where rare and little known, reported on dry waste ground, Jackson, Barton, and Mississippi counties. Flowering in July-August.

TRIBE XII. TRIPSACEAE

79. TRIPSACUM L. GAMAGRASS

Perennials; inflorescence terminal and axillary, consisting of 1-3 spikes; upper portion of each spike staminate with continuous rachis, falling entire, the lower part pistillate, eventually fragmenting into rachis joints with spikelet attached; staminate spikelets 2-flowered, in pairs, the lower one sessile, the upper pedicellate; pistillate spikelets 1-flowered, solitary, appressed in the recess of the hard, thickened rachis joint.

1. **Tripsacum dactyloides** (L.) L. EASTERN GAMAGRASS. Fig. 252.

Plants forming large clumps, rhizomatous; culms leafy, 1-2 m. tall or more; ligule a fringe of hairs less than 1 mm. long; leaf blades coarse, glabrous, with scabrous margins, 1-2 cm. wide; terminal spikes 2 or 3, digitate, as much as 20-25 cm. long, the axillary spikes solitary; pistillate spikelets about 8-9 mm. long, recessed in the thick rachis joint; staminate spikelets narrower, about 10 mm. long.

Distribution: Eastern and southern United States, west to Nebraska and Texas; also West Indies, Mexico, and South America.

Missouri. Swales, low prairies, waste ground, on moist soils, general, but not common. Flowering in June-July.

Related plants also placed in the Tripsaceae include the following. Like *Tripsacum,* these have unisexual spikelets and are monoecious.

Coix Lacryma-jobi L. Job's Tears, of tropical origin, is characterized by its hard, smooth, bead-like grains. It is commonly cultivated as a garden ornament.

Euchlaena mexicana Schrad. Commonly called teosinte, this species occurs wild in Mexico and Guatemala. It is considered one of the closest relatives of corn. Teosinte bears a resemblance to the latter in having the staminate spikelets invested in a tassel arrangement, but the grains are extremely hard and few in number. Fertile hybrids have been produced from crossing teosinte with corn.

Zea Mays L. The corn plant is the only important grain to originate in the Americas. It has been cultivated in the Western Hemisphere since prehistoric times, and includes numerous races and varieties. The ancestry of corn, or maize, has been studied intensively, but its exact origin is still unknown.

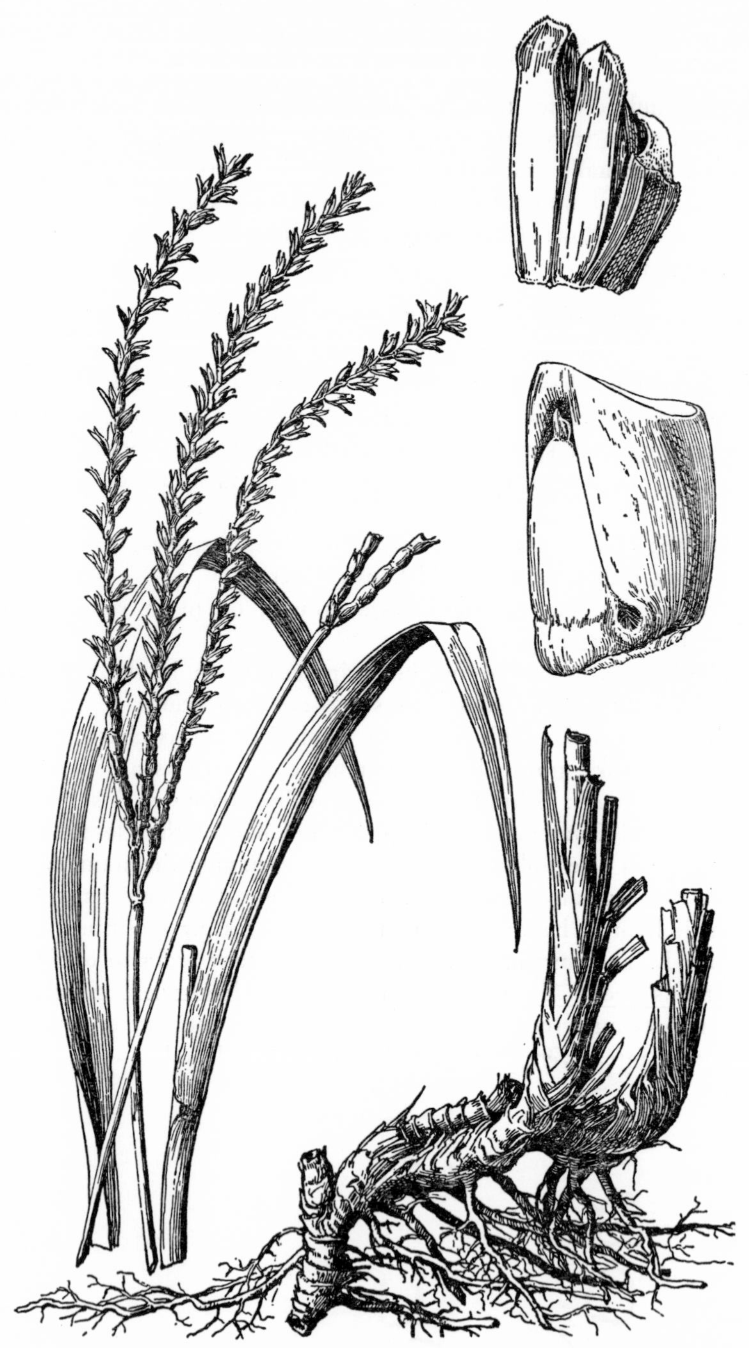

FIG. 252.—*Tripsacum dactyloides.* Plant, × ½; pistillate spikelets with rachis joint and pair of staminate spikelets with rachis joint, × 5.

THE VEGETATION OF MISSOURI

The principal plant formations of the Middle West are Grassland and Deciduous Forest. An intermingling of these systems occurs over a broad transition region, with westerly extensions of forest following stream dissection. A third, more restricted life form is the Coniferous type. All three formations are represented in Missouri.

Geologic history and parent materials are important factors contributing to the rich and varied flora of Missouri vegetation. The northern part of the state was covered by Kansan drift while the southern part was not glaciated. The southern limits of drift correspond in general to the Missouri River Valley which traverses the state from west to east. The inter-stream topography of the drift region is flat to generally rolling, with parent material of varying texture and depth. On the level terrain, soils are characteristically heavy with resultant slow drainage. Bordering the Missouri River in particular, loess deposits of the post-glacial period have accumulated to great depth to produce a distinctive river-hill topography. Soils developing under these conditions are deep, porous, and well-drained. Diminishing accumulations of generally finer loess also covered extensive areas of glacial till.

South of the glacial boundary the state has had a much longer history of soil development and plant occupation, which may be measured in millions of years. Parts of the east-central Ozarks, centered in Iron, Madison, and St. Francois counties, are among the oldest exposed land areas in North America. In the highland region in general, geologic weathering and development of soils from the ancient underlying rocks date back to periods of uplift in Paleozoic and even pre-Cambrian times. Non-residual soils are of lesser extent and are derived chiefly from local loess deposits and stream alluvium. In southeastern Missouri, Crowley's Ridge is a distinctive land form elevated above the surrounding lowlands. Small spring-fed drainages traverse the lower slopes and in conjunction with sandy-textured soils provide numerous moist, well-drained plant habitats. Extensive dolomitic glades occur in the White River region of the southwestern Ozarks. The soils are shallow and droughty in contrast to deeper profiles developed from cherty limestones.

Rainfall in the state varies from about 32 to 35 inches per year in the northwestern section to slightly over 50 inches in the southeastern lowlands of the "bootheel." This regional difference in annual precipitation is due largely to the relatively drier winter condition toward the northwest. Amounts received in the growing season, however, are more nearly similar, averaging 25-30 inches.

The general pattern of native vegetation is shown on the accompanying map.[1] Prairie grasslands occurred extensively in the drift region north of the Missouri River, and south of glacial border in the west-central and western counties. In the eastern portion of the drift region, mainly east of the Chariton River drainage, flat, poorly-drained prairies formerly were common. Relic examples are still found in scattered localities, including Callaway, Audrain, Randolph, Macon, and Adair counties. West of this region, the upland prairie

1. Adapted from Transeau, *Ecology,* Vol. 16, 1935, and modified to include additional types.

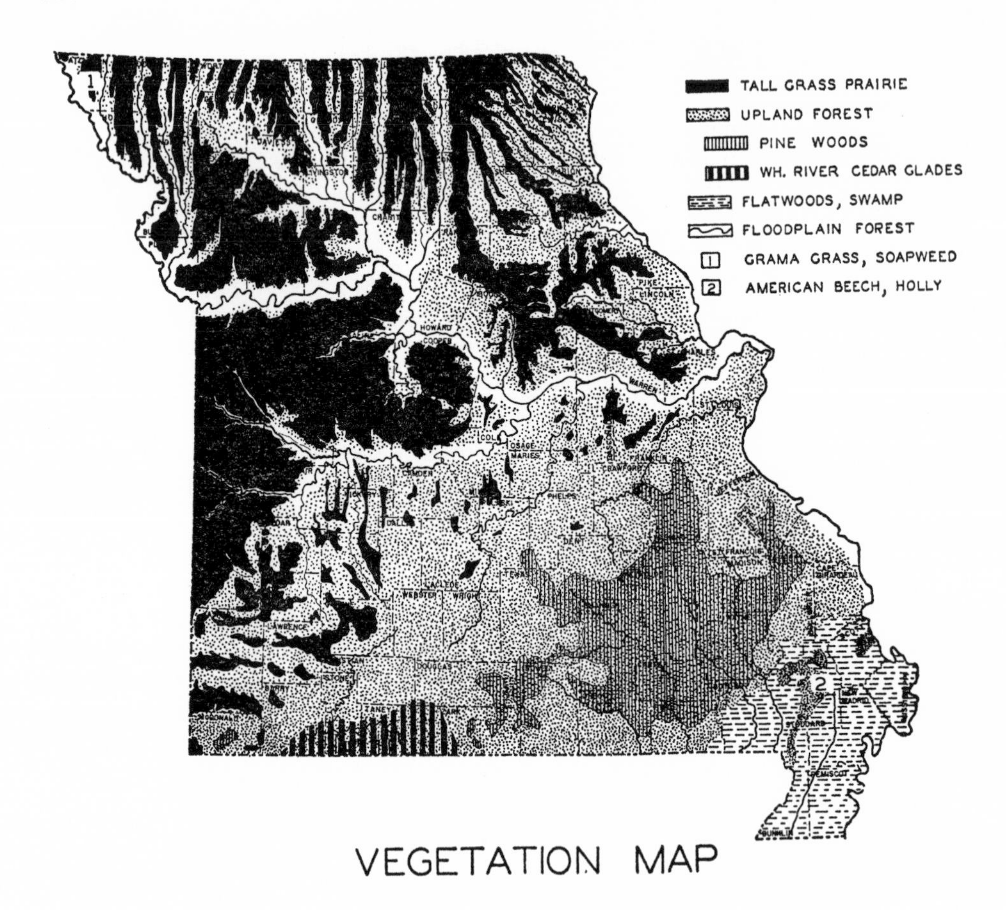

VEGETATION MAP

topography becomes more undulating, drained by broad valleys of flood plain forest and slough prairies, such as that of the Grand River. South of the drift border in the western part of the state, the present-day prairies are more extensive than those north of the Missouri River. Here the soils are variable in depth, and are frequently shallow, with outcroppings of rock. Such tracts which still remain are utilized as hay and pasture lands. In the White River region of the Missouri Ozarks, extending into Northern Arkansas as well, distinctive glade prairies occur on dolomitic outcrops. In addition to the prairie complement of grasses and herbs, arborescent species of scrubby form, including Eastern red cedar, *Juniperus virginiana,* are normally present in the glades.

The principal grass species of the Prairie Association in Missouri include the bluestems, *Andropogon Gerardi* and *A. scoparius;* Indian grass, *Sorghastrum nutans*; wild rye, *Elymus canadensis*; Junegrass, *Koeleria cristata*; dropseed, *Sporobolus heterolepis*; switchgrass, *Panicum virgatum*; sloughgrass, *Spartina pectinata;* and sideoats grama, *Boutelous curtipendula*. The latter is a typical species of dry, limestone prairies and loessial bluffs. Other species are less widely distributed. Bluejoint, *Calamagrostis canadensis,* occurs in damp swales of the northern counties. Another species having a northerly distribution, occupying swales and bottomlands, is the common reed, *Phragmites communis* var. *Ber-*

landieri. Porcupine grass, *Stipa spartea,* a species of the dry upland, is found primarily in the western and northern parts of the state. Restricted species which are more common in the arid, western plains occur in northwestern Missouri. These are found on dry loessial hills bordering the Missouri River, mainly in Atchison and Holt counties. Alkali sacaton, *Sporobolus airoides*; the grama grasses, *Bouteloua gracilis* and *B. hirsuta*; and buffalo grass, *Buchloe dactyloides,* are found in these habitats. Another associated plains species in these habitats is the soapweed, *Yucca glauca.*

The Oak-Hickory Association is the principal upland forest type in Missouri. It occurs throughout the state and is most extensive and highly developed in the Ozark region. Several oak species are widespread and common, including white oak, *Quercus alba*; northern red oak, *Q. rubra*; and black oak, *Q. velutina.* The bur oak, *Q. macrocarpa,* is also common, occurring generally on lower ground or along streams. Post oak, *Q. stellata,* and chinquapin, *Q. Muhlenbergii,* are found in xeric habitats, the latter usually on calcareous soils. A principal hickory of upland sites is shagbark, *Carya ovata.* Bitternut hickory, *C. cordiformis,* is also general but occupies more moist sites. Common species of sloughs and prairie drainages are pin oak, *Q. palustris,* and shingle oak, *Q. imbricaria.* These oaks are less important in stands toward the south, particularly in the Ozark region. Southern species, common in Ozark stands, includes scarlet oak, *Q. coccinea*; southern red oak, *Q. falcata*; and blackjack, *Q. marilandica.* The latter, however, is not limited to the Ozarks. This species, post oak, and also black hickory, *C. texana,* are characteristic of a dry forest type in the glade region. Southwestward extensions of this hardwood complex occur in Oklahoma and Texas.

Sugar maple, *Acer saccharum,* and basswood, *Tilia americana,* are frequent dominants in a secondary association restricted to more moist sites than those of the widespread oak communities. Associated species are northern red oak, white oak, bitternut, and red elm, *Ulmus rubra.* Distinctive species with local ranges in Missouri include American beech, *Fagus grandifolia,* and holly, *Ilex opaca.* Both are limited to several southeastern counties and are best exemplified in moist, sandy habitats of Crowley's Ridge.

The distribution of shortleaf pine in Missouri is confined to the Ozark region, primarily in the eastern and southern counties. It is the only native pine in the state. Stands of mixed oak and pine occur on xeric ridges and slopes, which are generally the less favorable sites. Extensive pineries were once an abundant resource in the timber industry. One remnant stand of large specimens may be observed today in Shannon County. The map indicates the principal range of pine in Missouri; however, scattered trees and small stands occur also in adjacent areas outside the depicted boundary (Liming, 1946).

The southeastern lowlands provide distinctive plant habitats not found elsewhere in the state. Flatwoods and swamp vegetation were typical before drainage, but important areas still remain. Forest species include bald cypress, *Taxodium distichum*; tupelo, *Nyssa aquatica*; sweet gum, *Liquidambar styraciflua*; and overcup oak, *Q. lyrata.*

Typical grasses of the dry upland woods and glades are numerous, many of which are in the genus *Panicum.* Other genera with native species occurring in these habitats are *Danthonia, Sphenopholis, Muhlenbergia, Sporobolus, Aristida, Paspalum* and *Andropogon.* In moist or shaded situations, various species of *Bromus, Festuca, Poa, Diarrhena, Elymus, Cinna, Muhlenbergia, Leersia, Paspalum* and *Panicum* are present. In old field vegetation, broomsedge, *Andropogon virginicus,* is a distinctive successional type, most general in the central and southern parts of the state.

GLOSSARY

Abaxial. The side away from the central axis.
Acuminate. Pointed, with narrow, gradually tapering sides.
Acute. Pointed, the sides broader, more abruptly tapered.
Adaxial. The side near the central axis.
Annual. Persisting only one season. See winter annual.
Anther. Pollen-bearing structure of the stamen.
Anthesis. Time of flowering, the full opening of the flower.
Antrorse. Pointing upward or forward, as applied to pubescence, bristles. The opposite of retrorse.
Appressed. Lying close to axis or surface.
Articulate. Jointed.
Articulation. Point of natural separation, or breaking away, as the florets separating above the glumes.
Attenuate. Long, narrow-pointed.
Auricle. Ear-like appendage or lobe at the base of the leaf blade.
Awl-shaped. Narrow, needle-like.
Awn. Usually elongate, slender bristle or projection from the apex or dorsal surface, as of a lemma.
Axil. The upper angle between branch, stalk, or sheath and the main axis.
Axillary. In the axil.
Axis. The main stem or stalk.
Bearded. Having tuft of hairs, as at the nodes or at the base of spikelets or florets.
Biennial. Persisting two seasons.
Bifid. Two-pointed apex.
Bisexual. With both stamens and pistil, referring to perfect flowers.
Blade. Part of the leaf which is above the sheath.
Bract. A usually small, scale-like appendage.
Callus. Pointed, stiff projection at the base of the floret in some grasses.
Capillary. Delicate, hairlike.
Caryopsis. The grain or fruit in grasses, the mature ovary.
Cespitose. Referring to plants forming tufts or bunches.
Ciliate. With fringe of hairs, as on the margins of leaf blades.
Cleistogamous. Referring to flowers which remain unopened and are self-fertilized.
Collar. Outside juncture of the leaf blade and its sheath.
Compressed. Flattened, usually forming a keel.
Continuous rachis. Remaining intact, not disarticulating.
Contracted inflorescence. One which is narrow, with close branching, usually dense though not always.
Culm. The grass stem, characterized by having solid joints or nodes and mostly hollow internodes.
Decumbent. Prostrate or touching the ground, as applied to the culm.
Diffuse inflorescence. One which is open, with wide-spreading branches.
Digitate. Attachment of spikes or racemes from the summit of the main flowering stalk, as in Crabgrass.
Dioecious. Referring to species in which the male and female flowers are on separate plants, as in Buffalo Grass.
Disarticulating. Breaking or separating at the joints when mature.
Dorsal. Back side, or the side away from the main axis.
Dorsal compression. Referring to spikelets flattened from the dorsal side, the midvein rounded, not keeled.
Erose. Irregular or jagged.
Exserted. Extended.
Fasciculate. Closely bunched or in clusters.
Fertile. Producing fruit or grain.
Floret. Part of the spikelet comprising the lemma and palea, and the flower.
Fruit. In grasses called the grain or caryopsis, the ripened ovary.
Geniculate. Bent, as at the joints of the culm.
Glabrous. Smooth, lacking pubescence of any kind.
Glaucous. With a whitish to bluish-green color, as on the foliage.

Glumes. Pair of empty (sterile) bracts or scales below the floret(s).
Habit. Characteristic form of growth, as spreading or upright stems.
Habitat. The natural site in which the plant is found.
Hirsute. With coarse hairs.
Hispid. With stiff hairs.
Hyaline. Thin, or translucent.
Imbricate. Overlapping.
Indurate. Hard, firm.
Inflorescence. The flowering portion, as a panicle, raceme, or spike.
Internode. The part of the culm between two successive nodes.
Involute. With inrolled margins, as of a leaf blade.
Keel. The ridge or fold formed by the midvein.
Lateral compression. Referring to spikelets flattened from the sides, forming the keel at the midvein.
Lemma. One bract of the floret, opposing the palea.
Ligule. Membranous or hairy collar-like projection at the inside juncture of the blade and sheath.
Lodicules. Minute scales at the base of some grass flowers, considered to be a vestigial perianth.
Monoecious. Referring to species with staminate and pistillate flowers on the same plant.
Mucronate. Ending abruptly in a minute, usually sharp tip.
Nerve. Vein of a leaf blade, or of a bract such as a glume or lemma.
Node. Joint of the culm.
Oblong. Longer than broad, widest through the middle.
Obovate. Broadest above the middle, opposite of ovate.
Obsolete. Reduced in size, or absent.
Obtuse. Blunt or rounded, as an apex.
Orbicular. Circular in outline.
Ovate. Broadest below the middle, egg-shaped.
Palea. One bract of the floret, opposing the lemma, and usually the smaller of the two.
Panicle. A branching inflorescence, a compound raceme.
Papillose. Referring to a surface with minute glandlike protuberances or pimples.
Pedicel. The stalk of an individual spikelet.
Perennial. Persisting two or more growing seasons.
Perfect. With both stamens and pistil, referring to bisexual flowers.
Pilose. With soft, straight hairs.
Pistillate. Referring to flowers with a pistil only, lacking stamens.
Plumose. Feathery pubescent.
Puberulent. With minute pubescence.
Pubescent. General condition of hairiness on various surfaces, such as blades, sheaths or spikelets.
Pulvinus. A glandlike swelling at the base of panicle branches.
Raceme. An inflorescence type consisting of a simple, unbranched axis bearing pedicillate spikelets along its length.
Rachilla. The jointed axis of the spikelet on which the florets are borne.
Rachis. The unbranched axis of a raceme or spike.
Retrorse. Pointing backward.
Rhizome. A horizontal underground stem, rooting at the nodes, and having scales.
Rudimentary. Small or imperfectly developed.
Scabrous. Rough to the touch, as the surface of some leaf blades.
Scarious. Thin, membraneous, translucent, not green.
Secund. Arranged on one side, as spikelets along the rachis.
Serrate. With minute teeth, as the margin of some leaf blades.
Sessile spikelet. Lacking a pedicel.
Sheath. Part of the leaf below the blade which envelops the culm.
Spathe-like sheath. Enlarged, somewhat inflated sheaths enveloping part of the inflorescence of some grasses.
Spike. An inflorescence type consisting of a simple, unbranched axis with sessile spikelets along its length.
Spikelet. The basic unit of the inflorescence, consisting of the glumes and one or more florets.

Staminate. Referring to flowers with stamens only, lacking a pistil.
Sterile. Lacking both stamens and pistil.
Stipitate. With a short stipe or stalk.
Stolon. A horizontal stem, usually above ground, rooting at the nodes and producing new plants.
Subulate. Narrow, needle-like, referring to an apex.
Truncate. Straight across, as if cut off.
Villous. With long, soft hairs.
Winter annual. Germinating in the fall, continuing growth and flowering the following spring, not persisting afterward.

BIBLIOGRAPHY

Anderson, Dennis. 1959. Personal communication. Botany Dept., Iowa State University, Ames, Iowa.

Ashe, W. W. 1898. The dichotomous group of *Panicum* in the eastern United States. Journ. Elisha Mitch. Sci. Soc. 15: 22-62.

Boyle, W. S. 1945. A cytotaxonomic study of the North American species of *Melica*. Madrona 8: 1-26.

Bush, B. F., and Cameron Mann. 1885. First Supplement to the Flora of Jackson County, Missouri.

Church, G. L. 1954. Interspecific hybridization in eastern *Elymus*. Rhodora 56: 185-197.

Fairbrothers, D. E. 1956. Nomenclatural change in the grass genus *Echinochloa*. Rhodora 58: 48-49.

———. 1959. Morphological variation of *Setaria Faberii* and *S. viridis*. Brittonia 10: 44-48.

Fassett, N. C. 1950. Grasses of Wisconsin, University of Wisconsin Press, Madison, Wisconsin.

Featherly, H. I. 1938. A new *Triodia* from Oklahoma. Rhodora 40: 243-244.

Fernald, M. L. 1936. Plants from the outer coastal plain of Virginia. Rhodora 38: 376-404.

———. 1943. Five common rhizomatous species of *Muhlenbergia*. Rhodora 45: 221-239.

———. 1950. Gray's Manual of Botany, ed. 8. American Book Co., New York.

Fernald, M. L. and Ludlow Griscom. 1935. Contributions from the Gray Herbarium of Harvard University, No. CVII. Rhodora 37: 137-147.

Garber, E. D. 1950. Cytotaxonomic studies in the genus *Sorghum*. Calif. Univ. Publ. 23: 283-361.

Gates, F. C. 1936. Grasses in Kansas. Kansas State Board of Agriculture, Topeka, Kansas.

Gilly, C. L. 1943. A preliminary investigation of the North American canes (*Arundinaria*). Bull. Torr. Club 70: 297-309.

Gleason, H. A. Change of name for certain plants of the 'Manual Range.' Phytologia 4: 20-25.

———. 1952. The New Britton and Brown Illustrated Flora of Northeastern United States and Adjacent Canada. Vol. 1. New York Botanical Garden, New York.

Hegi, Gustav. 1906. Illustrierte Flora von Mittel-Europa. Vol. 1. Universität Müchen, Müchen, Germany.

Henrard, J. Th. 1950. Monograph of the Genus *Digitaria*. University of Leyden, Leyden, The Netherlands.

Hitchcock, A. S. 1933. New species and new names of grasses from Texas. Journ. Wash. Acad. Sci. 23: 449-456.

———. 1951. Manual of the Grasses of the United States. U.S.D.A. Misc. Publ. 200., ed. 2. U.S.D.A., Wash., D. C.

Hubbard, C. E. 1954. Grasses: A Guide to their Structure, Identification, Uses, and Distribution in the British Isles. Rich, Clay and Co., Ltd., Bungay, Suffolk, England.

Hubbard, F. T. 1915. A Taxonomic study of *Setaria italica* and its immediate allies. Am. Journ. Bot. 2: 169-198.

Huskins, C. L. 1946. Fatuoid, speltoid, and related mutation of oats and wheat. Bot. Rev. 12: 457-514.

Kucera, C. L. 1953. Additional notes on the grasses of Boone County, Missouri. Rhodora 55: 289-290.

———. 1954. *Eragrostis curvula* in Missouri. Rhodora 56: 273-274.

———. 1957. A new *Tridens* record from Missouri. Rhodora 59: 72.

Liming, F. S. 1946. The range and distribution of shortleaf pine in Missouri. U.S.D.A. Central States Forest Exp. Sta. Tech. Paper 106. Central States Forest Exp. Sta., Columbus, Ohio.

MacKenzie, K. K., B. F. Bush, *et al.* 1902. Manual of the Flora of Jackson County, Missouri. Kansas City, Missouri.

Mangelsdorf, P. C. and R. B. Reeves. 1931. Hybridization of maize, *Tripsacum* and *Euchlaena*. Journ. of Heredity 22: 329-343.

McFadden, E. S. and E. R. Sears. 1946. The origin of *Triticum spelta* and its free threshing hexaploid relatives. Journ. of Heredity 37: 81-89.

Mobberly, D. G. 1956. Taxonomy and distribution of the genus *Spartina*. Iowa State Coll. Journ. Sci. 30: 471-574.

Muhlenbach, Viktor. 1957. Adventitious and escape plants new to Missouri. Rhodora 59: 27-31.

Palmer, E. J. and J. A. Steyermark. 1935. An Annotated Catalogue of the Flowering Plants of Missouri. Ann. Missouri Bot. Gard. 22: 375-758.

———. 1955. Plants new to Missouri. Rhodora 57: 310-319.

———. 1958. Plants new to Missouri. Brittonia 10: 109-120.

Philipson, W. R. 1937. A revision of the British species of *Agrostis*. Journ. Linnean Soc. London 51: 73-151.

Pilger, R. 1940. Reihe Glumiflorae, Gramineae III (Band 14 e. in Die Naturlichen Pflanzenfamilien.) Published by J. W. Edwards, Ann Arbor, Michican, 1945.

Pohl, R. W. 1947. A taxonomic study of the grasses of Pennsylvania. Am. Midl. Nat. 38: 513-604.

Raven, P. H. 1960. The correct name for rescue grass. Brittonia 12: 219-221.

Sarker, P. and G. L. Stebbins. 1956. Morphological evidence concerning the origin of the 'B' genome in wheat. Am. Journ. Bot. 43: 297-304.

Skinners, L. H. 1954. Notes on north Texas grass. Rhodora 56: 25-38.

Snowden, J. D. 1936. The Cultivated Races of Sorghum. Adlaid & Son, Ltd., London, England.

Stapledon, R. G. 1928. Cocksfoot grass (*Dactylis glomerata* L.): ecotypes in relation to the biotic factor. Journ. Ecology 16: 71-104.

Stebbins, G. L., Jr., J. I. Valencia and R. Marie Valencia. 1946. Artificial and natural hybrids in the Gramineae, Tribe Hordeae II. *Agropyron, Elymus* and *Hordeum*. Am. Journ. Bot. 33: 579-586.

Steyermark, J. A. 1940. The first recorded occurrence of *Distchlis spicata* in the central interior of the United States. Rhodora 42: 22-24.

———. 1958-59. Personal communications. Barrington, Illinois.

Steyermark, J. A. and C. L. Kucera. 1961. New combinations in grasses. Rhodora 63: 24-26.

———. 1958-59. Personal Communications. Barrington, Illinois.

Swallen, Jason. 1955, 1959. Personal communications. U. S. Nat. Herb., Washington, D. C.

Transeau, E. N. 1935. The prairie peninsula. Ecology 16: 423-437.

Van Schaack, Geo. B. 1954. *Calamagrostis insperata* in Missouri. Rhodora 56: 43.

Wagnon, H. K. 1952. A revision of the genus *Bromus,* Section Bromopsis, of North America. Brittonia 7: 415-480.

Weinstraub, F. C. 1953. Grasses introduced into the United States. U.S.D.A. For. Ser. Handbook 58. U.S.D.A., Wash., D. C.

INDEX

Tribes, genera, species, and subspecific taxa are listed. Common names are also indexed. Page numbers printed in boldface refer to the principal entry. Synonyms are printed in italic.

ABOUT THE AUTHOR

CLAIR L. KUCERA, a native of Iowa, received his B.S. (1947), A.M. (1948), and Ph.D. (1950) degrees in botany from Iowa State University. In 1950 he joined the staff at the University of Missouri, where he is now professor of botany and chairman of the department. His primary research interests have been in the native grass flora and ecology of the mid-American prairie; a number of his papers resulting from this research have appeared in botanical journals, including *Ecology, Ecological Monographs, American Midland Naturalist, Bulletin of the Torrey Botanical Club, Iowa State College Journal of Science,* and *Rhodora.* Professor Kucera is a member of several professional societies and at present is chairman of the Central States Section of the Botanical Society of America.